Reviews of Plasma Physics

VOPROSY TEORII PLAZMY

ВОПРОСЫ ТЕОРИИ ПЛАЗМЫ

Authorized translation from the Russian by **Herbert Lashinsky**
University of Maryland

Reviews of Plasma Physics

Edited by Acad. M. A. Leontovich

Volume 1

CONSULTANTS BUREAU · NEW YORK · 1965

The original text was published in Moscow in 1963 by the press Gosatomizdat,
for the State Committee for the Peaceful Uses of Atomic Energy.

Library of Congress Catalog Card Number 64-23244

Printed in the United States of America

FOREWORD

This volume marks the beginning of the publication of a number of review collections devoted to various aspects of plasma theory. The reader would obviously like to have a single treatise containing a complete presentation of the theory from a unified point of view. With this thought in mind, two years ago the authors started to write a comprehensive monograph on plasma theory. In the process, however, it became clear that this task could not be accomplished, since a complete and definitive theory for the description of real plasmas is not yet available.

For instance, not more than ten years ago it seemed self-evident that as far as dynamic behavior is concerned a plasma should not differ from an ordinary gas; thus, one assumed that the theory of transport effects in a plasma, i.e., electrical conductivity, thermal conductivity, diffusion, etc., could be developed by complete analogy with the corresponding Chapman-Enskog theory for gases. Such a theory was in fact developed through the efforts of many workers and is now called the "classical" theory, although ten or twenty years is scarcely sufficient for this designation to be appropriate.

Unfortunately further work, primarily experimental, has shown that the behavior of a real plasma is quite different from that predicted by the classical theory. This difference is a result of the variety of instabilities that can develop in a plasma; these instabilities produce a broad spectrum of noise and fluctuations which, in turn, have an important effect on the averaged plasma parameters. For this reason, any complete plasma theory must necessarily contain an analysis of the nonlinear (and frequently turbulent) behavior of a plasma; at the present time theories of this kind are only in their infancy.

Nonetheless, the outlines of a complete future theory are beginning to be discernible and, in certain cases, elements of this theory are in satisfactory form.

If one considers a low-density completely ionized plasma consisting of only one species, and concentrates on the dynamics of the problem, neglecting such things as elementary processes, radiation (optical), and so on, a theory can be developed (in explicit or implicit form) that describes an essentially artificial object; this theory takes account of particle interactions and can be derived completely on a classical basis using Maxwell's equations for the fields and Newton's equations for the charged particles.*

It is obvious that a statistical description must be used in this case.

By integrating the Liouville equation over all particles except one, over all particles except two, and so on, one obtains the hierarchy of equations due to Bogolyubov which is solved by expansion in powers of a small parameter, the reciprocal of the number of particles in a Debye sphere. This procedure leads to a kinetic equation with self-consistent fields and a collision term in the Landau form.

At this point the problem of collective processes is first encountered. Even in a weakly nonequilibrium plasma the collision term in the Landau form yields only logarithmic accuracy. It was first shown by B. I. Davydov that the thermal Langmuir oscillations make a contribution to the collision term in an equilibrium plasma; this contribution is smaller than that due to two-particle collisions by a factor equal to the Coulomb logarithm. This means that in a moderately nonequilibrium plasma account must be taken of "thermal" fluctuations of the electric field, which can have an appreciable effect on transport processes.

In a highly nonequilibrium plasma the situation can become extremely complicated: specifically, the fluctuation amplitudes in such a plasma can become so large that the interaction between various modes becomes important; this feature marks the transition to turbulence in a plasma. In a highly nonequilibrium plasma the two-body interactions become insignificant in this second stage so that the temporal behavior of the averaged quantities is, on the whole, determined by the collective effects of the various fluctuations. It is evident that the various concepts that have been developed for the description of ordinary gases do not apply in such a plasma.

In other words, in contrast with an ordinary gas, which possesses only one inherent characteristic time (the time between collisions), a plasma exhibits a rather large number of characteristic times. In a plasma in thermodynamic equilibrium these times are the periods characteristic of various kinds of oscillations; in a highly nonequilibrium plasma these times are the

*This statement is not completely accurate. In a high-temperature plasma a quantum-mechanical analysis must be used even to obtain the thermodynamic quantities (the classical collision integral diverges).

characteristic times for the growth of instabilities and the exchange of energy between various instability modes.

If one neglects this "microturbulence" and proceeds using the kinetic equation with the usual collision term the theory can be developed in two directions. In the case of slow plasma motion the Chapman-Enskog method is used to solve the kinetic equation. This method leads naturally to two-fluid hydrodynamics and, in most cases of practical interest, can be reduced further to single-fluid hydrodynamics, i.e., the magnetohydrodynamic description. In the other limiting case, in which the characteristic time of the problem is much shorter than the time between collisions, the collision term can be neglected and the model is that of a collisionless plasma described by the Vlasov equation. If a strong magnetic field is present use can be made of an expansion in the ratio of the mean Larmor radius to the characteristic scale length. The resulting equation is frequently called the drift approximation to the kinetic equation. At the present time the magnetohydrodynamic equations, the two-fluid description, and the Vlasov equation have all been applied in the solution of a large variety of problems; in particular, it has been found possible to investigate linear (and certain nonlinear) oscillations, plasma stability, and particular turbulent plasma states.

In these pages we hope to illuminate for the reader some of the above-mentioned problems of plasma theory. We certainly do not aspire to a comprehensive description of all plasma effects, but are biased (in accordance with the major interests of the majority of the authors) toward the development of ideas pertaining to the problem of controlled thermonuclear fusion. This bias is manifest, for example, in our analyses of the structure of lines of force of a magnetic field and of the motion of particles in electromagnetic fields, in which we give primary attention to the problem of confining particles by means of external fields. Similarly, in our presentation of the basic results of the classical theory of transport effects we stress transport theory for a plasma in a magnetic field. In the first few volumes of this series we shall present relatively detailed reviews of plasma equilibrium and hydromagnetic stability, small oscillations and kinetic instabilities of a plasma in a magnetic field, radiation from a high-temperature plasma, nonlinear oscillations, and plasma turbulence. The reader will find that very little space in this series is devoted to problems associated with classical gas discharges.

It is hoped to publish three volumes of these review collections in 1963. The first of these is devoted to certain general problems in the description of a plasma; the second to problems associated with the containment of a high-temperature plasma by an electromagnetic field, and the third to the theory of plasma oscillations. In subsequent volumes we propose to investigate radiation and fluctuations in a plasma and selected problems in magnetohydrodynamic and plasma turbulence.

M. Leontovich

TRANSLATOR'S PREFACE

In the interest of speed and economy the notation of the original text has been retained so that the cross product of two vectors **A** and **B** is denoted by [**AB**], the dot product by (**AB**), the Laplacian operator by Δ, the curl by rot, etc. It might also be worth pointing out that the temperature is frequently expressed in energy units in the Soviet literature so that the Boltzmann constant will be missing in various familar expressions. In matters of terminology, whenever possible several forms are used when a term is first introduced, e. g., magnetoacoustic and magnetosonic waves, "probkotron" and mirror machine, etc. It is hoped in this way to help the reader to relate the terms used here with those in existing translations and with the conventional nomenclature. In general the system of literature citation used in the bibliographies follows that of the American Institute of Physics "Soviet Physics" series; when a translated version of a given citation is available only the English translation is cited, unless reference is made to a specific portion of the Russian version. Except for the correction of some obvious misprints the text is that of the original.

We wish to express our gratitude to Academician Leontovich for kindly providing the latest corrections and additions to the Russian text, and especially for some new material, which appears for the first time in the American edition.

College Park, Maryland

April 1965

CONTENTS

MOTION OF CHARGED PARTICLES IN ELECTROMAGNETIC FIELDS IN THE DRIFT APPROXIMATION

D. V. Sivukhin

§ 1. Motion of a Charged Particle in a Constant Uniform Magnetic Field

1. The motion of a particle in an external electromagnetic field is described by the equations

$$\dot{\mathbf{r}} = \mathbf{v}, \tag{1.1}$$

$$\dot{\mathbf{p}} = e\left\{\mathbf{E} + \frac{1}{c}[\mathbf{vB}]\right\}, \tag{1.2}$$

where **E** and **B** are the electric and magnetic fields respectively; c is the velocity of light in vacuum; **r** is the radius vector giving the particle position; e, **v**, and **p** ≡ m**v** are the particle charge, velocity, and momentum. The absolute Gaussian system of units is used.

At relativistic velocities the mass m must be treated as a variable and is given by the expression

$$m = \frac{m_0}{\sqrt{1 - \frac{v^2}{c^2}}}, \tag{1.3}$$

from which it follows that

$$(mc)^2 = (m_0c)^2 + p^2. \tag{1.4}$$

If there is no electric field, so that the magnetic field is time-independent, Eq. (1.2) becomes

$$\dot{\mathbf{p}} = \frac{e}{c}[\mathbf{vB}]. \tag{1.5}$$

Taking the scalar product of both sides of this equation with $\mathbf{p} \equiv m\mathbf{v}$ yields

$$\mathbf{p}\dot{\mathbf{p}} = \frac{1}{2}\frac{d}{dt}(p^2) = 0,$$

whence it follows that the length of the vector $\mathbf{p}$ is independent of the time. The particle mass m, as follows from Eq. (1.4), is also time independent. Hence the length of the vector $\mathbf{v}$ and the total particle energy both remain constant

$$\mathcal{E} = mc^2 = \frac{m_0 c^2}{\sqrt{1 - \frac{v^2}{c^2}}} = \text{const}. \tag{1.6}$$

The energy remains constant because the force exerted on the particle by the magnetic field is perpendicular to the velocity $\mathbf{v}$ and thus does no work.

2. Of the various particular cases in which Eqs. (1.1) and (1.2) can be integrated in closed form special interest attaches to that in which the particle moves in a constant uniform magnetic field $\mathbf{B}$. For the present purposes this case is important because it represents the zeroth approximation in the analysis of particle motion in strong magnetic fields with weak spatial inhomogeneities, or in strong magnetic fields when weak electric fields are also present. Using the zeroth approximation as a basis it is possible to obtain a first approximation, which represents an approximate description of particle motion in electromagnetic fields of this kind. This first-order theory is only an approximation to the actual motion of a particle. It does not describe the small rapid oscillations of the particle about the trajectory characteristic of the smooth motion. This first-order approximation is called the drift approximation. The present review is devoted to the development of this approximate theory. At this point it will be convenient to recapitulate the basic features of the motion of a particle in a constant uniform magnetic field, although these results are presumed to be familiar to the reader.

The total velocity $\mathbf{v}$ can be decomposed into a velocity $\mathbf{v}_{\parallel}$ along the field $\mathbf{B}$ and a velocity $\mathbf{v}_{\perp}$ perpendicular to $\mathbf{B}$

$$\mathbf{v} = \mathbf{v}_{\parallel} + \mathbf{v}_{\perp}. \tag{1.7}$$

Since the mass m remains constant in the motion, using Eq. (1.5) we can find expressions for $\mathbf{v}_{\parallel}$ and $\mathbf{v}_{\perp}$:

$$\dot{\mathbf{v}}_{\parallel} = 0, \tag{1.8}$$

$$m\dot{\mathbf{v}}_{\perp} = \frac{e}{c}[\mathbf{v}_{\perp}\mathbf{B}]. \tag{1.9}$$

It follows from Eq. (1.8) that $\mathbf{v}_{\parallel}$ = const, that is to say, the particle motion in the direction of the magnetic field is uniform. Equation (1.9) shows that the rate of change of the vector $\mathbf{v}_{\perp}$ is perpendicular to $\mathbf{v}_{\perp}$ itself. Hence the change in $\mathbf{v}_{\perp}$ as a function of time can be represented as a rotation characterized by an angular velocity $\boldsymbol{\omega}$. The vector $\boldsymbol{\omega}$ is found from the equation

$$\dot{\mathbf{v}}_{\perp} = [\boldsymbol{\omega}\mathbf{v}_{\perp}] = \frac{e}{mc}[\mathbf{v}_{\perp}\mathbf{B}], \tag{1.10}$$

which yields*

$$\boldsymbol{\omega} = -\frac{e\mathbf{B}}{mc}. \tag{1.11}$$

The angular velocity $\boldsymbol{\omega}$ is evidently constant in both length and direction. Thus, $\mathbf{v}_{\perp}$, which does not change length, rotates uniformly around the magnetic field at an angular velocity

$$\omega = -\frac{eB}{mc}, \tag{1.12}$$

called the c y c l o t r o n f r e q u e n c y.† The corresponding period of rotation $|T = 2\pi/\omega|$ is called the c y c l o t r o n p e r i o d.

The motion of the particle perpendicular to the magnetic field is also a uniform gyration around a circle at the same angular velocity $\boldsymbol{\omega}$. The radius of this circle is

---

*Equation (1.10) describes $\boldsymbol{\omega}$ to within an arbitrary term parallel to $\mathbf{v}_{\perp}$. However, adding a term of this kind to Eq. (1.11) changes nothing physically since this corresponds to rotation of $\mathbf{v}_{\perp}$ around its own axis with no resulting change in $\mathbf{v}_{\perp}$ itself.

†The quantity ω is sometimes called the L a r m o r f r e q u e n c y. We shall not use this nomenclature because in other connections "Larmor frequency" sometimes refers to a frequency which is one-half ω.

$$\left|a_\perp\right| = \left|\frac{v_\perp}{\omega}\right| = \left|\frac{mcv_\perp}{eB}\right| \qquad (1.13)$$

and the circle itself is called the Larmor circle. For a positively charged particle the angular velocity vector $\boldsymbol{\omega}$ is in the opposite direction to **B**; for a negatively charged particle it is in the direction of **B**. This rule can be stated more graphically through the introduction of the magnetic moment μ, which arises as a consequence of the gyration of the particle around the Larmor circle:

$$\boldsymbol{\mu} = \frac{I}{c}\mathbf{S} = \frac{IS}{c}\cdot\frac{\boldsymbol{\omega}}{|\omega|}, \qquad (1.14)$$

where $I = (e/2\pi)|\omega|$ is the mean current associated with the gyrating particle, and $S = \pi a_\perp^2$ is the area of the Larmor circle. Using the values of ω and $a_\perp$ from Eqs. (1.12) and (1.13) we find

$$\boldsymbol{\mu} = -\frac{mv_\perp^2}{2B^2}\mathbf{B}. \qquad (1.15)$$

It is then obvious that regardless of the sign of the charge the magnetic moment $\boldsymbol{\mu}$ associated with the gyration around the Larmor circle is always in the opposite direction to the magnetic field **B**. This is essentially an expression of the general principle known in electrodynamics as Lenz's law. If a magnetic field varies from zero to some fixed value B an electric field is produced during the time in which the magnetic field is changing; the electric field accelerates the particle while the magnetic field constrains the particle to gyrate around the field direction. By Lenz's law the direction of particle gyration must be such that the magnetic field produced by the motion tends to reduce the rate-of-rise of the external field. Since the magnetic field produced by the particle gyrating in the Larmor circle can be represented as that of a magnetic dipole with dipole moment $\boldsymbol{\mu}$, it follows from Lenz's law that the vectors $\boldsymbol{\mu}$ and B must always be in opposite directions.

The analysis of uniform motion along a magnetic field then leads to the following conclusion. In a constant uniform magnetic field a charged particle gyrates uniformly around the Larmor circle whose center is displaced parallel or antiparallel to the vector B at a fixed velocity $\mathbf{v}_\parallel$. The resulting motion traces out a helix at a speed v. The axis of the helix is parallel to B. In Fig. 1 the motion along the helix is shown for positively and negatively charged particles. The center of the Larmor circle moves with uniform rectilinear motion along the axis of the helix. It should be emphasized that in general this center is not the center of curvature of the helix along which the particle moves. These points coincide only in the particular case in which the helix degenerates into a circle.

3. We now find the radius vector **R** giving the position of the center of the Larmor circle. If **r** is the particle radius vector then

$$\mathbf{v}_\perp = [\boldsymbol{\omega}\,(\mathbf{r} - \mathbf{R})].$$

Taking the vector product of this equation with $\boldsymbol{\omega}$ and using Eq. (1.11) we have

$$\mathbf{R} = \mathbf{r} + \frac{mc}{eB^2}[\mathbf{v}_\perp \mathbf{B}] \tag{1.16}$$

or

$$\mathbf{R} = \mathbf{r} + \frac{mc}{eB^2}[\mathbf{vB}]. \tag{1.17}$$

A right-handed triad of mutually perpendicular unit vectors is now introduced:

$$\mathbf{h} = [\mathbf{n}_1\mathbf{n}_2];\ \ \mathbf{n}_1 = [\mathbf{n}_2\mathbf{h}];\ \ \mathbf{n}_2 = [\mathbf{h}\mathbf{n}_1], \tag{1.18}$$

the first unit vector, ($\mathbf{h}$), is along the magnetic field and the second ($\mathbf{n}_1$) is in the direction of the transverse particle velocity:

$$\mathbf{h} = \frac{\mathbf{B}}{B},\qquad \mathbf{n}_1 = \frac{\mathbf{v}_\perp}{v_\perp}. \tag{1.19}$$

In this notation

$$\mathbf{v} = v_\parallel \mathbf{h} + v_\perp \mathbf{n}_1. \tag{1.20}$$

Two parameters are now introduced

$$a_\perp = \frac{mcv_\perp}{eB} = \frac{cp_\perp}{eB}, \tag{1.21}$$

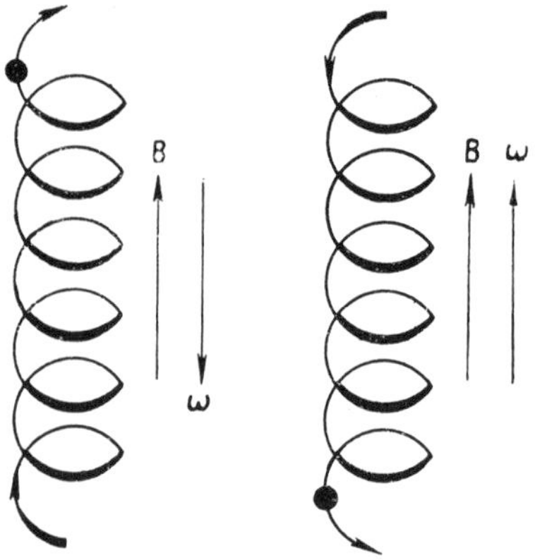

Positively charged particle   Negatively charged particle

Fig. 1

$$a_{\parallel} = \frac{mcv_{\parallel}}{eB} = \frac{cp_{\parallel}}{eB}; \tag{1.22}$$

the absolute magnitude of the first is equal to the radius of the Larmor circle. The second parameter $a_{\parallel}$ would have the same meaning if the transverse velocity of the particle were $v_{\parallel}$. Hence, the parameters $a_{\perp}$ and $a_{\parallel}$ considered together might be called the "Larmor lengths." From Eqs. (1.16) and (1.21) we then have

$$\mathbf{R} = \mathbf{r} - a_{\perp}\mathbf{n}_2. \tag{1.23}$$

It is now evident that the unit vector $\mathbf{n}_2$ points in the direction of the radius of the Larmor circle: for a positively charged particle this vector points from the center of the circle to the particle; for a negatively charged particle it points from the center.

§ 2. Motion of the Guiding Center

1. If the magnetic field is inhomogeneous, or if it varies in time, or if an electric field is present, the integration of the equations of motion (1.1) and (1.2) is a mathematical problem of extreme difficulty and cannot, in general, be carried out in closed form. To obtain all the details of the motion in actual cases it is then necessary to use complicated and tedious numerical methods of integrating these equations. Work along these lines has been carried out for many years by Stürmer in connection with the motion of charged particles in the magnetic field of the earth. The necessity and importance of investigations of this kind is evident. However, when such as approach is used it is difficult to obtain general results and to form a clear picture of the motion.

2. There is one particularly important case in which a good qualitative picture of the motion can be obtained if the details are not of interest; the motion can be described in general form without recourse to numerical integration of the equations of motion. This is the case if the magnetic field is strong and slowly varying in both time and space and if the electric field is weak. If these conditions are satisfied the effect of the electric field and the variation of the magnetic field in time and space can be taken into account by perturbation–theoretic methods and the motion can be described approximately.

If the above requirements are met, at any given instant of time the particle is gyrating rapidly in a Larmor circle of small radius around the direction of the magnetic field. The center of the Larmor circle, the so-called guiding center of the particle, moves along the magnetic field line and is also displaced slowly in the perpendicular direction. This displacement can be caused by a weak electric field or by a variation of the magnetic field. The particle motion is thus characterized by slow changes in the numerical values of the longitudinal and transverse particle velocities.

The conditions for which this approximate description of the motion is applicable are stated more rigorously as follows. First of all the magnetic and electric fields must not vary greatly in either magnitude or direction over a distance of the order of the Larmor lengths $a_\perp$ and $a_\parallel$ given by Eqs. (1.21) and (1.22). More precisely, if all variations are in the x direction the following inequalities must be satisfied:

$$\left| a_\parallel \frac{\partial \mathbf{B}}{\partial x} \right| \ll B; \quad \left| a_\perp \frac{\partial \mathbf{B}}{\partial x} \right| \ll B; \tag{2.1}$$

$$\left| a_\parallel \frac{\partial \mathbf{E}}{\partial x} \right| \ll E; \quad \left| a_\perp \frac{\partial \mathbf{E}}{\partial x} \right| \ll E. \tag{2.2}$$

The second requirement is that the electric field **E** must be weak. By this we mean that the change in particle velocity must be small in a time of the order of its period of gyration in the Larmor circle:

$$T = \left|\frac{2\pi}{\omega}\right| = \left|\frac{2\pi mc}{eB}\right|.$$

In this time period the particle velocity changes by an amount of order

$$\frac{eE}{m} T \approx c\frac{E}{B}.$$

This velocity change must be small compared with v:

$$c\frac{E}{B} \ll v. \tag{2.3}$$

A third requirement is that the transverse particle velocity $v_\perp$ must be large; in this case the projection of the particle motion in the plane perpendicular to **B** will not deviate greatly from circular motion in the Larmor circle in a time of order T. In other words, the velocity of particle gyration in the Larmor circle must be large compared with the velocity of the circle itself across the magnetic field. It is only under these conditions that the trajectory will be a helix.

However, the application of the drift-approximation equations, which will be derived below, does not depend on this limitation. If the gyration velocity of the particle in the Larmor circle is small (or comparable) with respect to the velocity with which the circle itself moves across the magnetic field the trajectory will not approximate a helix. Nonetheless, the particle trajectory (although perhaps a complicated curve) will still be a line that winds around the magnetic force line and is slowly displaced in the transverse direction. When the system of drift equations is derived below we will show that the third condition used in the derivation is not a necessary one.

3. The rapid gyrations of the particle in the Larmor circle are not of great interest and it is convenient to eliminate them from the equations of motion. This can be done by focusing attention on the motion of the guiding center rather than on the motion of the particle. It will be shown below that the motion of the guiding center consists of a smooth or regular motion upon which are superimposed rapid small oscillations or deviations.

The amplitudes of these oscillations are small compared with the radius of the Larmor circle since they represent the effects of perturbations due to the electric field or to the variation of the magnetic field, and these perturbations vanish when the particle moves in a uniform magnetic field. These small rapid oscillations of the guiding center are not of great interest and it is convenient to eliminate them in analyzing the "smoothed" motion. However, the expression for the velocity characterizing the smoothed motion of the guiding center contains the longitudinal and transverse velocities of the particle as parameters, or more precisely, the smoothed particle velocities. It is thus necessary to obtain equations describing the smoothed variations of the longitudinal and transverse velocites of the particle. The problem can then be formulated as follows.

Let it be required to find an expression for the velocity characterizing the smoothed motion of the guiding center and also to find equations describing the regular changes in the longitudinal and transverse velocities of the particle. The theory which analyzes the motion of a charged particle in electromagnetic fields in this formulation is known as drift theory or the drift approximation. The statement of the problem in this form is due to Alfvén [1] who obtained the equations of motion of drift theory in the simplest cases, starting with very physical but nonrigorous considerations. Later, Bogolyubov and Zubarev [2, 3] were able to obtain the drift equations in general form for motion at nonrelativistic velocities. These authors made use of the asymptotic method of integration of differential equations developed earlier by Krylov and Bogolyubov [13]. Using this technique Bogolyubov and Zubarev were able to develop a systematic scheme which, in principle, can be used to any order of approximation. However, even in the first approximation the calculations are extremely complicated and not very illuminating. A different derivation of the equations of drift theory is given below. This derivation is extremely instructive and is much simpler mathematically if one requires the same degree of accuracy as obtained with the Bogolyubov–Zubarev equations. The calculations become difficult in the higher approximations. The method is suitable for both relativistic and nonrelativistic velocities. A relativistic drift theory was first developed by Hellwig [4], who used a method differing from that given here as well as the Bogolyubov–Zubarev method.

Although drift equations suitable for relativistic velocities can be obtained, these equations are not covariant. This is because relativistically noncovariant conditions are used in the derivation of the drift equations;

for example, we require that the electric field must be small compared with the magnetic field.

In all of the work cited the drift equations are obtained in the first approximation. We shall also limit ourselves to this approximation.

4. Before proceeding we must establish precisely what is meant by the zeroth, first, second, and higher approximations. We shall regard the electric field as well as the space and time variations in the magnetic field as perturbations. By virtue of the Maxwell equation $\partial \mathbf{B}/\partial t = -c \operatorname{rot} \mathbf{E}$, the time variation of the magnetic field can be expressed in terms of the appropriate space derivatives of the electric field $\mathbf{E}$. Let G denote a small region of space whose linear dimensions are an order of magnitude greater than the Larmor lengths $|a_\perp|$ and $|a_\parallel|$ given by Eqs.(1.21) and (1.22). The fields $\mathbf{E}$ and $\mathbf{B}$ within these small regions can be expanded in powers of the coordinates. Our classification of an approximation order is then to be related to the various terms that make up this expansion. The zeroth approximation is the approximation in which the magnetic field in the region G is uniform and the electric field is neglected. In the first approximation the magnetic field in the region G is regarded as a linear function of the coordinates while the electric field is assumed to be uniform. Thus, in the first approximation the drift equations will contain $\mathbf{E}$, in addition to $\mathbf{B}$, and will also contain the first spatial derivatives of $\mathbf{B}$ to the first power. In the second approximation the magnetic field in G is assumed to be quadratic while the electric field is a linear function of the coordinates. This approximation can contain second spatial derivatives of $\mathbf{B}$ appearing to the first power. Combinations of the first derivatives of $\mathbf{B}$ as well as combinations with $\mathbf{E}$ can appear to the second power. The first spatial derivatives of $\mathbf{E}$ can appear only to the first power.

To make rapid estimates of the order of magnitude of various quantities we introduce the following scheme, which will be used in a somewhat provisional sense here, and justified in greater detail later:

zero-order quantities – the field $\mathbf{B}$;
first-order quantities – the field $\mathbf{E}$ and the first spatial derivatives of $\mathbf{B}$;
second-order quantities – first derivatives of $\mathbf{E}$ and second spatial derivatives of $\mathbf{B}$, etc.

In general the order of magnitude of the product of two or more quantities is equal to the sum of the orders of magnitude of the individual quantities.

The quantities being compared must obviously be of the same dimensionality. In this scheme it is therefore assumed that all coordinates with respect to which differentiation is carried out are d i m e n s i o n l e s s v a r i a b l e s. More precisely, the unit of length is taken to be the Larmor length $a_\perp$ or the Larmor length $a_\parallel$. For example, in differentiating the vector **B** we are to understand

$$\frac{\partial \mathbf{B}}{\partial\left(\dfrac{x}{a_\perp}\right)} = a_\perp \frac{\partial \mathbf{B}}{\partial x}$$

and

$$\frac{\partial \mathbf{B}}{\partial\left(\dfrac{x}{a_\parallel}\right)} = a_\parallel \frac{\partial \mathbf{B}}{\partial x},$$

where the x axis can be chosen at convenience. Both of these quantities have the meaning of changes in the vector **B** in distances of the order of $a_\perp$ and $a_\parallel$.

5. To second-order or higher accuracy the magnetic fields at the location of the particle $\mathbf{B} \equiv \mathbf{B}(\mathbf{r})$ and of the guiding center $\mathbf{B}_0 \equiv \mathbf{B}(\mathbf{R})$ are related by

$$\mathbf{B}(\mathbf{r}) = \mathbf{B}(\mathbf{R}) + (\mathbf{r} - \mathbf{R})\nabla\cdot\mathbf{B}$$

or, by virtue of Eq. (1.23),

$$\mathbf{B} = \mathbf{B}_0 + a_\perp (\mathbf{n}_2 \nabla)\mathbf{B}_0. \tag{2.4}$$

The vector $\mathbf{B}_0$ can be written in the form

$$\mathbf{B}_0 = \overline{\mathbf{B}}_0 + \delta\mathbf{B}_0, \tag{2.5}$$

where $\overline{\mathbf{B}}_0$ is a slowly varying vector while $\delta\mathbf{B}_0$ is a small correction associated with the oscillations of the guiding center about the smoothed trajectory. These oscillations do not appear in uniform magnetic fields. In nonuniform fields the oscillation amplitudes are proportional to the derivative $\partial\mathbf{B}/\partial x$. Hence, $\delta\mathbf{B}_0$, the increment in $\mathbf{B}_0$ over a distance corresponding to these amplitudes, is proportional to the square or product of these derivatives, so that $\delta\mathbf{B}_0$ is a quantity of second order or higher. Furthermore, since $\delta\mathbf{B}_0$ oscillates rapidly about this zero value these oscillations can be neglected in the present approximations. Finally, to within a rapidly oscillating second-order vector quantity we can write

$$\mathbf{B}_0 = \overline{\mathbf{B}}_0, \tag{2.6}$$

that is to say, the magnetic field $\mathbf{B}_0$ at the location of the guiding center can be regarded as a smoothly varying vector (to the degree of accuracy used here). The same considerations hold for the unit vector $\mathbf{h}_0$ in the direction of the magnetic field at the same point in space. This vector is related to the unit vector $\mathbf{h}$ by the expression*

$$\mathbf{h} = \mathbf{h}_0 + a_\perp (\mathbf{n}_2 \nabla) \mathbf{h}_0 \ . \tag{2.7}$$

Thus, both $\mathbf{B}$ and $\mathbf{h}$ can be written in the form

$$\mathbf{B} = \mathbf{B}_0 + \delta \mathbf{B}, \quad \mathbf{h} = \mathbf{h}_0 + \delta \mathbf{h}, \tag{2.8}$$

where $\mathbf{B}_0$ and $\mathbf{h}_0$ are slowly varying vectors while $\delta \mathbf{B} = a_\perp (\mathbf{n}_2 \nabla)\mathbf{B}_0$ and $\delta \mathbf{h} = a_\perp (\mathbf{n}_2 \nabla)\mathbf{h}_0$ are rapidly oscillating first-order vectors.

In similar fashion, the electric field at the location of the guiding center can be written in the form $\mathbf{E}_0$,

$$\mathbf{E}_0 = \overline{\mathbf{E}}_0 + \delta \mathbf{E}_0,$$

*If $\mathbf{h}_0$ is a unit vector, then by virtue of the identity $\mathbf{h}_0(\mathbf{n}_2 \nabla)\mathbf{h}_0 = 0$ it follows from Eq. (2.7) that $\mathbf{h}$ is also a unit vector, the point being that $\mathbf{h}^2$ differs from $\mathbf{h}_0^2$ by a second-order quantity that can be neglected. The identity we have used is a particular case of the identity

$$\mathbf{A} (\mathbf{C} \nabla) \mathbf{A} = 0, \tag{2.8a}$$

where $\mathbf{A}$ is a vector of fixed length ($\mathbf{A}^2$ = cost) and $\mathbf{C}$ is an arbitrary vector. The validity of Eq. (2.8a) is easily demonstrated by the following considerations. The quantity $(\mathbf{C}\nabla)\mathbf{A}$ is the derivative of the vector $\mathbf{A}$ in the direction of the vector $\mathbf{C}$ multiplied by $\mathbf{C}$. Since the length of $\mathbf{A}$ is fixed this derivative is a vector perpendicular to $\mathbf{A}$ and the identity in (2.8a) follows directly.

where $\overline{E}_0$ is a smoothly varying vector while δE_0 represents a rapidly varying third-order correction. Hence, to within a rapidly oscillating third-order term, the vector E_0 varies smoothly. To the same degree of accuracy the electric field $\mathbf{E} \equiv \mathbf{E}(\mathbf{r})$ at the location of the particle can be written in the form

$$\mathbf{E} = \mathbf{E}_0 + a_\perp (\mathbf{n}_2 \nabla) \mathbf{E}_0. \tag{2.9}$$

6. We now turn to the problem of computing the velocity of the guiding center and extracting the smoothly varying terms. By definition, R the radius vector of the guiding center is given by Eq. (1.17). Differentiating this expression with respect to time we find the velocity of the guiding center

$$\dot{\mathbf{R}} = \mathbf{v} + \frac{c}{eB^2}\left[\frac{d\mathbf{p}}{dt}\mathbf{B}\right] - \frac{2mc}{eB^3}\cdot\frac{dB}{dt}[\mathbf{v}\mathbf{B}] + \frac{mc}{eB^2}\left[\mathbf{v}\frac{d\mathbf{B}}{dt}\right].$$

We now replace dp/dt by Eq. (1.2), writing $\mathbf{B} = B\mathbf{h}$, and make use of Eqs. (1.18), (1.20), (1.21) and (1.22). Then

$$\dot{\mathbf{R}} = v_\parallel \mathbf{h} + \frac{c}{B^2}[\mathbf{E}\,\mathbf{B}] + a_\perp\left(\frac{1}{B}\cdot\frac{dB}{dt}\mathbf{n}_2 + \left[\mathbf{n}_1\frac{d\mathbf{h}}{dt}\right]\right) + \tag{2.10}$$
$$+ a_\parallel\left[\mathbf{h}\frac{d\mathbf{h}}{dt}\right].$$

The relations

$$\frac{dB}{dt} = \frac{\partial B}{\partial t} + (\mathbf{v}\nabla)B = \frac{\partial B}{\partial t} + v_\parallel(\mathbf{h}\nabla B) + v_\perp(\mathbf{n}_1\nabla B),$$
$$\frac{d\mathbf{h}}{dt} = \frac{\partial\mathbf{h}}{\partial t} + (\mathbf{v}\nabla)\mathbf{h} = \frac{\partial\mathbf{h}}{\partial t} + v_\parallel(\mathbf{h}\nabla)\mathbf{h} + v_\perp(\mathbf{n}_1\nabla)\mathbf{h}, \tag{2.11}$$

can be used to write Eq. (2.10) in the form

$$\dot{\mathbf{R}} = v_\parallel\mathbf{h} + \frac{c}{B^2}[\mathbf{E}\,\mathbf{B}] + a_\parallel v_\parallel[\mathbf{h}\cdot(\mathbf{h}\nabla)\mathbf{h}] +$$
$$+ a_\perp v_\perp\left\{\left(\mathbf{n}_1\frac{\nabla B}{B}\right)\mathbf{n}_2 + [\mathbf{n}_1\cdot(\mathbf{n}_1\nabla)\mathbf{h}]\right\} +$$
$$+ a_\perp v_\parallel\left\{\left(\mathbf{h}\frac{\nabla B}{B}\right)\mathbf{n}_2 + [\mathbf{n}_1\cdot(\mathbf{h}\nabla)\mathbf{h}] + [\mathbf{h}\cdot(\mathbf{n}_1\nabla)\mathbf{h}]\right\} +$$
$$+ a_\perp\left\{\frac{1}{B}\cdot\frac{\partial B}{\partial t}\mathbf{n}_2 + \left[\mathbf{n}_1\frac{\partial\mathbf{h}}{\partial t}\right]\right\} + a_\parallel\left[\mathbf{h}\frac{\partial\mathbf{h}}{\partial t}\right]. \tag{2.12}$$

This is the exact expression for the velocity of the guiding center. As expected, it contains a zero-order term $v_{\parallel}\mathbf{h}$ and terms of first order and higher resulting from the presence of the electric field and the variation in the magnetic field.

It is important to note, and this is expected from general considerations, that Eq. (2.12) does not contain rapidly varying zero-order terms. On the other hand, the particle velocity **v** does contain a rapidly oscillating zero-order term which results from the gyration of the particle around the magnetic force line. Thus, in converting from the motion of the particle to the motion of the guiding center we have raised the order of magnitude of the rapidly oscillating terms by one unit. This procedure simplifies considerably the problem of isolating the smooth motion from the rapidly oscillating motion and is the principal motivation for the introduction of the notion of a guiding center.

In accordance with the program mapped out above, we neglect in Eq. (2.12) all terms of second order or higher and all terms of first order describing "deviations" of the guiding center.*

All terms appearing in the last line of Eq. (2.12) can be neglected: these are all of second order since $\partial B/\partial t$ and $\partial \mathbf{h}/\partial t$ can be expressed in terms of the spatial derivatives of **E**.

The first-order terms in the second and third lines of Eq. (2.12) contain the rapidly rotating vectors $\mathbf{n}_1$ and $\mathbf{n}_2$ which appear as multiplicative factors for the slowly varying coefficients. To isolate these smoothly varying first-order terms we average them over the unperturbed motion of the unit vectors $\mathbf{n}_1$ and $\mathbf{n}_2$ regarding the coefficients of $\mathbf{n}_1$ and $\mathbf{n}_2$ as constant. The unperturbed motion of the vectors $\mathbf{n}_1$ and $\mathbf{n}_2$ is a uniform rotation around the vector **h**. When averaged over the rotation the third line in Eq. (2.12) vanishes since all terms in this line contain $\mathbf{n}_1$ and $\mathbf{n}_2$ to the first power. It remains to average the expressions $(\mathbf{n}_1\nabla B)\mathbf{n}_2$ and $[\mathbf{n}_1\cdot(\mathbf{n}_1\nabla)\mathbf{h}]$. For further development of this presentation, however, we shall find it convenient to take averages of more general expressions: $(\mathbf{n}_1\mathbf{A})\mathbf{n}_2$, $[\mathbf{n}_1\cdot(\mathbf{n}_1\nabla)\mathbf{A}]$ and several others in which **A** is an arbitrary fixed vector or a slowly varying vector.

---

*If will be shown in §4, that effects due to rapidly oscillating first-order terms can modify the smoothed velocity of the guiding center only to second order or higher.

We start by averaging the quantities $(\mathbf{n}_1\mathbf{A})\mathbf{n}_1$ and $(\mathbf{n}_2\mathbf{A})\mathbf{n}_2$. Both vectors $\mathbf{n}_1$ and $\mathbf{n}_2$ rotate uniformly about the direction of the vector $\mathbf{h}$. Since they are mutually perpendicular the phases of these rotations are shifted with respect to each other by a quarter period, which, at least to a first approximation, will have no effect on the average values. Hence, denoting the averaging operation by a bar over a quantity, on the one hand we can write

$$\overline{(\mathbf{n}_1\mathbf{A})\,\mathbf{n}_1} = \overline{(\mathbf{n}_2\mathbf{A})\,\mathbf{n}_2}.$$

On the other hand, the vector $\mathbf{A}$ can be decomposed in terms of the unit vectors $\mathbf{h}$, $\mathbf{n}_1$, and $\mathbf{n}_2$.

$$\mathbf{A} = (\mathbf{A}\,\mathbf{h})\,\mathbf{h} + (\mathbf{A}\mathbf{n}_1)\,\mathbf{n}_1 + (\mathbf{A}\mathbf{n}_2)\,\mathbf{n}_2.$$

Averaging this relation and comparing it with the one above we find

$$\overline{(\mathbf{n}_1\mathbf{A})\,\mathbf{n}_1} = \overline{(\mathbf{n}_2\mathbf{A})\,\mathbf{n}_2} = \frac{1}{2}\{\mathbf{A} - (\mathbf{h}\mathbf{A})\,\mathbf{h}\}. \qquad (2.13)$$

Replacing $\mathbf{A}$ by $[\mathbf{h}\mathbf{A}]$ and noting that

$$\mathbf{n}_1\,[\mathbf{h}\mathbf{A}] = [\mathbf{n}_1\mathbf{h}]\,\mathbf{A} = -(\mathbf{n}_2\mathbf{A}),$$

$$\mathbf{n}_2\,[\mathbf{h}\mathbf{A}] = [\mathbf{n}_2\mathbf{h}]\,\mathbf{A} = (\mathbf{n}_1\mathbf{A}),$$

we have

$$\overline{(\mathbf{n}_1\mathbf{A})\,\mathbf{n}_2} = -\overline{(\mathbf{n}_2\mathbf{A})\,\mathbf{n}_1} = \frac{1}{2}\,[\mathbf{h}\mathbf{A}]. \qquad (2.14)$$

At least to a first approximation the averages of the expressions $[\mathbf{n}_1\cdot(\mathbf{n}_1\nabla)\mathbf{A}]$ and $[\mathbf{n}_2\cdot(\mathbf{n}_2\nabla)\mathbf{A}]$, are equal. To find these averages it is simplest to make use of the identity*

$$\operatorname{rot}\mathbf{A} = [\mathbf{n}_1\cdot(\mathbf{n}_1\nabla)\,\mathbf{A}] + [\mathbf{n}_2\cdot(\mathbf{n}_2\nabla)\,\mathbf{A}] + [\mathbf{h}\cdot(\mathbf{h}\nabla)\,\mathbf{A}], \qquad (2.15)$$

*The validity of this identity and the identity

$$\operatorname{div}\mathbf{A} = \mathbf{n}_1\cdot(\mathbf{n}_1\,\nabla)\,\mathbf{A} + \mathbf{n}_2\cdot(\mathbf{n}_2\,\nabla)\,\mathbf{A} + \mathbf{h}\cdot(\mathbf{h}\,\nabla)\,\mathbf{A} \qquad (2.16)$$

are evident if we write the right side in a coordinate system in which the x axis is along $\mathbf{n}_1$, the y axis along $\mathbf{n}_2$ and the z axis along $\mathbf{h}$. In this coordinate system the right sides of Eqs. (2.15) and (2.16) become

$$\left[\mathbf{n}_1\,\frac{\partial}{\partial x}\cdot\mathbf{A}\right] + \left[\mathbf{n}_2\,\frac{\partial}{\partial y}\cdot\mathbf{A}\right] + \left[\mathbf{h}\,\frac{\partial}{\partial z}\cdot\mathbf{A}\right] = [\nabla\,\mathbf{A}] = \operatorname{rot}\mathbf{A};$$

$$\left(\mathbf{n}_1\,\frac{\partial}{\partial x}\cdot\mathbf{A}\right) + \left(\mathbf{n}_2\,\frac{\partial}{\partial y}\cdot\mathbf{A}\right) + \left(\mathbf{h}\,\frac{\partial}{\partial z}\cdot\mathbf{A}\right) = (\nabla\,\mathbf{A}) = \operatorname{div}\mathbf{A}.$$

which yields

$$\overline{[\mathbf{n}_1\cdot(\mathbf{n}_1\nabla)\mathbf{A}]} = \overline{[\mathbf{n}_2\cdot(\mathbf{n}_2\nabla)\mathbf{A}]} = \frac{1}{2}\operatorname{rot}\mathbf{A} - \frac{1}{2}[\mathbf{h}\cdot(\mathbf{h}\nabla)\mathbf{A}]. \quad (2.17)$$

Similarly, from the identity in (2.16) we have

$$\overline{\mathbf{n}_1\cdot(\mathbf{n}_1\nabla)\mathbf{A}} = \overline{\mathbf{n}_2\cdot(\mathbf{n}_2\nabla)\mathbf{A}} = \frac{1}{2}\operatorname{div}\mathbf{A} - \frac{1}{2}\mathbf{h}\cdot(\mathbf{h}\nabla)\mathbf{A}. \quad (2.18)$$

Finally, scalar multiplication of **h** with Eq. (2.17) yields

$$\overline{\mathbf{n}_2\cdot(\mathbf{n}_1\nabla)\mathbf{A}} = -\overline{\mathbf{n}_1\cdot(\mathbf{n}_2\nabla)\mathbf{A}} = \frac{1}{2}(\mathbf{h}\operatorname{rot}\mathbf{A}). \quad (2.19)$$

Now, writing $A = \nabla B$ in Eq. (2.14) and $A = \mathbf{h}$ in Eq. (2.17) we find the values of the expressions of interest

$$\overline{(\mathbf{n}_1\nabla B)\,\mathbf{n}_2} \text{ and } \overline{[\mathbf{n}_1\cdot(\mathbf{n}_1\nabla)\mathbf{h}]}.$$

The last two terms in the first line in Eq. (2.12) do not contain rapidly varying first-order terms and can be used without change. It now remains to consider the zero-order term $v_{\parallel}\mathbf{h}$. A slowly varying velocity $v_{\parallel}$ can be written in the form $v_{\parallel} = \overline{v}_{\parallel} + \delta v_{\parallel}$ where $\overline{v}_{\parallel}$ is a smoothly varying quantity while $\delta v_{\parallel}$ is a rapidly oscillating first-order quantity. Using Eq. (2.8) and neglecting second order terms we find

$$v_{\parallel}\mathbf{h} = \overline{v}_{\parallel}\,\mathbf{h}_0 + (\overline{v}_{\parallel}\,\delta\,\mathbf{h} + \mathbf{h}_0\delta v_{\parallel}).$$

The terms contained in the curved brackets are of first order and describe deviations. They can be neglected in the approximation used here.

We denote by $\overline{v}_{\perp}$, $\overline{m}$, $\overline{a}_{\perp}$, . . . the smoothly varying terms in the quantities $v_{\perp}$, m, $a_{\perp}$, . . . (as was the case with $v_{\parallel}$) and make use of the identity

$$(\mathbf{h}\nabla)\,\mathbf{h} + [\mathbf{h}\operatorname{rot}\mathbf{h}] = 0, \quad (2.20)$$

which is easily obtained by taking the gradient of both parts of the relation $h^2 = 1$. Then, to a first approximation the velocity of the regular motion of the guiding center is given by

$$\bar{\mathbf{R}} = \left[\bar{v}_{\|} + \frac{1}{2}\bar{v}_{\perp}\bar{a}_{\perp}(\mathbf{h}_0 \operatorname{rot} \mathbf{h}_0)\right]\mathbf{h}_0 + \frac{c}{B_0^2}[\mathbf{E}_0\mathbf{B}_0] + \\ + \frac{1}{2}\bar{v}_{\perp}\bar{a}_{\perp}\left[\mathbf{h}_0 \cdot \frac{\nabla B_0}{B_0}\right] + \bar{v}_{\|}\bar{a}_{\|}[\mathbf{h}_0 \cdot (\mathbf{h}_0 \nabla)\mathbf{h}_0]. \tag{2.21}$$

Strictly speaking, by $\mathbf{B}_0$ and $\mathbf{E}_0$ we should understand the smoothly varying terms rather than the actual field at the location of a guiding center. However, the latter differs from the former by rapidly varying second-order terms which have been neglected. Hence, $\mathbf{B}_0$ and $\mathbf{E}_0$ can be taken to mean the fields at the location of the guiding center.

It is clear from the derivation that in this approximation the mass $\bar{m}$ can be obtained from the expression

$$\bar{m} = \frac{m_0}{\sqrt{1 - \frac{\bar{v}_{\|}^2 + \bar{v}_{\perp}^2}{c^2}}}. \tag{2.22}$$

Similarly,

$$\bar{p}_{\|} = \bar{m}\bar{v}_{\|}; \quad \bar{p}_{\perp} = \bar{m}\bar{v}_{\perp}; \tag{2.23}$$

$$\bar{a}_{\perp} = \frac{\bar{m}c\bar{v}_{\perp}}{eB_0} = \frac{c\bar{p}_{\perp}}{eB_0}; \tag{2.24}$$

$$\bar{a}_{\|} = \frac{\bar{m}c\bar{v}_{\|}}{eB_0} = \frac{c\bar{p}_{\|}}{eB_0}. \tag{2.25}$$

7. The first term in Eq. (2.21)

$$\left(\dot{\bar{\mathbf{R}}}\right)_{\|} = \left[\bar{v}_{\|} + \frac{1}{2}\bar{v}_{\perp}\bar{a}_{\perp}(\mathbf{h}_0 \operatorname{rot} \mathbf{h}_0)\right]\mathbf{h}_0 \tag{2.26}$$

gives the smoothed velocity associated with the motion of the guiding center in the direction of $\mathbf{h}_0$, that is to say, the motion in the direction of the magnetic line of force passing through the guiding center. It can also be interpreted as the smoothed velocity of the particle itself in the same direction. By virtue of Eq.(2.7), in our approximation the projection of the total particle velocity in the direction $\mathbf{h}_0$ is

$$\mathbf{v}\,\mathbf{h}_0 = (v_{\parallel}\,\mathbf{h} + \mathbf{v}_{\perp}\,\mathbf{n}_1)\,\{\mathbf{h} - \mathbf{a}_{\perp}\,(\mathbf{n}_2\,\nabla)\,\mathbf{h}_0\} =$$
$$= v_{\parallel} - v_{\perp}a_{\perp}\,\mathbf{n}_1\,(\mathbf{n}_2\,\nabla)\,\mathbf{h}_0 - v_{\parallel}a_{\perp}\,\mathbf{h}\,(\mathbf{n}_2\,\nabla)\,\mathbf{h}_0.$$

Averaging this expression in accordance with Eq. (2.19) we have

$$\overline{\mathbf{v}\mathbf{h}_0} = \bar{v}_{\parallel} + \frac{1}{2}\,\bar{v}_{\perp}\bar{a}_{\perp}\,(\mathbf{h}_0\,\mathrm{rot}\,\mathbf{h}_0),$$

which coincides with the projection of the velocity in Eq. (2.26) in the direction $\mathbf{h}_0$. Thus, the smoothed velocities of the particle and its guiding center in the direction of $\mathbf{h}_0$ are the same (to second-order accuracy).

8. The remaining terms in Eq. (2.21) give the smoothed velocity of the guiding center in the direction perpendicular to $\mathbf{h}_0$. This is the drift motion. The $(c/B_0^2)[\mathbf{E}_0\mathbf{B}_0]$ term is the velocity associated with the so-called electric drift. This velocity is determined completely by the instantaneous values of the electric and magnetic fields at the location of the guiding center. In particular, it is independent of mass as well as the magnitude and sign of the particle charge.*

The expression for the electric drift velocity allows an important generalization. The nature of the force $\mathbf{F} = e\mathbf{E}$ acting on the particle (in addition to the magnetic field) is completely unimportant. The force $\mathbf{F}$ need not be electrical, but can be of any nature whatsoever, for example, gravitational, or inertial, if the motion is considered in a noninertial reference system. The important requirement is that $\mathbf{F}$ must be "small" so that its effect can be treated as a small perturbation. If this condition is satisfied the component of the force perpendicular to the magnetic field $\mathbf{F}_{\perp}$ causes a particle drift, i. e., a smooth motion with velocity

$$\mathbf{w}_F = \frac{c}{eB^2}\,[\mathbf{F}\mathbf{B}]. \tag{2.27}$$

*According to Eq. (2.21) an electric drift should also exist for uncharged particles, a situation which is obviously absurd since electric and magnetic fields have no effect on an uncharged particle. In order to resolve this paradox let us allow the particle charge to approach zero. The Larmor lengths $a_{\parallel}$ and $a_{\perp}$ then become infinite and the criteria for the applicability of the drift theory (2.1) are no longer satisfied. Thus, Eq. (2.21) can not be used to analyze an uncharged particle and no paradox arises.

It is true, however, that the electric drift differs from all other drifts in the fact that its direction is independent of the sign of the particle charge. For this reason, a plasma located in mutually perpendicular uniform **E** and **B** fields will move as a whole with drift velocity $\mathbf{w} = (c/B^2)[\mathbf{EB}]$. On the other hand, in a gravitational field the positive and negative particles drift in opposite directions (if all other forms of drift are neglected).

9. The last two terms in Eq. (2.21) give the drift associated with any inhomogeneity in the magnetic field. This drift is due to the spatial variation of the magnitude or direction of the magnetic field. In the latter case the drift is called centrifugal drift. The origin of this nomenclature will be explained in the next section. At this point it is convenient to write the expression for the centrifugal drift $\mathbf{w}_c$ in somewhat different form.

The vector $\mathbf{h}_0$ is a unit vector tangent to the line of force at the location of the guiding center. By definition the curvature is

$$(\mathbf{h}_0 \nabla)\, \mathbf{h}_0 = \frac{1}{\varrho_0}\, \mathbf{N}_0, \qquad (2.28)$$

where ρ_0 is the radius of curvature of this line of force while $\mathbf{N}_0$ is the unit vector associated with the principal normal to the magnetic line of force at the same point. We introduce an additional unit vector, the binormal:

$$\mathbf{b}_0 = [\mathbf{h}_0 \mathbf{N}_0]. \qquad (2.29)$$

Thus, the centrifugal drift velocity can be written

$$\mathbf{w}_c = \frac{\bar{v}_\parallel \bar{a}_\parallel}{\varrho_0}\, \mathbf{b}_0 = -\frac{\bar{v}_\parallel^2}{\omega_0 \varrho_0}\, \mathbf{b}_0. \qquad (2.30)$$

The centrifugal drift velocity is always directed along the binormal to the magnetic line of force.

The drift caused by the inhomogeneity in the magnitude of the magnetic field can also be transformed quite conveniently. Use is made of the Maxwell equation

$$\operatorname{rot} \mathbf{B}_0 \equiv \operatorname{rot}(B_0 \mathbf{h}_0) = -[\mathbf{h}_0 \nabla B_0] + B_0 \operatorname{rot} \mathbf{h}_0 = \frac{4\pi}{c} \cdot \mathbf{j}_0,$$

where $\mathbf{j}_0$ is the electric current density at the location of the guiding center. Now $\mathbf{h}$ is replaced by $\mathbf{h}_0$ in the identity in (2.20) and the vector product of both sides of the resulting equation with $\mathbf{h}_0$ is taken. From Eqs. (2.28) and (2.29) we then have

$$\mathrm{rot}\,\mathbf{h}_0 = \frac{1}{\varrho_0}\mathbf{b}_0 + (\mathbf{h}_0 \cdot \mathrm{rot}\,\mathbf{h}_0)\,\mathbf{h}_0.$$

Finally, the scalar product of the preceding relation with $\mathbf{h}_0$ is taken. This procedure yields

$$\mathbf{h}_0\,\mathrm{rot}\,\mathbf{B}_0 = \mathbf{B}_0\,\mathrm{rot}\,\mathbf{h}_0.$$

As a result we have

$$\mathbf{B}_0\,\mathrm{rot}\,\mathbf{h}_0 = \frac{B_0}{\varrho_0}\mathbf{b}_0 + (\mathbf{h}_0\;\mathrm{rot}\,\mathbf{B}_0)\;\mathbf{h}_0 = \frac{B_0}{\varrho_0}\mathbf{b}_0 + \frac{4\pi}{c}\,\mathbf{j}_{0\parallel}.$$

The symbols $\mathbf{j}_{0\parallel}$ and $\mathbf{j}_{0\perp}$ denote the components of the current density parallel and perpendicular to the magnetic field. The drift velocity $\mathbf{w}_B$ is then

$$\mathbf{w}_B = \frac{1}{2B_0}\overline{v_\perp a_\perp}[\mathbf{h}_0\,\nabla\,B_0] = \frac{\overline{a_\perp v_\perp}}{2\varrho_0}\mathbf{b}_0 - 2\pi\frac{\overline{v_\perp a_\perp}}{cB_0}\cdot\mathbf{j}_{0\perp}. \tag{2.31}$$

If the density of current flow across the magnetic field is zero the velocity of the drift being considered is directed along the binormal to the magnetic line of force.

Thus, Eq. (2.21) can be written in the form

$$\dot{\overline{\mathbf{R}}} = \left[\bar{v}_\parallel + \frac{1}{2}\overline{v_\perp a_\perp}\;(\mathbf{h}_0\,\mathrm{rot}\,\mathbf{h}_0)\right]\mathbf{h}_0 + \frac{c}{B_0^2}\,[\mathbf{E}_0\mathbf{B}_0] -$$
$$-\frac{1}{\omega_0\varrho_0}\left(\overline{v_\parallel^2} + \frac{1}{2}\overline{v_\perp^2}\right)\mathbf{b}_0 - 2\pi\frac{\overline{v_\perp a_\perp}}{cB_0}\,\mathbf{j}_{0\perp}. \tag{2.32}$$

10. To a first approximation the velocity associated with the smoothed motion of the guiding center in the direction perpendiculat to $\mathbf{h}_0$ coincides with the velocity of the smoothed motion of the particle itself in the same direction. This result follows from the fact that the Larmor radius $a \equiv a_\perp$ is a constant in a uniform constant magnetic field. The Larmor radius can

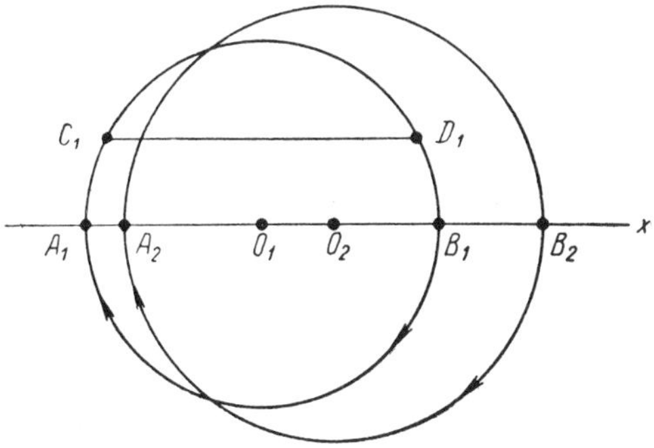

Fig. 2

only change as a result of spatial and temporal changes in the magnetic field. However, in a time interval of the order of the particle gyration period around the Larmor circle these changes will be of first order as compared with the Larmor radius itself. Having noted this point let us now consider the projection of the particle motion in the plane perpendicular to $\mathbf{h}_0$. At the initial time the particle gyrates in a Larmor circle of radius a_1 with center O_1 (Fig. 2). In a time $T \simeq 2\pi/\omega$ the center of the Larmor circle is displaced to O_2 and its radius becomes a_2. We take the direction of the smoothed motion of the guiding center to be along the x coordinate. The abscissa denoting the particle position is denoted by x and the abscissa of the guiding center by X. Assume that the initial and final particle positions are on the x axis. It is then evident from the figure that the particle displacement in a time T is

$$\Delta x = A_1A_2 = A_1O_1 + O_1O_2 + O_2A_2 = \Delta X - (a_2 - a_1) = \\ = \Delta X - \Delta a,$$

where $\Delta X = O_1O_2$ is the displacement of the guiding center. Hence the mean particle velocity $\Delta x/T$ during the same time will be smaller than the mean velocity of the guiding center $\Delta X/T$ by a quantity of first order $\Delta a/T$. If the particle were first located at the point B_1 and then moved to point B_2, its mean velocity would be

$$\frac{\Delta x}{T} = \frac{\Delta X}{T} + \frac{\Delta a}{T},$$

that is to say, a quantity greater than the mean velocity of the guiding center by an amount $\Delta a/T$. The mean of the two values coincides with the velocity of the guiding center $\Delta X/T$ if second-order quantities are neglected. Proceeding in the same way it is easily shown that the velocity averaged over a period T for a particle initially at C_1 is smaller (and for a particle initially at D_1 is larger) than the mean velocity of the guiding center by first-order quantities. However, if second-order quantities are neglected the arithmetic mean of these two velocities will equal the velocity of the guiding center. Thus, if the particle velocity is averaged over all possible positions on the Larmor circle, to a first approximation the result coincides with the mean velocity of the guiding center. But obviously the transverse velocity of the particle averaged in this way (with accuracy to second order) is the smoothed velocity in the direction perpendicular to $\mathbf{h}_0$. This proves our statement. In the proof we have neglected the rapid deviations of the particle from its Larmor circle. However, as has already been emphasized, the amplitudes of these oscillations are of first-order compared with the Larmor radius and they disappear when averages are taken; to a first approximation these deviations have no effect on the smoothed motion of the particle.

We have shown earlier that to a first approximation the smoothed velocity of the particle equals the smoothed velocity of the guiding center; we can now conclude that this statement holds for the total velocities as well. It is precisely this result that justifies the introduction of the guiding center because in the final analysis we are interested in the motion of the particle itself and not in the motion of an imaginary mathematical point related to the particle.

11. In the derivation of all expressions in this section it has been assumed that the drift velocity is small compared with the transverse velocity of the particle $v_\perp$. In particular, this refers to the electric drift. The derivation thus assumes that the following condition is satisfied:

$$v_\perp \gg c\frac{E_\perp}{B}. \tag{2.33}$$

It is necessary that the particle move along a helix that encircles the trajectory associated with the smoothed motion of the guiding center. If the condition in (2.33) is not satisfied the particle does not move along a helix. However, the particle trajectory does not necessarily have to be a helix. It is important to note that all the formulas for the velocity of the guiding center that have been obtained in the present section apply even if (2.33) is not satisfied. The proof of this statement requires only a slight modification of the derivations given above. Assume that (2.33) is not satisfied, i. e., consider the case for which

$$v_{\perp} \lesssim c\,\frac{E_{\perp}}{B}\,.$$

Then

$$|a_{\perp}| = \left|\frac{mcv_{\perp}}{eB}\right| \lesssim \left|\frac{mc^2}{eB^2}\cdot E_{\perp}\right|,$$

$$|a_{\perp}v_{\perp}| \lesssim \left|\frac{mc^3}{eB^3}\cdot E_{\perp}^2\right|.$$

Because of the small factors $E_{\perp}$ and $E^2_{\perp}$ the third line in Eq. (2.12) becomes a second-order quantity and the second line becomes a third-order quantitiy. Thus, these lines can be neglected, as can the corresponding terms in Eq. (2.21). Equation (2.21) remains valid. However, now the particle does not move along a helix but describes some complicated curve about the trajectory associated with the smoothed motion of the guiding center.

§ 3. Origin of the Drifts

1. In order to obtain a better understanding of the results of the preceding section we now consider particular cases of particle motion in electromagnetic fields, in which the origin of the drift can be understood from simple physical considerations. For simplicity we consider nonrelativistic cases only.

2. Electric drift. Assume that the electric and magnetic fields are uniform and constant. We write the equations of motion in a reference system moving with respect to a fixed system with a constant velocity $\mathbf{w}_E$ whose value will be determined later. The velocity and momentum of the particle in the moving system are denoted by $\mathbf{v}'$ and $\mathbf{p}'$ respectively. Then, $\mathbf{v} = \mathbf{v}' + \mathbf{w}_E$, $\mathbf{p} = \mathbf{p}' + m\mathbf{w}_E$ and Eq. (1.2) can be written

$$\dot{\mathbf{p}}' = e\left\{\mathbf{E} + \frac{1}{c}\,[\mathbf{v}'\mathbf{B}]\right\} + \frac{e}{c}\left[\mathbf{w}_E\cdot\mathbf{B}\right].$$

The velocity $\mathbf{w}_E$ is now chosen to make $(\mathbf{B}\mathbf{w}_E) = 0$ and $\mathbf{E}_\perp + (1/c)[\mathbf{w}_E \mathbf{B}] = 0$ where $\mathbf{E}_\perp$ is the electric field component perpendicular to the vector $\mathbf{B}$. The velocity $\mathbf{w}_E$ is determined uniquely by these conditions and is found to be

$$\mathbf{w}_E = \frac{c}{B^2}[\mathbf{E}_\perp \mathbf{B}] = \frac{c}{B^2}[\mathbf{E}\mathbf{B}]. \tag{3.1}$$

The equation of motion assumes the form

$$\frac{d\mathbf{p}'}{dt} = e\left\{\mathbf{E}_\parallel + \frac{1}{c}[\mathbf{v}'\mathbf{B}]\right\}, \tag{3.2}$$

where $\mathbf{E}_\parallel$ is the component of the electric field in the direction of $\mathbf{B}$. We now note that Eq. (3.2) has the same form as Eq. (1.2) but that the perpendicular component of the electric field $\mathbf{E}_\perp$ has been eliminated. It may then be concluded that the effect of the component $\mathbf{E}_\perp$ is to cause the particle to move across the magnetic field with a fixed velocity given by Eq. (3.1). This motion is called the electric drift.

From the derivation just given it is evident that the nature of the force $\mathbf{F} = e\mathbf{E}$ that acts on the particle (in addition to the magnetic field) is unimportant. For example, $\mathbf{F}$ can be a gravitational force or an inertial force if the motion is considered in a noninertial system of reference. The only important requirement is that $\mathbf{F}$ must be constant. If this condition is satisfied the component of this force $\mathbf{F}_\perp$ perpendicular to the magnetic field causes a particle drift, that is to say, a uniform motion of the particle with a constant velocity

$$\mathbf{w}_F = \frac{c}{eB^2}[\mathbf{F}\mathbf{B}]. \tag{3.3}$$

At first glance it would appear that we have not imposed any limitation on the magnitude of the field $\mathbf{E}$. However this is not the case. The point is that we have used nonrelativistic equations of motion. In general, the electric field $\mathbf{E}$ or the force $\mathbf{F}$ will accelerate a particle. If the quantities are large enough the particle will acquire a velocity comparable with the velocity c, in a time of the order of the cyclotron period $T = |2\pi mc/eB|$ in which case the nonrelativistic equations no longer apply. During a time T the longitudinal velocity of the particle increases by an amount

$$\Delta v_{\parallel} = \frac{eE_{\parallel}}{m} T = 2\pi c \frac{E_{\parallel}}{B} .$$

This velocity increment must also be small compared with c, giving the criterion $E_{\parallel} \ll B$. Similarly, the drift velocity must be small compared with c and consequently we require $E_{\perp} \ll B$. Thus, for nonrelativistic equations to apply it is necessary that

$$E \ll B \tag{3.4}$$

or

$$\frac{F}{e} \ll B. \tag{3.5}$$

If these conditions are not satisfied, the problem becomes relativistic. The relativistic equations of motion can, in fact, be integrated exactly for constant **B**, **E**, and **F** [5] but we shall not treat this problem here.

3. The results that have been obtained can be easily generalized to the case of inhomogeneous fields. All that is necessary is that the field **E** be weak and that the field **B** be slowly varying (in space and time). Then the velocity $\mathbf{w}_E$ given by Eq. (3.1) will be a first-order quantity and its variation over a cyclotron period T will be of second order. Neglecting second-order quantities in the course of short time intervals ($\approx$ T) we can regard the velocity $\mathbf{w}_E$ as constant. Transforming to a reference system moving with velocity $\mathbf{w}_E$ and employing the same reasoning as that given above we again reach the conclusion that the effect of the transverse component of the electric field **E** or the force **F** is such as to result only in the appearance of a drift with velocity given by Eq. (3.1) or Eq. (3.3). However, when the inhomogeneity in the fields **B** and **E** is taken into account this result holds only to a first approximation.

4. The origin of the electric drift and the drift caused by a constant force **F** can be easily understood from the following considerations [6]. Let us consider the projection of the particle trajectory in the plane perpendicular to the magnetic field **B**, which is assumed to be constant and uniform. Take this plane to be the plane of the figure (Figs. 3 and 4) and assume that the magnetic field is directed toward the reader. If there were no electric field the projection in question would be a circle of radius $a_{\perp}$. A positively charged particle would gyrate in the clockwise direction and a negatively charged particle in the counter-clockwise direction (Figs. 3 and 4 left).

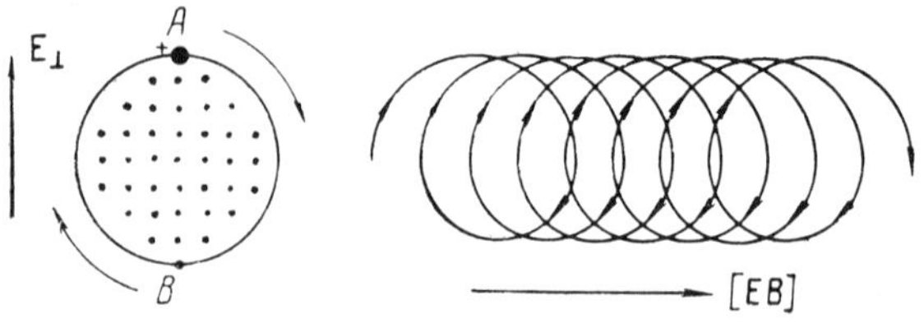

Fig. 3

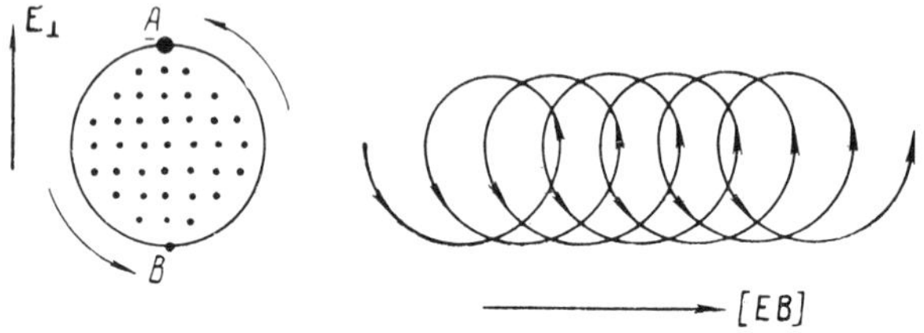

Fig. 4

Now let us consider the effect if the electric field $\mathbf{E}_\perp$ is directed upward. For the positively charged particle the velocity $v_\perp$ will then be a maximum at A and a minimum at B. Furthermore, at A the forces due to the electric and magnetic fields act in opposite directions; at B they act in the same direction. For these reasons the curvature of the projection of the trajectory $1/r$ in the upper part is smaller than in the lower part, as is evident from the expressions

$$\frac{1}{r} = \frac{eB}{mv_\perp c} - \frac{eE_\perp}{mv_\perp^2} \qquad \text{(at A)}$$

$$\frac{1}{r} = \frac{eB}{mv_\perp c} + \frac{eE_\perp}{mv_\perp^2}. \qquad \text{(at B)}$$

As a result the circle is converted into a curve that does not close on itself; in the motion along this curve the projection of the particle is slowly displaced to the right (Fig. 3). This displacement is the electric drift. The analogous projection of the trajectory for a negatively charged particle is shown in Fig. 4. In both cases the particle drift is to the right, i. e., the direction of the electric drift is independent of the sign of the charge as it should be.

5. The nature of the electric drift has been fairly well explored. However, it is of interest to go beyond the limits of the drift approximation because it is easy to find an exact solution to the problem if the fields **E** and **B** are constant and uniform. We first transform to a reference system that moves uniformly with the velocity given by Eq. (3.1). Then, from Eq. (3.2)

$$\dot{\mathbf{p}}'_{\parallel} = e\mathbf{E}, \tag{3.6}$$

$$\dot{\mathbf{p}}'_{\perp} = \frac{e}{c}\left[\mathbf{v}'_{\perp}\cdot\mathbf{B}\right]. \tag{3.7}$$

Equation (3.6) describes the uniformly accelerated motion of a particle in the direction of the magnetic field while Eq. (3.7) describes the uniform gyration of the particle around a Larmor circle of radius $|a_{\perp}| = |mcv'_{\perp}/eB|$ at the cyclotron frequency $\omega = -(eB/mc)$. In order to obtain the total particle velocity with respect to a fixed reference system we must add to these two velocities the constant velocity $\mathbf{w}_E$ associated with the moving reference system. This procedure leads to the following result.

In the nonrelativistic approximation the motion of a particle in constant uniform electric and magnetic fields consists of three motions: uniform acceleration along the magnetic line of force, uniform gyration around the Larmor circle, and a drift motion with constant velocity $\mathbf{w}_E = (c/B^2)[\mathbf{EB}]$. This result can also be obtained very easily from Eq. (2.10) if we note that $d\mathbf{B}/dt = 0$ in this case. Thus, the role of the electric field is twofold: The parallel component $\mathbf{E}_{\parallel}$ produces an acceleration in the direction of the magnetic field while the perpendicular component $\mathbf{E}_{\perp}$ causes a drift in the transverse direction with velocity $\mathbf{w}_E = (c/B^2)[\mathbf{EB}]$.

The uniform acceleration along **B** and the uniform drift motion perpendicular to **B** combine to give a parabolic motion. But in addition to this parabolic motion there is the uniform gyration around the Larmor circle. Consequently, in general, the motion describes a helix or a wavy curve that encircles the indicated parabola.

If the electric and magnetic fields are perpendicular to each other then $\mathbf{E}_{\parallel} = 0$. In this case the motion along the magnetic field is uniform and the parabola is replaced by a straight line. The trajectory of the particle will then be a helix or a wavy curve encircling this line.

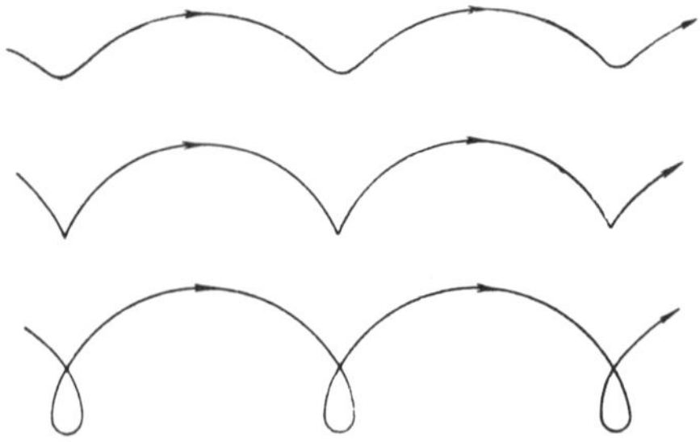

Fig. 5

Let us consider the particular situation in which **E** and **B** are perpendicular to each other and $v_{\parallel} = 0$. In this case the particle trajectory is a plane curve. The curve is obtained by combining the uniform gyration of the particle around the Larmor circle and the uniform rectilinear motion in the direction perpendicular to the electric and magnetic fields, i. e., in a direction lying in the plane of the circle. Consequently the particle trajectory is a cycloid which is stretched, normal, or compressed depending on the ratio of the angular Larmor velocity to the velocity of the center of the circle (See Fig. 5 in which the magnetic field is perpendicular to the plane of the figure).

6. Drift in a magnetic field whose magnitude varies in space (constant direction). The drift mechanism in this case is similar to that in the electric drift. Assume that the magnetic field is perpendicular to the plane of the figure and directed toward the reader. In Fig. 6 we show the projection of the particle trajectory in this plane. It is assumed that grad B is directed upward. Since the magnetic field is stronger in the upper part while the magnitude of the velocity v remains constant, the Larmor radius $a_{\perp}$ is reduced in the displacement from the lower region to the upper region. In other words, the curvature in the upper part of the projection of the trajectory is larger than in the lower part. For this reason the projected trajectory does not close on itself; the particle drifts to the left if it is positively charged and to the right if it is negatively charged (Fig. 6 applies for a positively charged particle). In general the drift is in the direction of [**h** grad B].

The drift velocity $\mathbf{w}_B$ is easily determined. Let grad B be in the y direction and take the x axis to be perpendicular to it and to **B** (Fig. 7). By definition the curvature is

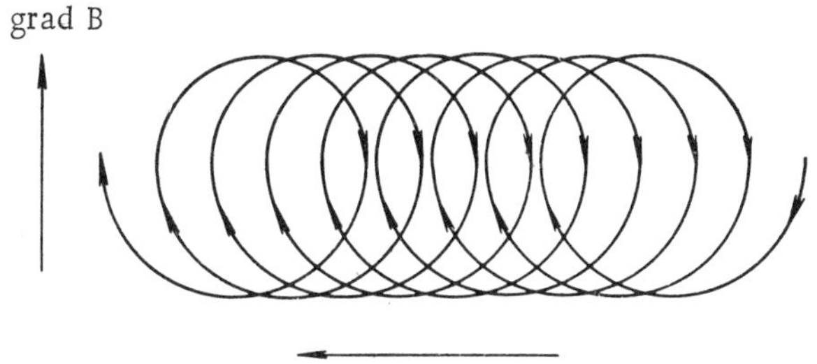

Fig. 6

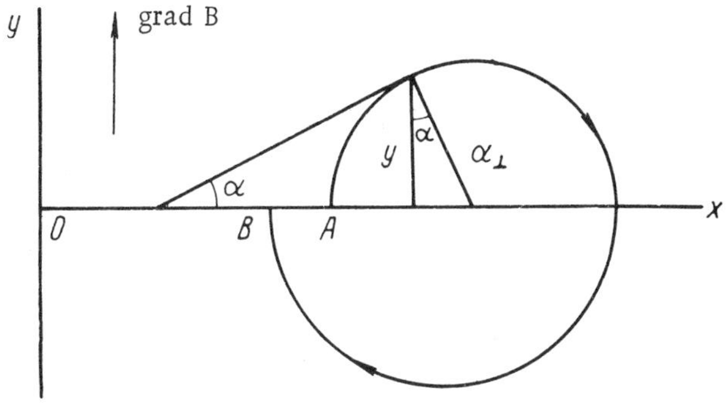

Fig. 7

$$\frac{1}{a_\perp} = -\frac{d\alpha}{ds},$$

where α is the angle between the x axis and the tangent to the projection of the trajectory, while the differentiation is carried out along the trajectory (the minus sign indicates that the angle α decreases as s increases). It is obvious that $dx = ds \cos\alpha$ and thus

$$dx = -a_\perp \cos\alpha \, d\alpha.$$

We expand $a_\perp(y)$ in powers of y and retain the linear term

$$a_\perp = a_\perp(0) + \frac{da_\perp}{dy} y.$$

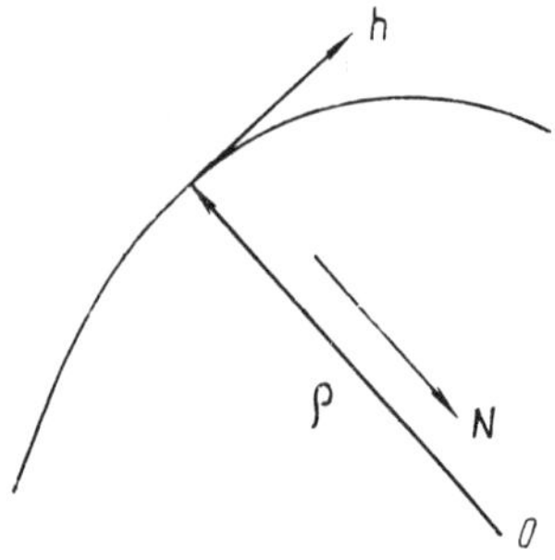

Fig. 8

We now find the increment in the abscissa $\Delta x = AB$ when the particle moves from the initial position A to B (Fig. 7). This increment is evidently

$$\Delta x = -\frac{da_\perp}{dy} \int_{\frac{\pi}{2}}^{\frac{\pi}{2}-2\pi} y \cos \alpha \, d\alpha.$$

To find Δx to a first approximation it is sufficient to take y in the zeroth approximation in the integration, i. e., $y = a_\perp \cos \alpha$. Computing the integral and dividing Δx by the cyclotron period $T = 2\pi a_\perp / v_\perp$, we find the drift velocity

$$w_B = \frac{v_\perp}{2} \frac{da_\perp}{dy}. \tag{3.8}$$

Since $a_\perp = \text{const}/B$ this result can be reduced to the form

$$w_B = -\frac{a_\perp v_\perp}{2B} \cdot \frac{dB}{dy}, \tag{3.9}$$

in agreement with (2.30).

7. Centrifugal drift. We now investigate the effect of curvature of the lines of force. Let us introduce a local coordinate system that rotates with angular velocity $\boldsymbol{\Omega}$ around the center of curvature of the line of force O (Fig. 8). In a fixed reference system the equation of motion of a particle is

$$m\,\mathbf{a}_{abs} = \mathbf{f}, \tag{3.10}$$

where $\mathbf{a}_{abs}$ is the particle acceleration in this system while **f** is the total force acting on the particle. Using the Coriolis theorem we can write the equation of motion in the rotating coordinate system

$$m\,\mathbf{a}_{rel} = \mathbf{f} + 2m\,[\mathbf{v}_{rel}\,\mathbf{\Omega}] - m\,[\mathbf{\Omega}\,[\mathbf{\Omega}\boldsymbol{\rho}]] - m\,[\dot{\mathbf{\Omega}}\boldsymbol{\rho}], \tag{3.11}$$

where $\mathbf{a}_{rel}$ and $\mathbf{v}_{rel}$ are the acceleration and velocity of the particle in the rotating coordinate system while $\boldsymbol{\rho}$ is a radius vector drawn from the center of curvature O to the particle. The total particle velocity is $\mathbf{v} = \mathbf{v}_{rest} + \mathbf{v}_{rel}$ where $\mathbf{v}_{rest} = [\mathbf{\Omega}\boldsymbol{\rho}]$ is the rest velocity, i.e., the velocity the particle would have if it were at rest in the rotating coordinate system. We choose $\mathbf{\Omega}$ so that

$$\mathbf{v}_{\parallel} = \mathbf{v}_{rest} = [\mathbf{\Omega}\boldsymbol{\rho}], \qquad (\mathbf{\Omega}\boldsymbol{\rho}) = 0.$$

Then

$$\mathbf{v}_{rel} = \mathbf{v}_{\perp},$$

$$\mathbf{\Omega} = -\frac{v_{\parallel}}{\rho^2}\,[\mathbf{h}\boldsymbol{\rho}]. \tag{3.12}$$

If **N** is the unit vector associated with the principal normal to the line of force while $\mathbf{b} = [\mathbf{hN}]$ is the unit vector associated with the binormal, then $\boldsymbol{\rho} = -\rho\mathbf{N}$ and

$$\mathbf{\Omega} = \frac{v_{\parallel}}{\rho}\,\mathbf{b}. \tag{3.13}$$

By the definition of curvature

$$(\mathbf{h}\nabla)\,\mathbf{h} = \frac{\mathbf{N}}{\rho}, \tag{3.14}$$

whence, by vector multiplication with **h** we find

$$\frac{\mathbf{b}}{\rho} = [\mathbf{h}\cdot(\mathbf{h}\nabla)\,\mathbf{h}]. \tag{3.15}$$

It is evident from Eqs. (3.13) and (3.15) that the vector $\boldsymbol{\Omega}$ is a first-order quantity. Its rapidly varying part is a second-order quantity. Thus, terms containing $\dot{\boldsymbol{\Omega}}$, both second-order or higher, can be neglected. For this reason the change in the length of the radius vector $\boldsymbol{\rho}$ in time can also be neglected. Further, the transverse velocity $\mathbf{v}_\perp$ can be resolved along the unit vectors for the principal normal $\mathbf{N}$ and the binormal $\mathbf{b}$, i. e., this velocity can be written in the form $\mathbf{v}_\perp = \mathbf{v}_N\mathbf{N} + v_b\mathbf{b}$. An expression for the Coriolis force is then obtained from Eqs. (3.12) and (3.13):

$$\mathbf{F}_C = 2m\,[\mathbf{v}_{\text{rel}}\,\dot{\boldsymbol{\Omega}}] = 2mv_N\,\Omega\,[\mathbf{N}\mathbf{b}] = 2mv_N\,\Omega\,\mathbf{h}.$$

To a first approximation Eq. (3.11) then becomes

$$m\mathbf{a}_{\text{rel}} = \mathbf{f} + m\Omega^2\boldsymbol{\varrho} + 2mv_N\Omega\,\mathbf{h}. \tag{3.16}$$

This expression is the equation of motion written to a first approximation in the local rotating coordinate system we have chosen. This coordinate system is chosen in such a way that the magnetic field at points traversed by the moving particle is, to a first approximation, *always in the same direction*. The transformation to this rotating coordinate system is then equivalent to straightening out the lines of force, i. e., to a first approximation the relative motion occurs as though the lines of force were straight lines. Then, we must add two inertial forces in Eq. (3.16) for the relative motion – the centrifugal force $\mathbf{F}_c = m\Omega^2\boldsymbol{\rho} = -(mv^2_\parallel/\rho)\,\mathbf{N}$ and the Coriolis force $\mathbf{F}_C = 2mv_N\Omega\mathbf{h}$. *The effect of the curvature of the magnetic lines of force is thus equivalent to the effects of centrifugal and Coriolis forces.* Since the Coriolis force is along the tangent to the line of force its effect is manifest only in a change in the longitudinal component of the total velocity $\mathbf{v} = v_\parallel\mathbf{h} + \mathbf{v}_{\text{rel}}$. *The centrifugal force only affects the transverse motion of the particle.* In accordance with Eq. (3.3) this force produces a drift with velocity

$$\mathbf{w}_c = \frac{c}{eB}\,[\mathbf{F}_c\cdot\mathbf{h}] = \frac{mv_\parallel^2\,c}{eB\varrho}\,[\mathbf{h}\mathbf{N}] = -\frac{v_\parallel^2}{\omega\varrho}\,\mathbf{b}, \tag{3.17}$$

which is the same as Eq. (2.29) when the appropriate changes in notation are made.

§ 4. Smoothing and Averaging of Quantities Containing Rapidly Varying Terms

1. Equations (2.21), (2.22), (2.24), and (2.25) do not comprise the complete system of equations required for the drift approximation. They must be supplemented by the two equations that determine the slowly varying velocities $\overline{v}_{\parallel}$ and $\overline{v}_{\perp}$ or, what is the same thing, the slowly varying momenta $\overline{p}_{\parallel} = \overline{m}\overline{v}_{\parallel}$ and $\overline{p}_{\perp} = \overline{m}\overline{v}_{\perp}$. These slowly varying quantities can be obtained from $v_{\parallel}$ and $v_{\perp}$ or $p_{\parallel}$ and $p_{\perp}$ by *smoothing*, i.e., by removal of all rapidly varying terms. The smoothed quantities will be denoted by symbols with a bar above them. We now consider methods by which the values of the smoothed quantities can be obtained with the required accuracy.

2. Let $f(t)$ be any quantity characterizing a particle or field at a given point. All such $f(t)$ functions with which we shall deal can be divided into two classes.

Functions of the first class consist of a slowly and smoothly varying term plus a rapidly varying term of *zero order*. In the zeroth approximation, i. e., in the absence of an electric field and space-time inhomogenieties in the magnetic field, these functions are *strictly periodic and do not degenerate into constant fields*. Quantities of this kind are, for example, $\mathbf{v}$, $\mathbf{p}$, $\mathbf{v}_{\perp}$, $\mathbf{n}_1$, $\mathbf{n}_2$ . . . and their projections on fixed coordinate axes.

The second class contains quantities that can be written in the form of a sum of a slowly varying term plus a rapidly varying term of *first-order or higher*. In the zeroth approximation these functions degenerate into *constant functions*. Typical functions of this kind are m, $v_{\parallel}$, $v_{\perp}$, $p_{\parallel}$, $p_{\perp}$, $\mathbf{B}$, $\mathbf{h}$, ...

Smoothing a quantity is essentially the removal of the rapidly varying term. We have used this procedure, for example, in the derivation of Eqs. (2.13) and (2.14). The difficulty here is the fact that one is not clear on how to isolate the "rapidly varying" term. This can usually be done easily with an accuracy up to a smoothly varying quantity which is one order of magnitude higher than the rapidly varying term. Examples are the smoothing procedures used in §2. If the quantity belongs to the second class this method of smoothing introduces an error which, in general, is of second order. In many cases an error of this magnitude is unimportant. However, if this method is applied to a quantity of the first class the error will be of first order and generally unacceptable. In these cases, and in all cases in which high accuracy is required, the smoothing can be carried out by means of intermediate averaging operations. Different methods of averaging are available. Let us consider the following method.

Every position of a particle is characterized by a cyclotron frequency $|\omega| = |eB/mc|$ and a cyclotron period

$$T(t) = \left|\frac{2\pi}{\omega}\right| = \left|\frac{2\pi mc}{eB}\right|. \tag{4.1}$$

We define the "averaged cyclotron period" by the relation

$$\widetilde{T}(t) = \frac{1}{2\widetilde{T}(t)} \int_{t-\widetilde{T}(t)}^{t+\widetilde{T}(t)} T(t')\,dt'. \tag{4.2}$$

Similarly, we can define the mean value of a function $f(t)$ for time t according to the expression

$$\widetilde{f}(t) = \frac{1}{2\widetilde{T}(t)} \int_{t-\widetilde{T}(t)}^{t+\widetilde{T}(t)} f(t')\,dt'. \tag{4.3}$$

When $f(t) \equiv T(t)$ Eq. (4.3) becomes Eq. (4.2). The averaged function $\widetilde{f}(t)$ will, in general, contain a rapidly varying part in addition to the smoothly varying term. For this reason the averaging operation in Eq. (4.3) is denoted by a wavy line in contrast with the straight lines denoting smoothing operations in which all rapidly varying terms are removed.

3. In general, the averaging operation in Eq. (4.3) raises the order of the rapidly varying term by one unit. In this case the smoothed functions obtained from $f(t)$ and $\widetilde{f}(t)$ can differ from each other by a slowly and smoothly varying quantity whose order of smallness exceeds that of $f(t)$ by at least two units.

To prove this statement we write the function $f(t)$ in the form

$$f(t) = \overline{f(t)} + \delta(t), \tag{4.4}$$

where $\delta(t)$ is a rapidly varying term. Expanding $\overline{f(t')}$ in powers of $(t'-t)$, and retaining the quadratic term, we find from Eq. (4.3)

$$\widetilde{f(t)} = \overline{f(t)} + \left\{\frac{1}{6}\frac{d^2\overline{f}}{dt^2}[\widetilde{T(t)}]^2 + \widetilde{\delta(t)}\right\}. \qquad (4.5)$$

Let us assume first that $f(t)$ is a function of the first class. Then $\widetilde{\delta(t)}$ vanishes rigorously in the zeroth approximation. Consequently, in the presence of an electric field or inhomogeneities in the magnetic fields the function $\widetilde{\delta(t)}$ is of first order or higher. The same holds true for any rapidly varying term that may be contained in $\widetilde{\delta(t)}$. The quantity $\frac{1}{6}(d^2f/dt^2)[\widetilde{T(t)}]^2$ is of second order or higher. Hence, the rapidly varying term in $\widetilde{f(t)}$ will be of first order or higher—the averaging operation (4.3) has increased the order of the rapidly varying term by at least one unit.

The functions $\overline{f(t)}$ and $\delta(t)$ are not determined uniquely for a given calculational accuracy. Using this arbitrariness $\delta(t)$ can be chosen so that the smoothly varying term in $\widetilde{\delta(t)}$ either vanishes altogether or becomes a second-order quantity compared with $\overline{f(t)}$. If this were not the case we would change $\delta(t)$ to a smoothly varying term of corresponding order, including it in $\overline{f(t)}$. Thus the additional term contained in Eq. (4.5) (in the curly brackets) and its smoothly varying part must be at least of order two and both parts of the theorem are proved for the case being considered.

The proof also holds if the function $f(t)$ belongs to the second class. It is sufficient to note that in this case $\delta(t)$ can be written in the form of a sum of terms of the form $\varepsilon\delta_1(t)$, where ε is first order or higher while $\delta_1(t)$ is a rapidly varying function such that $\widetilde{\delta_1(t)}$ vanishes in the zeroth approximation.

The theorem that has been proved here provides the basic approach for the methods used in the present review. If it is necessary to smooth a function $f(t)$, and simple removal of its rapidly varying part (which can be done by inspection) does not give the required accuracy, the accuracy can be improved by starting with the averaged function $\widetilde{f(t)}$, and smoothing it. The function $\widetilde{f(t)}$ can be smoothed more easily than the function $f(t)$ because the rapidly varying terms in $\widetilde{f(t)}$ are of higher order than the analogous terms in $f(t)$. In essence the same approach has been used in §2: Converting from the motion of the particle to the motion of its guiding center serves the purpose of raising the order of the rapidly varying terms.

4. In conclusion we wish to examine the possiblity of interchanging the operations of smoothing and differentiation with respect to time. For this purpose let us assume that $f(t)$ is a quantity of zero order, that is to say, it does not vanish in zero order. The generalization to higher orders is not difficult.

Replacing $f(t)$ by $\dot{f}(t)$ in Eq. (4.3) we have

$$\widetilde{\dot{f}}(t) = \frac{1}{2\widetilde{T}(t)} \int_{t-\widetilde{T}(t)}^{t+\widetilde{T}(t)} \dot{f}(t')\,dt' = \frac{f[t+\widetilde{T}(t)] - f[t-\widetilde{T}(t)]}{2\widetilde{T}(t)}.$$

Differentiating Eq. (4.3) with respect to time and using this result we find

$$\dot{\widetilde{f}}(t) = \widetilde{\dot{f}}(t) + \frac{\dot{\widetilde{T}}(t)}{\widetilde{T}(t)}\left\{\frac{f[t+\widetilde{T}(t)] + f[t-\widetilde{T}(t)]}{2} - \widetilde{f}(t)\right\}$$

or

$$\dot{\widetilde{f}}(t) = \widetilde{\dot{f}}(t) + \frac{\dot{\widetilde{T}}(t)}{\widetilde{T}(t)}\left\{\frac{\Delta f(t) - \Delta f[t-\widetilde{T}(t)]}{2} + [f(t) - \widetilde{f}(t)]\right\}, \quad (4.6)$$

where

$$\Delta f(t) = f[t + \widetilde{T}(t)] - f(t).$$

The quantity $\Delta f(t)$ vanishes for motion in a constant uniform magnetic field. Thus, in the general case $\Delta f(t)$ will be of first order and $\Delta f(t) - \Delta f[t - \widetilde{T}(t)]$ of second order. The order of the expression in the curly brackets in Eq. (4.6) is then generally determined by $f(t) - \widetilde{f}(t)$. When $f(t) \equiv T(t)$, $f(t) - \widetilde{f}(t) \equiv T(t) - \widetilde{T}(t)$ is of first order since $T(t)$ is a function of the second class. It then follows from Eq. (4.6) that

$$\dot{\widetilde{T}}(t) = \widetilde{\dot{T}}(t), \quad (4.7)$$

if an error of higher order compared with $\dot{\widetilde{T}}(t)$ can be tolerated. The derivative $\dot{T}(t)$ also refers to functions of the second class so that the rapidly varying term in $\widetilde{\dot{T}}(t)$ will be of second order. By virtue of Eq. (4.7) this statement also applies for the rapidly varying term in $\dot{\widetilde{T}}(t)$. Thus, to a rapidly varying term of second order $\dot{\widetilde{T}}(t)$ is a smoothly varying quantity of first order. If $f(t)$ is a function of the first class then $f(t) - \widetilde{f}(t)$ is a rapidly varying quantity of zero order and Eq. (4.6) yields

$$\dot{\widetilde{f}}(t) = \widetilde{\dot{f}}(t) + \text{rapidly varying terms of first order of smallness.} \quad (4.8)$$

However, if $f(t)$ is a function of the second class then

$$\dot{\widetilde{f(t)}} = \widetilde{\dot{f}(t)} + \text{rapidly varying terms of second order of smallness.} \tag{4.9}$$

The quantity $\dot{f}(t)$ is a function of the second class so that the rapidly varying part contained in $\widetilde{\dot{f}(t)}$ will be of second order. When rapidly varying parts of first order are smoothed they can have an effect on smoothly varying second-order terms. Similarly rapidly varying second-order terms can have an effect on third-order terms when smoothed. Hence, smoothing Eqs. (4.8) and (4.9) we find

$$\dot{\overline{f(t)}} = \overline{\dot{f}(t)}. \tag{4.10}$$

This relation is true to second-order accuracy for functions of the first class and to third-order accuracy for functions of the second class. Below, we will, in general, only smooth functions of the second class and the relation in Eq. (4.10) can be regarded as rigorously true for the accuracy used in our calculations. *To this degree of accuracy the operations of smoothing and time differentiation commute.*

§ 5. Complete System of Equations of Motion in the Drift Approximation

1. In order to find the smoothed velocity of the guiding center in the *first approximation* using Eqs. (2.21) or (2.32) it is sufficient to determine $\overline{v}_\perp$ in the *zeroth approximation* since this parameter contains first-order factors exclusively. Consequently, the derivative $\dot{\overline{v}}_\perp$ must be found to a higher approximation, i. e., the first approximation. The point here is that the parameter $\overline{v}_\perp = \int \dot{\overline{v}}_\perp \, dt$ must be known at any instant of time during the interval in which the motion is being considered. This time interval can contain a large number of cyclotron periods. *In integration over a large time interval, however, the order of magnitude of a quantity is reduced:* in general, first-order quantities become zero-order quantities and second-order quantities become first-order quantities. The parameter $\overline{v}_\parallel$ multiplies the *zero-order* quantity $\mathbf{h}_0$. For this reason this parameter must be found with high accuracy, i. e., it must be determined to a *first approximation* while its derivative $\dot{\overline{v}}_\parallel$ must be found to a *second approximation.* It is evident that no error will be committed if the derivative $\dot{\overline{v}}_\perp$ is computed to the same, i. e., the second, approximation. We shall follow this procedure below since a knowledge of the derivative $\dot{\overline{v}}_\perp$ in this approximation is of interest in its own right. Moreover, since we have not eliminated motion with relativistic velocities it is convenient to use the smoothed momenta $\overline{p}_\parallel$ and $\overline{p}_\perp$ rather than the smoothed velocities $\overline{v}_\parallel$ and $\overline{v}_\perp$; these momenta and velocities are related by Eq. (2.23). Thus, we must consider the problem of finding the derivatives $\dot{\overline{p}}_\parallel$ and $\dot{\overline{p}}_\perp$ to a second approximation.

2. Writing **p** in the form $\mathbf{p} = p_\parallel \mathbf{h} + p_\perp \mathbf{n}_1$, from Eq. (1.2) we have

$$\frac{dp_\parallel}{dt}\mathbf{h} + p_\parallel\frac{d\mathbf{h}}{dt} + \frac{dp_\perp}{dt}\mathbf{n}_1 + p_\perp\frac{d\mathbf{n}_1}{dt} = e\left\{\mathbf{E} + \frac{v_\perp}{c}[\mathbf{n}_1\mathbf{B}]\right\}.$$

Taking the scalar product of this equation with **h** and then with $\mathbf{n}_1$ we find the exact expressions

$$\left.\begin{aligned}\dot{p}_\parallel &= e(\mathbf{E}\mathbf{h}) + p_\perp\left(\mathbf{n}_1\cdot\frac{d\mathbf{h}}{dt}\right);\\ \dot{p}_\perp &= e(\mathbf{E}\mathbf{n}_1) - p_\parallel\left(\mathbf{n}_1\cdot\frac{d\mathbf{h}}{dt}\right),\end{aligned}\right\} \qquad (5.1)$$

where we have made use of the relation $(\mathbf{n}_1\mathbf{h}) = 0$, from which it follows that

$$\mathbf{h}\frac{d\mathbf{n}_1}{dt} + \mathbf{n}_1\frac{d\mathbf{h}}{dt} = 0. \qquad (5.2)$$

The second relation in (2.11) can be used to write Eq. (5.1) in the form

$$\left.\begin{aligned}\dot{p}_\parallel &= e(\mathbf{E}\mathbf{h}) + v_\parallel p_\perp \mathbf{n}_1\cdot(\mathbf{h}\nabla)\mathbf{h} + \\ &+ v_\perp p_\perp \mathbf{n}_1\cdot(\mathbf{n}_1\nabla)\mathbf{h} + p_\perp\left(\mathbf{n}_1\cdot\frac{\partial\mathbf{h}}{\partial t}\right);\\ \dot{p}_\perp &= e(\mathbf{E}\mathbf{n}_1) - v_\parallel p_\parallel \mathbf{n}_1\cdot(\mathbf{h}\nabla)\mathbf{h} - \\ &- v_\perp p_\parallel \mathbf{n}_1\cdot(\mathbf{n}_1\nabla)\mathbf{h} - p_\parallel\left(\mathbf{n}_1\cdot\frac{\partial\mathbf{h}}{\partial t}\right).\end{aligned}\right\} \qquad (5.3)$$

The momenta $p_\parallel(t)$ and $p_\perp(t)$ are quantities that have been called functions of the second class in the preceding section. The relation in (4.10) holds for functions of this kind if third-order quantities are neglected. Hence the problem of computing $\dot{\overline{p}}_\parallel$ and $\dot{\overline{p}}_\perp$ to a second approximation reduces to the smoothing of the right sides of Eq. (5.3) in the same approximation.

Calculations to a second approximation are rather tedious. We defer these calculations to §§ 7 and 8. Here we limit ourselves to calculating the derivatives $\dot{\overline{p}}_{\|}$ and $\dot{\overline{p}}_{\perp}$ to a first approximation. The accuracy of this approximation is sufficient for the analysis of many problems. The point here is that the motion of the guiding center along a magnetic line of force is a "rapid" motion since the associated velocity contains a term of zero order $\overline{v}_{\|}\mathbf{h}_0$. In many problems involving longitudinal motion only this $\overline{v}_{\|}\mathbf{h}_0$ term need be considered and all higher order terms can be neglected. This procedure has been used by Bogolyubov and Zubarev [2, 3]. On the other hand, motion across the magnetic field (drift) is a "slow" motion. In order to treat the smoothed transverse motion of the guiding center properly the second-order terms must be retained. Thus if different degrees of accuracy are tolerable for computing the longitudinal and transverse motions of the guiding center, it is sufficient to find both $\dot{\overline{p}}_{\|}$ and $\dot{\overline{p}}_{\perp}$ to a first approximation.

3. The right sides of Eq. (5.3) are quantities of first order. Hence, to a first approximation the rapidly varying terms in Eq. (5.3) can be smoothed immediately without the intermediate averaging operation. If Eq. (2.18) is used, taking account of in (2.8) it is easy to show that

$$\dot{\overline{p}}_{\|} = e(\mathbf{E}_0\mathbf{h}_0) + \frac{1}{2}\overline{p}_{\perp}\overline{v}_{\perp}\,\mathrm{div}\,\mathbf{h}_0;$$
$$\dot{\overline{p}}_{\perp} = -\frac{1}{2}\overline{p}_{\|}\overline{v}_{\perp}\,\mathrm{div}\,\mathbf{h}_0. \tag{5.4}$$

The equations (2.21), (2.22), (2.23), (2.24), (2.25), and (5.4) form the complete system of equations of the drift approximation. It will now be found convenient to modify the notation; specifically, we will henceforth omit the bars over all quantities, understanding $\dot{\mathbf{R}}$, $p_{\|}$, $p_{\perp}$, and . . . to mean the smoothed values of the corresponding quantities. Furthermore, we omit the subscript 0 on $\mathbf{B}_0$, $\mathbf{E}_0$, . . ., taking **B**, **E**, . . . to be the fields at the location of the guiding center.* Using this notation we have

$$\dot{\mathbf{R}} = v_{\|}\mathbf{h} + \frac{c}{B^2}[\mathbf{EB}] + \frac{v_{\perp}a_{\perp}}{2}\left[\mathbf{h}\frac{\nabla B}{B}\right] + v_{\|}a_{\|}\,[\mathbf{h}\cdot(\mathbf{h}\nabla)\,\mathbf{h}]; \tag{5.5}$$

$$\dot{p}_{\|} = e(\mathbf{Eh}) + \frac{1}{2}p_{\perp}v_{\perp}\,\mathrm{div}\,\mathbf{h}; \tag{5.6}$$

---

*The notation used earlier will be used below in certain cases in the proof and derivation of formulas. Final results, however, will be given in the new notation.

$$p_\perp = -\frac{1}{2} p_\parallel v_\perp \operatorname{div} \mathbf{h}. \tag{5.7}$$

Here we have introduced the relations

$$p_\parallel = m v_\parallel; \qquad p_\perp = m v_\perp; \tag{5.8}$$

$$m = \frac{m_0}{\sqrt{1 - \frac{v_\parallel^2 + v_\perp^2}{c^2}}}; \tag{5.9}$$

$$a_\parallel = \frac{c p_\parallel}{eB}; \qquad a_\perp = \frac{c p_\perp}{eB}. \tag{5.10}$$

Equation (5.7) can now be written in the form

$$\dot{\mathbf{R}} = v_\parallel \mathbf{h} + \frac{c}{B^2}[\mathbf{EB}] - \frac{1}{\omega \varrho}\left(v_\parallel^2 + \frac{v_\perp^2}{2}\right)\mathbf{b} - 2\pi \frac{v_\perp a_\perp}{cB} \mathbf{j}_\perp. \tag{5.11}$$

The equations in (5.6) and (5.7) can also be replaced by two equivalent equations. One of these is the energy equation. It can be obtained by multiplying Eqs. (5.6) and (5.7) by $p_\parallel$ and $p_\perp$, respectively, and adding. This procedure yields

$$\frac{d}{dt}\left(\frac{p^2}{2}\right) = e p_\parallel (\mathbf{Eh}) \tag{5.12}$$

or, by virtue of Eq. (1.4),

$$\frac{d}{dt}(mc^2) = e(\mathbf{E}\mathbf{v}_\parallel). \tag{5.13}$$

The second equation is found by integration of Eq. (5.7). Since div **B** = 0, then

$$\operatorname{div} \mathbf{h} = \operatorname{div} \frac{\mathbf{B}}{B} = \left(\mathbf{B} \cdot \nabla \frac{1}{B}\right). \tag{5.14}$$

Furthermore, since the transverse velocity of the guiding center is a first-order quantity, to second-order accuracy we have

$$\frac{d}{dt}\frac{1}{B} = \frac{\partial}{\partial t}\frac{1}{B} + \left(\mathbf{v}_\parallel \cdot \nabla \frac{1}{B}\right) \approx v_\parallel \left(\mathbf{h} \cdot \nabla \frac{1}{B}\right),$$

and Eq. (5.7) becomes

$$\frac{d}{dt}\frac{p_\perp^2}{B} = 0,$$

whence

$$\frac{p_\perp^2}{B} = \text{const.} \tag{5.15}$$

The quantity $p_\perp^2/B$ is then an integral of the motion. However, it is not an exact integral, but rather an approximate integral of the motion. It obtains as a consequence of the fact that the electric field is small and that the variations of **B** in space and time are slow. This kind of approximate integral of the motion is called an adiabatic invariant. The quantity in (5.15) is an adiabatic invariant. The general theory of adiabatic invariants has been considered by Kruskal [16].

4. The relation in (5.15) can be written in two equivalent forms. First, it is evident that to second-order accuracy the average magnetic flux Φ through the Larmor circle of the particle is $\pi a_\perp^2 B$, or by virtue of Eq. (5.10),

$$\Phi = \frac{\pi c^2}{e^2}\frac{p_\perp^2}{B}. \tag{5.16}$$

Comparing this expression with Eq. (5.15) we see that the average magnetic flux through the Larmor circle is the adiabatic invariant

$$\Phi = \pi a_\perp^2 B = \text{const.} \tag{5.17}$$

Second, as is evident from Eq. (1.15), the average magnetic moment of a particle gyrating in a Larmor circle is

$$\mu = \frac{1}{2m}\frac{p_\perp^2}{B} = \frac{p_\perp v_\perp}{2B}. \tag{5.18}$$

This means that $m\mu$ is an adiabatic invariant:

$$m\mu = \text{const.} \tag{5.19}$$

In particular, for nonrelativistic motion

$$\mu = \text{const.} \tag{5.20}$$

If the magnetic moment is introduced in Eq. (5.6) and Eq. (5.14) is used, Eq. (5.6) can be easily reduced to the form

$$\dot{p}_{\parallel} = (e\mathbf{E} - \mu \nabla B)\,\mathbf{h}. \tag{5.21}$$

This equation has a simple physical meaning. The quantity $e\mathbf{E}$ is the force exerted on the particle by the electric field. Since the particle gyrating around the Larmor circle has a mean magnetic moment $\mu\mathbf{h}$ the magnetic field exerts on it an average additional force $\mu(\mathbf{h}\nabla)\mathbf{B}$. The projection of this force in the direction of $\mathbf{h}$ is $\mu(\mathbf{h}\nabla B)$. The force $e\mathbf{E}$ then produces the change in the longitudinal momentum of the particle.

§ 6. More Exact System of Equations of Motion in the Drift Approximation

1. The system of drift equations given by Bogolyubov and Zubarev, which we have obtained in the preceding section, is not completely self-consistent because the transverse velocity of the regular motion of a particle is found to a first approximation while the longitudinal motion is only determined to the zeroth approximation. This lack of self-consistency was removed by Braginskii [7]. Using the technique given by Bogolyubov and Zubarev, Braginskii analyzed the motion of a particle at nonrelativistic velocities and found expressions for the derivatives $\dot{\overline{v}}_{\parallel}$ and $\dot{\overline{v}}_{\perp}$ to a second approximation. We have obtained the Braginskii equation in a form also applicable for relativistic motion. As explained in the preceding section, for this purpose it is necessary to smooth the right sides of Eq. (5.3) in the second approximation. Although this appears to be simple, in fact it is found the calculations are extremely laborious and can obscure the important points. For this reason, in the present section we give the complete system of drift equations without proof; the derivation is given in §8 following the development of some of the required mathematical apparatus in §7. The reader who is not interested in these proofs can omit both of these sections as well as §9 without impairing the understanding of what follows.

The self-consistent system of drift equations is of the following form in first approximation

$$\dot{\mathbf{R}} = \left[v_{\parallel} + \frac{1}{2} v_{\perp} a_{\perp} (\mathbf{h} \operatorname{rot} \mathbf{h})\right]\mathbf{h} + \frac{c}{B^2}[\mathbf{E}\mathbf{B}] +$$

$$+\frac{1}{2}v_{\perp}a_{\perp}\left[\mathbf{h}\frac{\nabla B}{B}\right]+v_{\parallel}a_{\parallel}\,[\mathbf{h}\cdot(\mathbf{h}\nabla)\,\mathbf{h}]; \tag{6.1}$$

$$\dot{p}_{\parallel}=e\,(\mathbf{E}\mathbf{h})+\frac{1}{2}v_{\perp}p_{\perp}\operatorname{div}\mathbf{h}+ea_{\parallel}\,(\mathbf{E}\,[\mathbf{h}\cdot(\mathbf{h}\nabla)\,\mathbf{h}])-$$

$$-\frac{a_{\parallel}p_{\perp}v_{\perp}}{2}\left(\frac{\nabla B}{B}\,[\mathbf{h}\cdot(\mathbf{h}\nabla)\,\mathbf{h}]\right)-\frac{a_{\parallel}p_{\perp}v_{\perp}}{2}\,\mathbf{h}\operatorname{rot}(\mathbf{h}\nabla)\,\mathbf{h}; \tag{6.2}$$

$$\dot{p}_{\perp}=-\frac{1}{2}v_{\perp}p_{\parallel}\operatorname{div}\mathbf{h}-\frac{ea_{\perp}}{2}\,(\mathbf{h}\operatorname{rot}\mathbf{E})+\frac{ea_{\perp}}{2}\left(\mathbf{E}\left[\mathbf{h}\,\frac{\nabla B}{B}\right]\right)+$$

$$+\frac{ea_{\perp}}{2}\,(\mathbf{E}\mathbf{h})(\mathbf{h}\operatorname{rot}\mathbf{h})+\frac{a_{\parallel}v_{\parallel}p_{\perp}}{2}\left(\frac{\nabla B}{B}\,[\mathbf{h}\cdot(\mathbf{h}\nabla)\,\mathbf{h}]\right)+$$

$$+\frac{1}{2}a_{\parallel}p_{\perp}v_{\parallel}\,\mathbf{h}\operatorname{rot}(\mathbf{h}\nabla)\,\mathbf{h}. \tag{6.3}$$

Equations (5.8), (5.9), and (5.10) still hold without change. Here, however, we adopt the modified notation introduced at the end of the preceding section.

2. Equations (6.1), (6.2), and (6.3) can be simplfied, following Braginskii [7], by the introduction of the new momenta and the corresponding velocities

$$\left.\begin{aligned} P_{\parallel}&=p_{\parallel}+\frac{1}{2}p_{\perp}a_{\perp}\,(\mathbf{h}\operatorname{rot}\mathbf{h});\\ P_{\perp}&=p_{\perp}-\frac{1}{2}p_{\parallel}a_{\perp}\,(\mathbf{h}\operatorname{rot}\mathbf{h}); \end{aligned}\right\} \tag{6.4}$$

$$\left.\begin{aligned} V_{\parallel}&=v_{\parallel}+\frac{1}{2}v_{\perp}a_{\perp}\,(\mathbf{h}\operatorname{rot}\mathbf{h});\\ V_{\perp}&=v_{\perp}-\frac{1}{2}v_{\parallel}a_{\perp}\,(\mathbf{h}\operatorname{rot}\mathbf{h}). \end{aligned}\right\} \tag{6.5}$$

The meaning of $V_{\parallel}$ and $P_{\parallel}$ has been given in §2. These quantities represent the smoothed projections of the particle velocity and momentum in the direction of the magnetic field at the location of the guiding center. It is also easily shown that $V_{\perp}$ and $P_{\perp}$ are the smoothed values of the particle velocity and momentum perpendicular to this direction. The last statement is easily demonstrated by means of Eqs. (6.4) and (6.5); to the required degree of accuracy

$$P_{\parallel}^2 + P_{\perp}^2 = p_{\parallel}^2 + p_{\perp}^2;$$
$$V_{\parallel}^2 + V_{\perp}^2 = v_{\parallel}^2 + v_{\perp}^2. \qquad (6.6)$$

In writing Eqs. (6.1), (6.2), and (6.3) in terms of the new variables we have used the identity in (2.20). Taking the curl of both sides of this identity we have

$$\text{rot}\,(\mathbf{h}\nabla)\,\mathbf{h} = -\,\text{rot}\,[\mathbf{h}\,\text{rot}\,\mathbf{h}] = -(\text{rot}\,\mathbf{h}\nabla)\,\mathbf{h} +$$
$$+ (\mathbf{h}\nabla)\,\text{rot}\,\mathbf{h} + \text{div}\,\mathbf{h}\cdot\text{rot}\,\mathbf{h},$$

whence*

$$\mathbf{h}\cdot\text{rot}\,(\mathbf{h}\nabla)\,\mathbf{h} = \mathbf{h}\cdot(\mathbf{h}\nabla)\,\text{rot}\,\mathbf{h} + (\mathbf{h}\,\text{rot}\,\mathbf{h})\,\text{div}\,\mathbf{h}. \qquad (6.7)$$

It also follows from the identity in (2.20) that

$$\text{rot}\,\mathbf{h}\cdot(\mathbf{h}\nabla)\,\mathbf{h} = 0. \qquad (6.8)$$

Now, using identities (6.7) and (6.8) and the relation

$$\text{div}\,\mathbf{B} \equiv \text{div}\,(B\,\mathbf{h}) = \mathbf{h}\nabla\,B + B\,\text{div}\,\mathbf{h}, \qquad (6.9)$$

it is easy to show that

$$\dot{\mathbf{R}} = V_{\parallel}\,\mathbf{h} + \frac{c}{B^2}\,[\mathbf{EB}] + \frac{1}{2}V_{\perp}a_{\perp}\left[\mathbf{h}\cdot\frac{\nabla B}{B}\right] + V_{\parallel}a_{\parallel}\,[\mathbf{h}\cdot(\mathbf{h}\nabla)\,\mathbf{h}]; \qquad (6.10)$$

$$\dot{P}_{\parallel} = e\,(\mathbf{Eh}) - \frac{1}{2B}\,V_{\perp}P_{\perp}\,(\mathbf{h}\nabla\,B) + ea_{\parallel}\,(\mathbf{E}\,[\mathbf{h}\cdot(\mathbf{h}\nabla)\,\mathbf{h}]) -$$
$$- \frac{a_{\parallel}P_{\perp}V_{\perp}}{2B}\,(\nabla\,B\,[\mathbf{h}\cdot(\mathbf{h}\nabla)\,\mathbf{h}]); \qquad (6.11)$$

---

*This identity is used in transformation of the derivative of rot **h**. Specifically, in the required approximation

$$\mathbf{h}\,\frac{d}{dt}\,\text{rot}\,\mathbf{h} = v_{\parallel}\,\mathbf{h}\cdot(\mathbf{h}\nabla)\,\text{rot}\,\mathbf{h} = v_{\parallel}\,\mathbf{h}\cdot\text{rot}\,(\mathbf{h}\nabla)\,\mathbf{h} - v_{\parallel}\,(\mathbf{h}\,\text{rot}\,\mathbf{h})\,\text{div}\,\mathbf{h}.$$

$$\dot{P}_{\perp} = \frac{1}{2B} V_{\perp} P_{\parallel} (\mathbf{h}\nabla B) - \frac{ea_{\perp}}{2} (\mathbf{h} \operatorname{rot} \mathbf{E}) + \frac{ea_{\perp}}{2B} (\mathbf{E} [\mathbf{h}\nabla B]) + \\ + \frac{a_{\parallel} V_{\parallel} P_{\perp}}{2B} (\nabla B [\mathbf{h} \cdot (\mathbf{h}\nabla) \mathbf{h}]). \tag{6.12}$$

3. Equations (6.11) and (6.12) can be replaced by two equivalent equations. One of these expresses the conservation of energy. The energy expression is obtained if Eqs. (6.11) and (6.12) are multiplied by $P_{\parallel}$ and $P_{\perp}$, respectively, and then added. We find

$$\frac{1}{2m} \frac{dP^2}{dt} = \frac{d}{dt} (mc^2) = e (\mathbf{E}\dot{\mathbf{R}}) - \frac{ea_{\perp} V_{\perp}}{2} (\mathbf{h} \operatorname{rot} \mathbf{E}). \tag{6.13}$$

The first term on the right side of Eq. (6.13) represents the work done by the electric field on the particle, assuming the particle to be moving with the velocity of the guiding center $\dot{\mathbf{R}}$. The second term is related to the work performed by the solenoidal electric field on the particle gyrating in the Larmor circle. It is evident that within the required accuracy P and $V_{\perp}$ can be replaced by p and $v_{\perp}$. We note that the magnetic field does not appear in Eq. (6.13). This result is reasonable since the magnetic field does no work.

In order to obtain the second equation we rewrite Eq. (6.12) in the form

$$\dot{P}_{\perp} = \frac{P_{\perp}}{2B} (\dot{\mathbf{R}} \nabla B) - \frac{ea_{\perp}}{2} (\mathbf{h} \operatorname{rot} \mathbf{E}). \tag{6.14}$$

Since

$$\frac{dB}{dt} = \frac{\partial B}{\partial t} + (\dot{\mathbf{R}} \nabla B),$$

then

$$\dot{P}_{\perp} = \frac{P_{\perp}}{2B} \cdot \frac{dB}{dt} - \frac{ea_{\perp}}{2} \left\{ \mathbf{h} \operatorname{rot} \mathbf{E} + \frac{1}{c} \frac{\partial B}{\partial t} \right\}. \tag{6.15}$$

The expression in the curly brackets vanishes by virtue of the Maxwell equation rot $\mathbf{E}$ + $(1/c)(\partial B/\partial t) = 0$ and we find

$$\dot{P}_{\perp} = \frac{P_{\perp}}{2B} \frac{dB}{dt}. \tag{6.16}$$

Integration of this last equation yields

$$\frac{P_{\perp}^2}{B} = \text{const}, \tag{6.17}$$

i.e., the quantity $P^2_{\perp}/B$ is an adiabatic invariant to second order. In order to obtain this invariant we have explicitly used the Maxwell equation $\text{rot}\,\mathbf{E} + (1/c)(\partial B/\partial t) = 0$. If the particle is subject to other force fields in addition to the electromagnetic field $P^2_{\perp}/B$ may not be an adiabatic invariant. If an additional force $\mathbf{F}$ acts on the particle Eq. (6.16) assumes the form

$$\dot{P}_{\perp} = \frac{P_{\perp}}{2B}\frac{dB}{dt} - \frac{a_{\perp}}{2}\,\mathbf{h}\,\text{rot}\,\mathbf{F}. \tag{6.18}$$

However Eq. (6.17) still applies if the force field is such that $\mathbf{h}\,\text{rot}\,\mathbf{F} = 0$. In particular, this is the case when the force $\mathbf{F}$ is derivable from a potential.

4. The system of drift equations can be written in the convenient form

$$\left.\begin{aligned} \dot{\mathbf{R}} &= V_{\parallel}\mathbf{h} + \frac{c}{B^2}[\mathbf{E}\mathbf{B}] + \frac{V_{\perp}a_{\perp}}{2B}[\mathbf{h}\nabla B] + V_{\parallel}a_{\parallel}[\mathbf{h}\cdot(\mathbf{h}\nabla)\,\mathbf{h}];\\ \frac{d}{dt}(mc^2) &= e(\mathbf{E}\,\dot{\mathbf{R}}) - \frac{ea_{\perp}V_{\perp}}{2}(\mathbf{h}\,\text{rot}\,\mathbf{E});\\ \frac{P_{\perp}^2}{B} &= \text{const}. \end{aligned}\right\} \tag{6.19}$$

These equations are supplemented by the relations

$$\left.\begin{aligned} &P_{\parallel} = mV_{\parallel};\quad P_{\perp} = mV_{\perp};\\ &m = \frac{m_0}{\sqrt{1 - \dfrac{V_{\parallel}^2 + V_{\perp}^2}{c^2}}};\\ &a_{\parallel} = \frac{cP_{\parallel}}{eB};\quad a_{\perp} = \frac{cP_{\perp}}{eB}. \end{aligned}\right\} \tag{6.20}$$

We note finally that Eq. (6.11) reduces to

$$\dot{P}_{\parallel} = (e\mathbf{E} - \mu\nabla B)\left(\mathbf{h} + \frac{a_{\parallel}}{\varrho}\mathbf{b}\right), \tag{6.21}$$

where μ is the magnetic moment of the particle gyrating in a Larmor circle, ρ is the radius of curvature of the line of force passing through the guiding center, and $\mathbf{b}$ is the unit vector associated with the binormal to this line of force.

§ 7. Derivation of Certain Auxiliary Relations

1. In order to derive the equations in the preceding section it is necessary to smooth the right sides of Eq. (5.3), retaining smoothly varying terms of second order. For this purpose we must find explicit expressions for m, $\mathbf{E}$, $\mathbf{h}$, $v_{\parallel}$, $p_{\parallel}$, $v_{\perp}$, $p_{\perp}$, and $\mathbf{n}_1$ (starting with accuracy to first-order terms inclusively) that are valid for small time intervals (of the order of a cyclotron period). If these expressions are substituted in Eq. (5.3) the first and second order terms on the right sides of the resulting equations are explicitly separated. It is then easy to carry out the smoothing operation either by direct removal of the oscillating terms or by means of the intermediate averaging operation described in §4. It is the purpose of the present section to find these expressions and to derive the required smoothing formulas.

As a preliminary step we introduce certain auxiliary relations in which it is assumed that the vectors $\mathbf{n}_1$ and $\mathbf{n}_2$ are taken in the zeroth approximation, that is to say, it is assumed that these vectors gyrate uniformly around the vector $\mathbf{h}$ with angular velocity $\boldsymbol{\omega} = -e\mathbf{B}/mc$.

2. The time derivatives of $\mathbf{n}_1$ and $\mathbf{n}_2$ can be written

$$\left.\begin{aligned} \dot{\mathbf{n}}_1 &= [\boldsymbol{\omega}\mathbf{n}_1], \\ \dot{\mathbf{n}}_2 &= [\boldsymbol{\omega}\mathbf{n}_2]. \end{aligned}\right\} \tag{7.1}$$

Using the relations in (1.11) and (1.18) these expressions can be reduced to the form

$$\left.\begin{aligned} \dot{\mathbf{n}}_1 &= \omega\mathbf{n}_2, \\ \dot{\mathbf{n}}_2 &= -\omega\mathbf{n}_1, \end{aligned}\right\} \tag{7.2}$$

whence

$$\left.\begin{aligned}\int \mathbf{n}_1\,dt &= -\frac{1}{\omega}\,\mathbf{n}_2 + \text{const},\\ \int \mathbf{n}_2\,dt &= \frac{1}{\omega}\,\mathbf{n}_1 + \text{const}.\end{aligned}\right\} \tag{7.3}$$

The relations in (7.2) and (7.3) are essentially formulas for the differentiation and integration of the sine and cosine functions written in vector form. Integrating by parts we can show easily that

$$\left.\begin{aligned}\int t\mathbf{n}_1\,dt &= -\frac{t}{\omega}\mathbf{n}_2 + \frac{1}{\omega^2}\,\mathbf{n}_1 + \text{const},\\ \int t\mathbf{n}_2\,dt &= \frac{t}{\omega}\mathbf{n}_1 + \frac{1}{\omega^2}\,\mathbf{n}_2 + \text{const},\end{aligned}\right\} \tag{7.4}$$

$$\left.\begin{aligned}\int t^2\mathbf{n}_1 dt &= \frac{1}{\omega}\left(\frac{2}{\omega^2} - t^2\right)\mathbf{n}_2 + \frac{2t}{\omega^2}\,\mathbf{n}_1 + \text{const},\\ \int t^2\mathbf{n}_2 dt &= \frac{1}{\omega}\left(-\frac{2}{\omega^2} + t^2\right)\mathbf{n}_1 + \frac{2t}{\omega^2}\,\mathbf{n}_2 + \text{const}.\end{aligned}\right\} \tag{7.5}$$

Let **A** be an arbitrary constant vector or a slowly and smoothly varying vector characterizing the field at the location of the particle. Neglecting the time derivatives of this vector compared with the derivatives of the rapidly varying vectors $\mathbf{n}_1$ and $\mathbf{n}_2$, by virtue of Eq. (7.2) we have

$$\left.\begin{aligned}\frac{d}{dt}\{\mathbf{n}_1\cdot(\mathbf{n}_1\nabla)\,\mathbf{A}\} &= -\frac{d}{dt}\{\mathbf{n}_2\cdot(\mathbf{n}_2\nabla)\,\mathbf{A}\} =\\ &= \omega\,\{\mathbf{n}_2\cdot(\mathbf{n}_1\nabla)\,\mathbf{A} + \mathbf{n}_1\cdot(\mathbf{n}_2\nabla)\mathbf{A}\};\\ \frac{d}{dt}\{\mathbf{n}_2\cdot(\mathbf{n}_1\nabla)\,\mathbf{A}\} &= \frac{d}{dt}\{\mathbf{n}_1\cdot(\mathbf{n}_2\nabla)\,\mathbf{A}\} =\\ &= \omega\,\{\mathbf{n}_2\cdot(\mathbf{n}_2\nabla)\,\mathbf{A} - \mathbf{n}_1\cdot(\mathbf{n}_1\nabla)\,\mathbf{A}\}.\end{aligned}\right\} \tag{7.6}$$

Evidently

$$\begin{aligned}\mathbf{n}_2\cdot(\mathbf{n}_1\nabla)\,\mathbf{A} + \mathbf{n}_1\cdot(\mathbf{n}_2\nabla)\,\mathbf{A} &= 2\mathbf{n}_2\cdot(\mathbf{n}_1\nabla)\,\mathbf{A} + \mathbf{n}_1\cdot(\mathbf{n}_2\nabla)\,\mathbf{A} - \mathbf{n}_2\cdot(\mathbf{n}_1\nabla)\,\mathbf{A} =\\ &= 2\mathbf{n}_2\cdot(\mathbf{n}_1\nabla)\,\mathbf{A} - \mathbf{h}\cdot\{[\mathbf{n}_1\cdot(\mathbf{n}_1\nabla)\,\mathbf{A}] + [\mathbf{n}_2\cdot(\mathbf{n}_2\nabla)\,\mathbf{A}]\},\end{aligned}$$

or, by virtue of the identity in (2.15),

$$\mathbf{n}_2\cdot(\mathbf{n}_1\nabla)\,\mathbf{A} + \mathbf{n}_1\cdot(\mathbf{n}_2\nabla)\,\mathbf{A} = 2\mathbf{n}_2\cdot(\mathbf{n}_1\nabla)\,\mathbf{A} - \mathbf{h}\,\mathrm{rot}\,\mathbf{A} = \\ = 2\mathbf{n}_1\cdot(\mathbf{n}_2\nabla)\,\mathbf{A} + \mathbf{h}\,\mathrm{rot}\,\mathbf{A}. \tag{7.7}$$

Similarly, using the identity in (2.16), we have

$$\mathbf{n}_2\cdot(\mathbf{n}_2\nabla)\,\mathbf{A} - \mathbf{n}_1\cdot(\mathbf{n}_1\nabla)\,\mathbf{A} = 2\mathbf{n}_2\cdot(\mathbf{n}_2\nabla)\,\mathbf{A} - \mathrm{div}\,\mathbf{A} + \mathbf{h}\cdot(\mathbf{h}\nabla)\,\mathbf{A} = \\ = -2\mathbf{n}_1\cdot(\mathbf{n}_1\nabla)\,\mathbf{A} + \mathrm{div}\,\mathbf{A} - \mathbf{h}\cdot(\mathbf{h}\nabla)\,\mathbf{A}. \tag{7.8}$$

Using the identities in (7.7) and (7.8) we can write Eq. (7.6) in the form

$$\left.\begin{aligned} &\frac{d}{dt}\{\mathbf{n}_1\cdot(\mathbf{n}_1\nabla)\,\mathbf{A}\} = -\frac{d}{dt}\{\mathbf{n}_2\cdot(\mathbf{n}_2\nabla)\,\mathbf{A}\} = \\ &= 2\omega\mathbf{n}_2\cdot(\mathbf{n}_1\nabla)\,\mathbf{A} - \omega\mathbf{h}\,\mathrm{rot}\,\mathbf{A} = \\ &= 2\omega\mathbf{n}_1\cdot(\mathbf{n}_2\nabla)\,\mathbf{A} + \omega\mathbf{h}\,\mathrm{rot}\,\mathbf{A}, \\ &\frac{d}{dt}\{\mathbf{n}_2\cdot(\mathbf{n}_1\nabla)\,\mathbf{A}\} = \frac{d}{dt}\{\mathbf{n}_1\cdot(\mathbf{n}_2\nabla)\,\mathbf{A}\} = \\ &= 2\omega\mathbf{n}_2\cdot(\mathbf{n}_2\nabla)\,\mathbf{A} - \omega\{\mathrm{div}\,\mathbf{A} - \mathbf{h}\cdot(\mathbf{h}\nabla)\,\mathbf{A}\} = \\ &= -2\omega\mathbf{n}_1\cdot(\mathbf{n}_1\nabla)\,\mathbf{A} + \omega\{\mathrm{div}\,\mathbf{A} - \mathbf{h}\cdot(\mathbf{h}\nabla)\,\mathbf{A}\}, \end{aligned}\right\} \tag{7.9}$$

whence

$$\int \mathbf{n}_1\cdot(\mathbf{n}_1\nabla)\,\mathbf{A}\,dt = -\frac{1}{2\omega}\mathbf{n}_2\cdot(\mathbf{n}_1\nabla)\,\mathbf{A} + \\ + \frac{t}{2}\{\mathrm{div}\,\mathbf{A} - \mathbf{h}\cdot(\mathbf{h}\nabla)\,\mathbf{A}\} + \mathrm{const} = \\ = -\frac{1}{2\omega}\mathbf{n}_1\cdot(\mathbf{n}_2\nabla)\,\mathbf{A} + \frac{t}{2}\{\mathrm{div}\,\mathbf{A} - \mathbf{h}\cdot(\mathbf{h}\nabla)\,\mathbf{A}\} + \mathrm{const};$$

$$\int \mathbf{n}_2\cdot(\mathbf{n}_2\nabla)\,\mathbf{A}\,dt = \frac{1}{2\omega}\mathbf{n}_2\cdot(\mathbf{n}_1\nabla)\,\mathbf{A} + \\ + \frac{t}{2}\{\mathrm{div}\,\mathbf{A} - \mathbf{h}\cdot(\mathbf{h}\nabla)\,\mathbf{A}\} + \mathrm{const} = \\ = \frac{1}{2\omega}\mathbf{n}_1\cdot(\mathbf{n}_2\nabla)\,\mathbf{A} + \frac{t}{2}\{\mathrm{div}\,\mathbf{A} - \mathbf{h}\cdot(\mathbf{h}\nabla)\,\mathbf{A}\} + \mathrm{const};$$

$$\int \mathbf{n}_2\cdot(\mathbf{n}_1\nabla)\,\mathbf{A}\,dt = \frac{1}{2\omega}\mathbf{n}_1\cdot(\mathbf{n}_1\nabla)\,\mathbf{A} + \frac{t}{2}\mathbf{h}\,\mathrm{rot}\,\mathbf{A} + \mathrm{const} = \\ = -\frac{1}{2\omega}\mathbf{n}_2\cdot(\mathbf{n}_2\nabla)\mathbf{A} + \frac{t}{2}\mathbf{h}\,\mathrm{rot}\,\mathbf{A} + \mathrm{const}; \tag{7.10}$$

$$\int \mathbf{n}_1\cdot(\mathbf{n}_2\nabla)\,\mathbf{A}\,dt = \frac{1}{2\omega}\,\mathbf{n}_1\cdot(\mathbf{n}_1\nabla)\,\mathbf{A} - \frac{t}{2}\,\mathbf{h}\,\mathrm{rot}\,\mathbf{A} + \mathrm{const} =$$

$$= \frac{1}{2\omega}\,\mathbf{n}_2\cdot(\mathbf{n}_2\nabla)\,\mathbf{A} - \frac{t}{2}\,\mathbf{h}\,\mathrm{rot}\,\mathbf{A} + \mathrm{const}. \qquad (7.10)$$

From the first two relations in Eq. (7.10) we obtain directly

$$\int \{\mathbf{n}_2\cdot(\mathbf{n}_2\nabla)\,\mathbf{A} - \mathbf{n}_1\cdot(\mathbf{n}_1\nabla)\,\mathbf{A}\}\,dt = \frac{1}{\omega}\,\mathbf{n}_2\cdot(\mathbf{n}_1\nabla)\,\mathbf{A} + \mathrm{const}. \qquad (7.11)$$

3. We take the x and y axes (with unit vectors $\mathbf{i}$ and $\mathbf{j}$) to be in the instantaneous directions of the vectors $\mathbf{n}_1$ and $\mathbf{n}_2$ at time t = 0. The z axis is along the vector $\mathbf{h}$. Thus

$$\mathbf{n}_1 = \mathbf{i}\cos\omega t + \mathbf{j}\sin\omega t; \quad \mathbf{n}_2 = -\mathbf{i}\sin\omega t + \mathbf{j}\cos\omega t. \qquad (7.12)$$

It is a simple matter to derive the relations

$$\left.\begin{aligned}
\mathbf{n}_1\cdot(\mathbf{n}_1\nabla)\,\mathbf{A} &= \frac{1}{2}\left(\frac{\partial A_x}{\partial x} + \frac{\partial A_y}{\partial y}\right) + \frac{1}{2}\left(\frac{\partial A_x}{\partial x} - \frac{\partial A_y}{\partial y}\right)\cos 2\omega t + \\
&\quad + \frac{1}{2}\left(\frac{\partial A_y}{\partial x} + \frac{\partial A_x}{\partial y}\right)\sin 2\omega t; \\
\mathbf{n}_2\cdot(\mathbf{n}_2\nabla)\,\mathbf{A} &= \frac{1}{2}\left(\frac{\partial A_x}{\partial x} + \frac{\partial A_y}{\partial y}\right) - \frac{1}{2}\left(\frac{\partial A_x}{\partial x} - \frac{\partial A_y}{\partial y}\right)\cos 2\omega t - \\
&\quad - \frac{1}{2}\left(\frac{\partial A_y}{\partial x} + \frac{\partial A_x}{\partial y}\right)\sin 2\omega t; \\
\mathbf{n}_2\cdot(\mathbf{n}_1\nabla)\,\mathbf{A} &= \frac{1}{2}\left(\frac{\partial A_y}{\partial x} - \frac{\partial A_x}{\partial y}\right) + \frac{1}{2}\left(\frac{\partial A_y}{\partial x} + \frac{\partial A_x}{\partial y}\right)\cos 2\omega t - \\
&\quad - \frac{1}{2}\left(\frac{\partial A_x}{\partial x} - \frac{\partial A_y}{\partial y}\right)\sin 2\omega t; \\
\mathbf{n}_1\cdot(\mathbf{n}_2\nabla)\,\mathbf{A} &= -\frac{1}{2}\left(\frac{\partial A_y}{\partial x} - \frac{\partial A_x}{\partial y}\right) + \frac{1}{2}\left(\frac{\partial A_y}{\partial x} + \frac{\partial A_x}{\partial y}\right)\cos 2\omega t - \\
&\quad - \frac{1}{2}\left(\frac{\partial A_x}{\partial x} - \frac{\partial A_y}{\partial y}\right)\sin 2\omega t;
\end{aligned}\right\} \qquad (7.13)$$

from which it follows that

$$\mathbf{n}_1\cdot(\mathbf{n}_1\nabla)\,\mathbf{A} + \mathbf{n}_2\cdot(\mathbf{n}_2\nabla)\,\mathbf{A} = \frac{\partial A_x}{\partial x} + \frac{\partial A_y}{\partial y} =$$

$$= \operatorname{div} \mathbf{A} - \mathbf{h}\cdot(\mathbf{h}\nabla)\,\mathbf{A};$$

$$\mathbf{n}_2\cdot(\mathbf{n}_1\nabla)\,\mathbf{A} - \mathbf{n}_1\cdot(\mathbf{n}_2\nabla)\,\mathbf{A} = \frac{\partial A_y}{\partial x} - \frac{\partial A_x}{\partial y} = \mathbf{h}\operatorname{rot}\mathbf{A};$$

$$\mathbf{n}_1\cdot(\mathbf{n}_1\nabla)\,\mathbf{A} - \mathbf{n}_2\cdot(\mathbf{n}_2\nabla)\,\mathbf{A} = \left(\frac{\partial A_x}{\partial x} - \frac{\partial A_y}{\partial y}\right)\cos 2\omega t + \left(\frac{\partial A_y}{\partial x} + \frac{\partial A_x}{\partial y}\right)\sin 2\omega t; \tag{7.14}$$

$$\mathbf{n}_1\cdot(\mathbf{n}_2\nabla)\,\mathbf{A} + \mathbf{n}_2\cdot(\mathbf{n}_1\nabla)\,\mathbf{A} = \left(\frac{\partial A_y}{\partial x} + \frac{\partial A_x}{\partial y}\right)\cos 2\omega t - \left(\frac{\partial A_x}{\partial x} - \frac{\partial A_y}{\partial y}\right)\sin 2\omega t.$$

4. The formulas that have been derived yield a simple method for solving the problem given at the beginning of the present section, i. e., the problem of finding expressions for m, **E**, **h**, and ... to a first approximation suitable for small intervals of time of the order of the cyclotron period T(t). As an example we find an expression for the particle mass. From the energy equation,

$$\frac{dm}{dt} = \frac{e}{c^2}(\mathbf{vE}) = \frac{e}{c^2}v_{\parallel}(\mathbf{hE}) + \frac{e}{c^2}v_{\perp}(\mathbf{n}_1\mathbf{E}).$$

To the degree of accuracy we have adopted all quantities on the right, with the exception of $\mathbf{n}_1$, can be assumed constant. These quantities can be taken out from under the integral sign, thereby introducing an error of second order at most. To this same degree of accuracy it is sufficient to take the rapidly rotating vector $\mathbf{n}_1$ in the zeroth approximation. Then

$$m(t) = \int \frac{e}{c^2}v_{\parallel}(\mathbf{hE})\,dt + \int \frac{e}{c^2}v_{\perp}(\mathbf{n}_1\mathbf{E})\,dt =$$

$$= \frac{e}{c^2}v_{\parallel}(\mathbf{hE})\int dt + \frac{e}{c^2}v_{\perp}\mathbf{E}\int \mathbf{n}_1\,dt,$$

whence, from the first expression in (7.3),

$$m(t) = \frac{ev_{\parallel}}{c^2}(\mathbf{hE})\,t - \frac{ev_{\perp}}{\omega c^2}(\mathbf{n}_2\mathbf{E}) + \text{const}.$$

The constant term can be determined as follows. The expression for m(t) is averaged using Eq. (4.3) and taking t = 0. When this average is taken the first two terms vanish and the constant term is found to be $\overline{m(0)}$.

Thus

$$m\,(t) = \widetilde{m\,(0)} + \delta m, \tag{7.15}$$

where

$$\delta m = \frac{ev_{\parallel}}{c^2}\,(\mathbf{hE})\,t - \frac{ev_{\perp}}{\omega c^2}\,(\mathbf{n}_2\mathbf{E}) \tag{7.16}$$

with a possible error of second order.

Similarly, from the relation

$$\frac{dB}{dt} = \frac{\partial B}{\partial t} + (\mathbf{v}\nabla)\,B \approx v_{\parallel}\,(\mathbf{h}\nabla B) + v_{\perp}\,(\mathbf{n}_1\nabla)\,B$$

we find

$$\left.\begin{aligned} B\,(t) &= \widetilde{B\,(0)} + \delta B; \\ \delta B &= v_{\parallel}\,(\mathbf{h}\nabla B)\,t - \frac{v_{\perp}}{\omega}\,(\mathbf{n}_2\nabla)\,B. \end{aligned}\right\} \tag{7.17}$$

Further

$$\left.\begin{aligned} \mathbf{h}\,(t) &= \widetilde{\mathbf{h}\,(0)} + \delta\mathbf{h}; \\ \delta\mathbf{h} &= v_{\parallel}\,t\,(\mathbf{h}\nabla)\,\mathbf{h} - \frac{v_{\perp}}{\omega}\,(\mathbf{n}_2\nabla)\,\mathbf{h}; \end{aligned}\right\} \tag{7.18}$$

$$\left.\begin{aligned} \mathbf{E}\,(t) &= \widetilde{\mathbf{E}\,(0)} + \delta\mathbf{E}; \\ \delta\mathbf{E} &= v_{\parallel}\,t\,(\mathbf{h}\nabla)\,\mathbf{E} - \frac{v_{\perp}}{\omega}\,(\mathbf{n}_2\nabla)\,\mathbf{E}. \end{aligned}\right\} \tag{7.19}$$

Finally, $p_{\parallel}(t)$ and $p_{\perp}(t)$ are found to a first approximation. For this purpose we integrate Eq. (5.3). Using the first formula in Eq. (7.10) and the relation*

$$\widetilde{\mathbf{n}_2\cdot(\mathbf{n}_1\nabla)\,\mathbf{A}} = \frac{1}{2}\,(\mathbf{h}\,\mathrm{rot}\,\mathbf{A}) \tag{7.20}$$

---

*This relation follows from the fact that $\mathbf{n}_2(\mathbf{n}_1\nabla)\mathbf{A}$ contains a rapidly varying first-order term so that the analogous term in $\overline{\mathbf{n}_2\,(\mathbf{n}_1\nabla)\,\mathbf{A}}$ will be of second order. Hence, $\widetilde{\mathbf{n}_2\,(\mathbf{n}_1\nabla)\,\mathbf{A}}$ must coincide with $\overline{\mathbf{n}_2\,(\mathbf{n}_1\nabla)\,\mathbf{A}}$. to within second-order errors. The value of the latter quantity is given by Eq. (2.19) and found to be $^1/_2(\mathbf{h}\ \mathrm{rot}\ \mathbf{A})$.

we find

$$\left.\begin{aligned} p_{\parallel}(t) &= \widetilde{p_{\parallel}(0)} + \delta p_{\parallel}; \\ \delta p_{\parallel} &= e(\mathbf{Eh})\,t - \frac{v_{\parallel}p_{\perp}}{\omega}\mathbf{n}_2\cdot(\mathbf{h}\nabla)\,\mathbf{h} - \frac{v_{\perp}p_{\perp}}{2\omega}\mathbf{n}_2\cdot(\mathbf{n}_1\nabla)\,\mathbf{h} + \\ &+ \frac{v_{\perp}p_{\perp}}{4\omega}(\mathbf{h}\,\mathrm{rot}\,\mathbf{h}) + \frac{v_{\perp}p_{\perp}}{2}\,t\,\mathrm{div}\,\mathbf{h}; \end{aligned}\right\} \quad (7.21)$$

$$\left.\begin{aligned} p_{\perp}(t) &= \widetilde{p_{\perp}(0)} + \delta p_{\perp}; \\ \delta p_{\perp} &= -\frac{e}{\omega}(\mathbf{E}\mathbf{n}_2) + \frac{v_{\parallel}p_{\parallel}}{\omega}\mathbf{n}_2\cdot(\mathbf{h}\nabla)\,\mathbf{h} + \\ &+ \frac{v_{\perp}p_{\parallel}}{2\omega}\mathbf{n}_2\cdot(\mathbf{n}_1\nabla)\,\mathbf{h} - \frac{v_{\perp}p_{\parallel}}{4\omega}(\mathbf{h}\,\mathrm{rot}\,\mathbf{h}) - \frac{v_{\perp}p_{\parallel}}{2}\,t\,\mathrm{div}\,\mathbf{h}. \end{aligned}\right\} \quad (7.22)$$

5. It is somewhat more difficult to find expressions for $\mathbf{n}_1(t)$ and $\mathbf{n}_2(t)$. By definition

$$\mathbf{n}_1 = \frac{\mathbf{p}_{\perp}}{p_{\perp}} = \frac{\mathbf{p} - p_{\parallel}\mathbf{h}}{p_{\perp}}.$$

Differentiating this expression with respect to time and using Eqs. (1.2) and (5.1) we find without difficulty

$$\frac{d\mathbf{n}_1}{dt} = -\frac{e}{mc}[\mathbf{B}\mathbf{n}_1] + \frac{1}{p_{\perp}}\left\{e(\mathbf{E}\mathbf{n}_2) - p_{\parallel}\left(\mathbf{n}_2\frac{d\mathbf{h}}{dt}\right)\right\}\mathbf{n}_2 - \left(\mathbf{n}_1\frac{d\mathbf{h}}{dt}\right)\mathbf{h}. \quad (7.23)$$

In contrast with all the preceding examples, in addition to containing first-order terms the derivative $d\mathbf{n}_1/dt$ contains the term $-(e/mc)[\mathbf{B}\mathbf{n}_1]$, which is of zero order; the presence of this term complicates the calculation. We must first separate from $\mathbf{n}_1$ the rapidly rotating zero-order vector $\mathbf{n}_1^0$ whose derivative would be $-(e/mc)[\mathbf{B}\mathbf{n}_1]$ in this order. The calculation of the small correction $\delta\mathbf{n}_1$ can then be reduced to a simple integration, completely analogous to the integration in the calculation of the quantities m, **B**, **h**, etc. Thus, the unit vector $\mathbf{n}_1$ is written in the form

$$\mathbf{n}_1 = \mathbf{n}_1^0 + \delta\mathbf{n}_1. \quad (7.24)$$

The uniformly rotating unit vector $\mathbf{n}_1^0$ is not determined uniquely but only to second-order accuracy. We exploit this arbitrariness and choose the vector $\mathbf{n}_1^0$ to satisfy the equation

$$\frac{d\mathbf{n}_1^0}{dt} = \left[\boldsymbol{\omega}_0 \mathbf{n}_1^0\right], \tag{7.25}$$

where ω_0 is the constant angular velocity

$$\boldsymbol{\omega}_0 = \frac{e\widetilde{\mathbf{B}(0)}}{\widetilde{m(0)}\, c}. \tag{7.26}$$

The vector $\mathbf{n}_1^0$ is still not determined uniquely because in our ordering there are still three arbitrary constants that determine the initial value of $\mathbf{n}_1^0$. These are related by only one equation so that $\mathbf{n}_1^0$ is unique to within a possible error of second order.

Now, substituting Eq. (7.24) in Eq. (7.23), using Eq. (7.25), and neglecting second-order quantities, we have

$$\frac{d}{dt}\delta\mathbf{n}_1 = -\frac{e}{c}\left[\delta\frac{\mathbf{B}}{m}\cdot\mathbf{n}_1\right] - \frac{e}{c}\left[\frac{\mathbf{B}}{m}\cdot\delta\mathbf{n}_1\right] + \\ + \frac{1}{p_\perp}\left\{e(\mathbf{E}\mathbf{n}_2) - p_\parallel\left(\mathbf{n}_2\frac{d\mathbf{h}}{dt}\right)\right\}\mathbf{n}_2 - \left(\mathbf{n}_1\frac{d\mathbf{h}}{dt}\right)\mathbf{h}, \tag{7.27}$$

where

$$\delta\frac{\mathbf{B}}{m} = \frac{\mathbf{B}}{m} - \frac{\widetilde{\mathbf{B}(0)}}{\widetilde{m(0)}} = \frac{m\delta\mathbf{B} - \mathbf{B}\delta m}{m^2}.$$

We note that it makes no difference whether we write ω_0, $\mathbf{n}_1^0$ or ω, $\mathbf{n}_1$ in the first-order terms since the difference only appears in second order. This feature will be used below without further comment.

Equation (7.27) is still not in convenient form for the calculation of $\delta\mathbf{n}_1$ because it contains $\delta\mathbf{n}_1$ on the right side and the value of this vector is not known in the first approximation. Hence, the integral of the right side of Eq. (7.27) can not be obtained directly and we are forced to use the following somewhat artificial approach. Since $\mathbf{n}_1$ and $\mathbf{n}_1^0$ are unit vectors it follows from (7.24) that to second order $\mathbf{n}_1\delta\mathbf{n}_1 = 0$. Hence, $\delta\mathbf{n}_1$ is perpendicular to $\mathbf{n}_1$ and can be expanded in terms of $\mathbf{n}_2$ and $\mathbf{h}$:

$$\delta \mathbf{n}_1 = \alpha \mathbf{n}_2 + \beta \mathbf{h}. \tag{7.28}$$

Thus

$$\alpha = (\mathbf{n}_2 \delta \mathbf{n}_1); \qquad \beta = (\mathbf{h} \delta \mathbf{n}_1).$$

The problem is now reduced to the calculation of the coefficients α and β. In order to carry out this calculation we must first find the time derivatives of these coefficients. When differentiating β with respect to time the vector $\mathbf{h}$ need not be differentiated since $\dot{\mathbf{h}}\delta\mathbf{n}_1$ is a second-order quantity. Furthermore, $\dot{\mathbf{n}}_2\delta\mathbf{n}_1 = -\omega\mathbf{n}_1\delta\mathbf{n}_1 = 0$. Finally, $\mathbf{h}\delta(\mathbf{B}/m) = \delta(B/m)$. Taking all these factors into account, from the preceding expressions and Eq. (7.27) we have

$$\left.\begin{aligned} \frac{d\alpha}{dt} &= -\frac{e}{c}\,\delta\frac{B}{m} + \frac{1}{p_\perp}\left\{e\,(\mathbf{E}\mathbf{n}_2) - p_\parallel\left(\mathbf{n}_2\frac{d\mathbf{h}}{dt}\right)\right\}; \\ \frac{d\beta}{dt} &= -\,\omega\,(\mathbf{n}_2\delta\mathbf{h}) - \left(\mathbf{n}_1\frac{d\mathbf{h}}{dt}\right). \end{aligned}\right\} \tag{7.29}$$

Here

$$\delta\frac{B}{m} = \frac{m\delta B - B\delta m}{m^2}. \tag{7.30}$$

The right side of Eq. (7.29) now only contains functions that may be regarded as known in a first approximation. Hence the coefficients to be determined, α and β, can be found from Eq. (7.29) by the same method of integration that was used earlier for finding the functions $m(t)$, $\mathbf{B}(t)$, etc.

We introduce Eq. (7.30) in Eq. (7.29) and replace δm, δB, and $\delta\mathbf{h}$ by the expressions in (7.16), (7.17), and (7.18). Now $d\mathbf{h}/dt$ is transformed using Eq. (2.11), and the $\partial\mathbf{h}/\partial t$ term is neglected. Integrating the expressions obtained for $d\alpha/dt$ and $d\beta/dt$ with respect to time and using Eqs. (7.3), (7.4), (7.10), and (7.11) we find

$$\left.\begin{aligned} \alpha = &-\frac{ev_\parallel t^2}{2mc}\left\{(\mathbf{h}\nabla B) + \frac{\omega}{c}(\mathbf{h}\mathbf{E})\right\} - \frac{v_\parallel t}{2}\,\mathbf{h}\,\mathrm{rot}\,\mathbf{h} + \\ &+ \frac{e}{\omega p_\perp}\left(1 + \frac{v_\perp^2}{c^2}\right)(\mathbf{E}\mathbf{n}_1) + \frac{ev_\perp}{mc\omega^2}(\mathbf{n}_1\nabla B) - \\ &- \frac{v_\parallel^2}{\omega v_\perp}\,\mathbf{n}_1\cdot(\mathbf{h}\nabla)\,\mathbf{h} - \frac{v_\parallel}{2\omega}\,\mathbf{n}_1\cdot(\mathbf{n}_1\nabla)\,\mathbf{h} + \mathrm{const}; \\ \beta = &-v_\parallel t\mathbf{n}_1\cdot(\mathbf{h}\nabla)\,\mathbf{h} + \frac{v_\perp}{\omega}\,\mathbf{n}_2\cdot(\mathbf{n}_1\nabla)\,\mathbf{h} + \mathrm{const}. \end{aligned}\right\} \tag{7.31}$$

The unit vector $\mathbf{n}_1$ is now determined by the expression $\mathbf{n}_1 = \mathbf{n}_1^0 + \alpha\mathbf{n}_2 + \beta\mathbf{h}$. It remains to determine the additive constants in Eq. (7.31). This problem cannot be solved uniquely since the uniformly rotating vector $\mathbf{n}_1^0$ has, up to this point, only been specified by the differential equation in (7.25), and is not yet determined uniquely. We take $\mathbf{n}_1^0$ to be perpendicular to $\widetilde{\mathbf{h}(0)}$. Furthermore, the constant in the expression for α is defined in such as way that α vanishes when $t = 0$. The value of this constant is not important in what follows and need not be computed. We shall, however, compute the constant in the expression for $\beta(t)$. Writing $t = 0$, we find $\mathbf{n}_1(0) = \mathbf{n}_1^0(0) + \beta\mathbf{h}(0)$; then, taking the scalar product with $\mathbf{h}(0)$ we find the initial value of β:

$$\beta(0) = -\mathbf{h}(0)\,\mathbf{n}_1^0(0).$$

By virtue of Eq. (7.18)

$$\mathbf{h}(0) = \widetilde{\mathbf{h}(0)} - \frac{v_\perp}{\omega}\{(\mathbf{n}_2\nabla)\,\mathbf{h}\}_0.$$

(The zero symbol means that the quantity enclosed in the curly brackets is taken at $t = 0$.) Now, since $\widetilde{\mathbf{h}(0)}$ is perpendicular to $\mathbf{n}_1^0$,

$$\beta(0) = \frac{v_\perp}{\omega}\{\mathbf{n}_1\cdot(\mathbf{n}_2\nabla)\,\mathbf{h}\}_0,$$

and $\beta(t)$ is determined uniquely. Thus, the additive constant in the expression for β is

$$\frac{v_\perp}{\omega}\{\mathbf{n}_1\cdot(\mathbf{n}_2\nabla)\,\mathbf{h} - \mathbf{n}_2(\mathbf{n}_1\nabla)\,\mathbf{h}\}_0.$$

Here the zero can be omitted because in the present approximation the result is independent of time by virtue of Eq. (7.14).

The form of Eq. (7.31) merits an additional remark. In place of the unit vector $\mathbf{n}_1^0$ we could have taken any other uniformly rotating vector characterized by an angular velocity differing from that given in Eq. (7.26) by a first-order constant $\delta\boldsymbol{\omega}_0$. Then, we would have added a term $[\delta\boldsymbol{\omega}_0\cdot\mathbf{n}_1]$ on the right side of Eq. (7.27). The first formula in Eq. (7.29) would then have contained an additional term $[\delta\boldsymbol{\omega}_0\cdot\mathbf{n}_1]\mathbf{n}_2 = (\delta\boldsymbol{\omega}_0\mathbf{h})$ while the second would have contained the additional term $[\delta\boldsymbol{\omega}_0 \cdot \mathbf{n}_1]\mathbf{h} = -(\delta\boldsymbol{\omega}_0\mathbf{n}_2)$. Integration of these terms in Eq. (7.31) would have led to additional terms $(\delta\boldsymbol{\omega}_0\mathbf{h})t$ and $-(1/\omega)(\delta\boldsymbol{\omega}_0\mathbf{n}_1)$. If the length of $\boldsymbol{\omega}_0$ is changed, but not its direction, then $\delta\omega_0 = \delta\omega_0 \widetilde{\mathbf{h}(0)}$ or, to second order, $\delta\boldsymbol{\omega}_0 = \delta\omega_0 \cdot \mathbf{h}$. Consequently, $(\delta\boldsymbol{\omega}_0\mathbf{n}_1) = \delta\omega_0(\mathbf{h}\mathbf{n}_1) = 0$ and the second equation in (7.31) remains unchanged while the first contains an additional term linear in t.

Thus, if $\mathbf{n}_1^0(t)$ is chosen to be perpendicular to $\widetilde{\mathbf{h}(0)}$ and it is required that the coefficient α vanish at $t = 0$, the following expressions are obtained for α and β:

$$\alpha = \frac{e}{\omega p_\perp}\left(1 + \frac{v_\perp^2}{c^2}\right)(\mathbf{E}\mathbf{n}_1) + \frac{ev_\perp}{mc\omega^2}(\mathbf{n}_1\nabla B) -$$

$$-\frac{v_\parallel^2}{\omega v_\perp}\mathbf{n}_1(\mathbf{h}\nabla)\mathbf{h} - \frac{v_\parallel}{2\omega}\mathbf{n}_1\cdot(\mathbf{n}_1\nabla)\mathbf{h} + (at^2 + bt + d); \qquad (7.32)$$

$$\beta = -v_\parallel t\mathbf{n}_1\cdot(\mathbf{h}\nabla)\mathbf{h} + \frac{v_\perp}{\omega}\mathbf{n}_1\cdot(\mathbf{n}_2\nabla)\mathbf{h}.$$

These expressions together with Eq. (7.24) and (7.28) then represent a solution to the problem. A polynomial of second degree $at^2 + bt + d$ with constant coefficients a, b, and d is a first-order quantity. It will be shown below that the presence of this polynomial does not affect the smoothing of the functions that will be considered below. The length of $\boldsymbol{\omega}_0$ can then be changed by an arbitrary first-order term without affecting the second equation in (7.32); in the first equation only the value of the coefficient in the linear term bt is affected. This arbitrariness can be used to simplify calculations.

6. We conclude this section by deriving several auxiliary expressions required for averaging and smoothing of quantities containing rapidly varying terms. Let us assume that **A** and **C** are constant, or smoothly and slowly varying, vectors while $\mathbf{n}_1$ and $\mathbf{n}_2$ are taken in the zeroth approximation. Equations of this kind have already been obtained, [specifically Eqs. (2.13), (2.14), (2.17), (2.18), and (2.19)]. We shall use these and similar expressions in the following section.

Our general approach to finding smoothed quantities is the following: In certain cases the quantity being smoothed can be written in the form of a constant (or a slowly and smoothly varying quantity) and a rapidly varying part of first order. In these cases smoothing reduces to the simple removal of the rapidly varying terms. We have followed this procedure, for example, in the derivation of Eqs. (2.13) and (2.14). In other cases the quantity being smoothed may contain rapidly varying terms of zero order. Then using Eq. (4.3) we first find the average of this quantity at zero time $t = 0$. In view of the arbitrariness in the time reference the mean value calculated this way can be easily given in a form that applies for any value of t. In general it will contain a rapidly varying part of first order which can be omitted. The basis for this method of smoothing was given in §4.

It is evident first of all that to the required accuracy

$$\overline{(\mathbf{A}\mathbf{n}_1)} = \overline{(\mathbf{A}\mathbf{n}_2)} = 0. \tag{7.33}$$

Further, taking the scalar product of Eq. (2.14) with **C** yields

$$\overline{(\mathbf{A}\mathbf{n}_1)(\mathbf{C}\mathbf{n}_2)} = \frac{1}{2}\overline{(\mathbf{h}[\mathbf{A}\mathbf{C}])}. \tag{7.34}$$

The expressions in (7.13) are orthogonal to the expressions $(\mathbf{n}_1\mathbf{C})$ and $(\mathbf{n}_2\mathbf{C})$ over a cyclotron period $T = 2\pi/\omega$. The following relations then obtain

$$\begin{aligned}
&\overline{\mathbf{n}_1(\mathbf{n}_1\nabla)\mathbf{A}\cdot(\mathbf{n}_1\mathbf{C})} = \overline{\mathbf{n}_2(\mathbf{n}_2\nabla)\mathbf{A}\cdot(\mathbf{n}_1\mathbf{C})} = \\
&= \overline{\mathbf{n}_2(\mathbf{n}_1\nabla)\mathbf{A}\cdot(\mathbf{n}_1\mathbf{C})} = \overline{\mathbf{n}_1(\mathbf{n}_2\nabla)\mathbf{A}\cdot(\mathbf{n}_1\mathbf{C})} = \\
&= \overline{\mathbf{n}_1(\mathbf{n}_1\nabla)\mathbf{A}\cdot(\mathbf{n}_2\mathbf{C})} = \overline{\mathbf{n}_2(\mathbf{n}_2\nabla)\mathbf{A}\cdot(\mathbf{n}_2\mathbf{C})} = \\
&= \overline{\mathbf{n}_2(\mathbf{n}_1\nabla)\mathbf{A}\cdot(\mathbf{n}_2\mathbf{C})} = \overline{\mathbf{n}_1(\mathbf{n}_2\nabla)\mathbf{A}\cdot(\mathbf{n}_2\mathbf{C})} = 0.
\end{aligned} \tag{7.35}$$

In order to smooth the expression $\mathbf{n}_1\cdot(\mathbf{h}\nabla)(\mathbf{n}_2\nabla)\mathbf{A}$ we write it in the form

$$\begin{aligned}
\mathbf{n}_1\cdot(\mathbf{h}\nabla)(\mathbf{n}_2\nabla)\mathbf{A} = {} & n_{1x}(\mathbf{h}\nabla)\left(n_{2x}\frac{\partial A_x}{\partial x} + n_{2y}\frac{\partial A_x}{\partial y}\right) + \\
& + n_{1y}(\mathbf{h}\nabla)\left(n_{2x}\frac{\partial A_y}{\partial x} + n_{2y}\frac{\partial A_y}{\partial y}\right)
\end{aligned}$$

and note that by virtue of Eq. (7.12)

$$\left.\begin{aligned}
&\overline{n_{1x}n_{2x}} = \overline{n_{1y}n_{2y}} = 0; \\
&\overline{n_{1x}n_{2y}} = -\overline{n_{2x}n_{1y}} = \frac{1}{2}.
\end{aligned}\right\} \tag{7.36}$$

Thus

$$\overline{\mathbf{n}_1 \cdot (\mathbf{h}\nabla)(\mathbf{n}_2\nabla)\mathbf{A}} = \frac{1}{2}(\mathbf{h}\nabla)\left(\frac{\partial A_x}{\partial y} - \frac{\partial A_y}{\partial x}\right)$$

or

$$\overline{\mathbf{n}_1 \cdot (\mathbf{h}\nabla)(\mathbf{n}_2\nabla)\mathbf{A}} = -\frac{1}{2}(\mathbf{h}\nabla)(\mathbf{h}\,\mathbf{rot}\,\mathbf{A}). \tag{7.37}$$

In particular, if $\mathbf{A} \equiv \mathbf{h}$

$$\overline{\mathbf{n}_1 \cdot (\mathbf{h}\nabla)(\mathbf{n}_2\nabla)\mathbf{h}} = -\frac{1}{2}(\mathbf{h}\nabla)(\mathbf{h}\,\mathrm{rot}\,\mathbf{h}). \tag{7.38}$$

This expression can be transformed easily. Applying the rule for differentiation of a product to (**h** rot **h**) we have

$$(\mathbf{h}\nabla)(\mathbf{h}\,\mathrm{rot}\,\mathbf{h}) = \mathrm{rot}\,\mathbf{h}\cdot(\mathbf{h}\nabla)\mathbf{h} + \mathbf{h}\cdot(\mathbf{h}\nabla)\,\mathrm{rot}\,\mathbf{h}.$$

The first term on the right side vanishes by virtue of the indentity in (6.8). Hence

$$(\mathbf{h}\nabla)(\mathbf{h}\,\mathrm{rot}\,\mathbf{h}) = \mathbf{h}\cdot(\mathbf{h}\nabla)\,\mathrm{rot}\,\mathbf{h} \tag{7.39}$$

or, by virtue of the identity in (6.7),

$$(\mathbf{h}\nabla)(\mathbf{h}\,\mathrm{rot}\,\mathbf{h}) = \mathbf{h}\cdot\mathrm{rot}\,(\mathbf{h}\nabla)\mathbf{h} - (\mathbf{h}\,\mathrm{rot}\,\mathbf{h})\,\mathrm{div}\,\mathbf{h}. \tag{7.40}$$

Thus

$$\overline{\mathbf{n}_1 \cdot (\mathbf{h}\nabla)(\mathbf{n}_2\nabla)\mathbf{h}} = -\frac{1}{2}\mathbf{h}\,\mathrm{rot}\,(\mathbf{h}\nabla)\mathbf{h} + \frac{1}{2}(\mathbf{h}\,\mathrm{rot}\,\mathbf{h})\,\mathrm{div}\,\mathbf{h}. \tag{7.41}$$

Similarly, expressing the relations in coordinate form and smoothing, it is easy to show that

$$\overline{\mathbf{n}_1 \cdot ((\mathbf{n}_2\nabla)\mathbf{A}\nabla)\mathbf{A}} = -\frac{1}{2}\{\mathrm{div}\,\mathbf{A} - \mathbf{h}(\mathbf{h}\nabla)\mathbf{A}\}(\mathbf{h}\,\mathrm{rot}\,\mathbf{A});\tag{7.42}$$

$$\overline{\mathbf{n}_1(\mathbf{n}_1\nabla)(\mathbf{n}_2\nabla)\mathbf{A}} = 0. \tag{7.43}$$

The last relation is a consequence of the fact that the functions n_{1x} and n_{1y} are orthogonal with respect to the functions $n_{1x}n_{2x}$ and $n_{1x}n_{2y}$ over a cyclotron period.

We now smooth the expression $\mathbf{n}_1(\mathbf{n}_1\nabla)\mathbf{A}\cdot\mathbf{n}_2(\mathbf{n}_1\nabla)\mathbf{C}$. Transforming this expression by means of Eq. (7.13) and averaging we have

$$\widetilde{\mathbf{n}_1(\mathbf{n}_1\nabla)\mathbf{A}\cdot\mathbf{n}_2(\mathbf{n}_1\nabla)\mathbf{C}} = \frac{1}{4}\left(\frac{\partial A_x}{\partial x} + \frac{\partial A_y}{\partial y}\right)\left(\frac{\partial C_y}{\partial x} - \frac{\partial C_x}{\partial y}\right) + \\ + \frac{1}{8}\left(\frac{\partial A_x}{\partial x} - \frac{\partial A_y}{\partial y}\right)\left(\frac{\partial C_y}{\partial x} + \frac{\partial C_x}{\partial y}\right) - \\ - \frac{1}{8}\left(\frac{\partial A_y}{\partial x} + \frac{\partial A_x}{\partial y}\right)\left(\frac{\partial C_x}{\partial x} - \frac{\partial C_y}{\partial y}\right).$$

The factors $\partial A_x/\partial x + \partial A_y/\partial y = \operatorname{div}\mathbf{A} - \mathbf{h}(\mathbf{h}\nabla)\mathbf{A}$ and $\partial C_y/\partial x - \partial C_x/\partial y = (\mathbf{h}\operatorname{rot}\mathbf{C})$ vary smoothly. The remaining factors are rapidly varying. One is easily convinced of this if the expressions

$$\frac{\partial A_y}{\partial x} + \frac{\partial A_x}{\partial y} = \mathbf{n}_2\cdot(\mathbf{n}_1\nabla)\mathbf{A} + \mathbf{n}_1\cdot(\mathbf{n}_2\nabla)\mathbf{A}$$

and

$$\frac{\partial A_x}{\partial x} - \frac{\partial A_y}{\partial y} = \mathbf{n}_1\cdot(\mathbf{n}_1\nabla)\mathbf{A} - \mathbf{n}_2\cdot(\mathbf{n}_2\nabla)\mathbf{A}$$

are compared with (7.14). Hence, as a result of smoothing we have

$$\overline{\mathbf{n}_1(\mathbf{n}_1\nabla)\mathbf{A}\cdot\mathbf{n}_2(\mathbf{n}_1\nabla)\mathbf{C}} = -\overline{\mathbf{n}_1(\mathbf{n}_1\nabla)\mathbf{A}\cdot\mathbf{n}_1(\mathbf{n}_2\nabla)\mathbf{C}} = \\ = \frac{1}{4}\{\operatorname{div}\mathbf{A} - \mathbf{h}(\mathbf{h}\nabla)\mathbf{A}\}(\mathbf{h}\operatorname{rot}\mathbf{C}). \quad (7.44)$$

Special analysis is required for the smoothing of secular terms, i.e., terms that contain the time t to the first or higher powers. These terms appear on the right side of Eq. (5.3) after the expressions for $v_{\parallel}$, $p_{\parallel}$, n_1 are substituted. The factors t or t^2 always appear in combination with coefficients that are quantities of second order.

The time origin is taken to be the time at which it is necessary to find the smoothed values of the derivatives $\dot{p}_{\parallel}$ and $\dot{p}_{\perp}$ in Eq. (5.3). Hence, the smoothed values of the secular terms must also be found at time t = 0. It then follows from the derivation of the secular terms given above that the time t can be taken for small values (of the order of several cyclotron periods).

Each secular term makes its own contribution to the rate of change of the momenta $p_{\parallel}$ and $p_{\perp}$. Averaging each term in accordance with Eq. (4.3) we replace the term corresponding to it in the instantaneous velocity by its mean value over the time interval (−T, +T); the middle of this time interval represents the zero time at which the corresponding rate of change is to be determined. If it is required to find the averaged rate of change at some other time, the time origin must be shifted in such a way that this new time becomes zero time. It is clear that by this means the mean value of a secular term can be determined for any instant of time. It can either vary smoothly and slowly or can contain rapidly varying terms. The latter will be of second order, in which case smoothing reduces to the simple neglect of these terms. Let us now consider an actual example of smoothing of secular terms that will be needed below. We start with $t\mathbf{n}_1(t)$ and $t\mathbf{n}_2(t)$. Using Eq. (7.4) we have

$$\widetilde{[t\mathbf{n}_1(t)]}_{t=0} = \frac{1}{2T}\left[-\frac{t}{\omega}\,\mathbf{n}_2(t) + \frac{1}{\omega^2}\,\mathbf{n}_1(t)\right]_{-T}^{+T}$$

By virtue of the periodicity of $\mathbf{n}_1(t)$ and $\mathbf{n}_2(t)$, $\mathbf{n}_1(T) = \mathbf{n}_1(-T) = \mathbf{n}_1(0)$ in the zeroth approximation; a similar relation holds for $\mathbf{n}_2$. Hence,

$$\widetilde{[t\mathbf{n}_1(t)]}_{t=0} = -\frac{1}{\omega}\,\mathbf{n}_2(0);$$

$$\widetilde{[t\mathbf{n}_2(t)]}_{t=0} = \frac{1}{\omega}\,\mathbf{n}_1(0).$$

If the time origin is shifted the corresponding terms are replaced by $-(1/\omega)\mathbf{n}_2(t)$ and $(1/\omega)\mathbf{n}_1(t)$. These are rapidly varying terms that disappear upon smoothing. Thus

$$\overline{t\mathbf{n}_1(t)} = \overline{t\mathbf{n}_2(t)} = 0. \qquad (7.45)$$

Similarly, using Eq. (7.5) we find

$$\overline{t^2\mathbf{n}_1(t)} = \overline{t^2\mathbf{n}_2(t)} = 0. \qquad (7.46)$$

The relations in (7.45) and (7.46) can be written in another form if they are projected on the fixed coordinate axes x and y. Thus

$$\overline{t\cos\omega t}=\overline{t\sin\omega t}=0; \quad (7.45a)$$

$$\overline{t^2\cos\omega t}=\overline{t^2\sin\omega t}=0. \quad (7.46a)$$

It is evident that these relations still hold if ω is replaced by 2ω; these relations can be used to carry out the smoothing operation several times. For example, in smoothing the quantity $t(\mathbf{A}\mathbf{n}_1)(\mathbf{C}\mathbf{n}_1)$ we direct the vector **A** along the x axis, having merged the xy coordinate plane with the (**A**, **C**) plane. The symbol δ denotes the angle between the vectors **A** and **C** so that

$$t(\mathbf{A}\mathbf{n}_1)(\mathbf{C}\mathbf{n}_1)=tAC\cos\omega t\cos(\omega t+\delta)=$$
$$=\frac{tAC}{2}\{\cos\delta+\cos o\cos 2\omega t-\sin\delta\sin 2\omega t\},$$

whence we conclude on the basis of Eq. (7.45a) that the smoothed term vanishes. Thus

$$\overline{t(\mathbf{A}\mathbf{n}_1)(\mathbf{C}\mathbf{n}_1)}=\overline{t(\mathbf{A}\mathbf{n}_1)(\mathbf{C}\mathbf{n}_2)}=0. \quad (7.47)$$

Similarly, from the form of Eq. (7.13), it follows without further calculation that*

$$\overline{t\mathbf{n}_2\cdot(\mathbf{n}_1\nabla)\mathbf{A}}=\overline{t\mathbf{n}_1\cdot(\mathbf{n}_2\nabla)\mathbf{A}}=\overline{t\mathbf{n}_1\cdot(\mathbf{n}_1\nabla)\mathbf{A}}=$$
$$=\overline{t\mathbf{n}_2\cdot(\mathbf{n}_2\nabla)\mathbf{A}}=0; \quad (7.48)$$

$$\overline{t^2\{\mathbf{n}_2(\mathbf{n}_1\nabla)\mathbf{A}+\mathbf{n}_1(\mathbf{n}_2\nabla)\mathbf{A}\}}=0. \quad (7.49)$$

All secular terms encountered below will be of the form given above. Hence, the smoothed values of all secular terms that we shall encounter below is zero.

---

*The reader should be cautioned against an improper understanding of the operations of averaging and smoothing of secular terms. It would be incorrect to perform these operations in the following way: first, average the secular term for an arbitrary time t, i.e., over the interval $(t-T,\ t+T)$ not taking $t=0$; then, carry out the smoothing operation. If this approach were used the result of applying the operation of averaging and smoothing to the secular term would explicitly contain the time t, which is obviously incorrect. The proper approach, as noted above, is as follows: first, carry out the averaging for time $t=0$, i.e., over the interval $(-T,+T)$; then, extend the result to any time; finally, perform the smoothing operation.

§ 8. Derivation of a Compatible System of Equations of Motion in the Drift Approximation

1. Using the results of the preceding section we can now derive the system of drift equations that were given in §6 without proof. For this purpose we must smooth the right parts of Eq. (5.3), which contain regular terms of second order, and neglect all terms of higher order as well as rapidly varying terms of second order.

In the first place we can neglect terms containing $\partial \mathbf{h}/\partial t$ in these equation since these are rapidly varying second-order quantities. Further, it is obvious that

$$\overline{(\mathbf{E}\mathbf{h})} = (\mathbf{E}_0\mathbf{h}_0). \tag{8.1}$$

In the first-order term $\mathbf{E}\mathbf{n}_1$ we replace $\mathbf{E}$ by the expression in Eq. (7.19) and $\mathbf{n}_1$ by the expression $\mathbf{n}_1 = \mathbf{n}_1^0 + \alpha\mathbf{n}_2 + \beta\mathbf{h}$. Then, neglecting third-order terms we have

$$\begin{aligned}\mathbf{E}\mathbf{n}_1 &= \widetilde{\mathbf{E}(0)}\,\mathbf{n}_1^0 + v_{\parallel} t\mathbf{n}_1(\mathbf{h}\nabla)\mathbf{E} - \\ &- \frac{v_\perp}{\omega}\mathbf{n}_1\cdot(\mathbf{n}_2\nabla)\mathbf{E} + \alpha(\mathbf{E}\mathbf{n}_2) + \beta(\mathbf{E}\mathbf{h}).\end{aligned} \tag{8.2}$$

We have not made any distinction between $\mathbf{n}_1$ and $\mathbf{n}_1^0$ or between $\widetilde{\mathbf{E}(0)}$ and $\mathbf{E}$ in the second-order terms since the differences between these terms appears only in third-order or higher. Thus, the vectors $\mathbf{n}_1$ and $\mathbf{n}_2$ in the second-order terms can be regarded as uniformly rotating so that all the averaging and smoothing formulas obtained in §7 can be used.

We average the first term in Eq. (8.2) at time t = 0. Using an angular velocity vector ω_0 of arbitrary length we have $\omega_0 = 2\pi/\widetilde{T(0)}$. When the first term is averaged $\widetilde{\mathbf{E}(0)}\,\mathbf{n}_1^0$ vanishes exactly since the vector $\widetilde{\mathbf{E}(0)}$ is a constant while the vector $\mathbf{n}_1^0$ rotates uniformly with angular velocity ω_0. Since our choice of the time origin is arbitrary this result applies for all values of t. In the smoothing operation the term $v_{\parallel} t\mathbf{n}_1(\mathbf{h}\nabla)\mathbf{E}$ vanishes by virtue of Eq. (7.45). By virtue of Eq. (2.19) the third term yields

$$-\overline{\frac{v_\perp}{\omega}\mathbf{n}_1\cdot(\mathbf{n}_2\nabla)\mathbf{E}} = \frac{v_\perp}{2\omega}(\mathbf{h}\,\mathrm{rot}\,\mathbf{E}) = -\frac{a_\perp}{2}(\mathbf{h}\,\mathrm{rot}\,\mathbf{E}).$$

On smoothing the fourth term $\alpha(\mathbf{E}\mathbf{n}_2)$ by means of Eqs. (7.32), (7.33), (7.45), (7.46), (7.34), and (7.35) we can show easily that

$$\overline{\alpha\,(\mathbf{En}_2)} = \frac{ev_\perp}{2mc\omega^2}(\mathbf{h}\,[\nabla B\cdot\mathbf{E}]) + \frac{v_\parallel^2}{2\omega v_\perp}(\mathbf{h}\,[\mathbf{E}\cdot(\mathbf{h}\nabla)\,\mathbf{h}]) =$$
$$= \frac{a_\perp}{2}\left(\mathbf{E}\left[\mathbf{h}\,\frac{\nabla B}{B}\right]\right) + \frac{a_\parallel v_\parallel}{2v_\perp}(\mathbf{E}\,[\mathbf{h}\cdot(\mathbf{h}\nabla)\,\mathbf{h}]).$$

Similarly, from Eqs. (7.32), (7.45), and (2.19) we find

$$\overline{\beta\,(\mathbf{Eh})} = -\frac{v_\perp}{2\omega}(\mathbf{h}\,\mathrm{rot}\,\mathbf{h})\,(\mathbf{Eh}) = \frac{a_\perp}{2}(\mathbf{Eh})\,(\mathbf{h}\,\mathrm{rot}\,\mathbf{h}).$$

Finally,

$$\overline{e\,(\mathbf{En}_1)} = -\frac{ea_\perp}{2}(\mathbf{h}\,\mathrm{rot}\,\mathbf{E}) + \frac{ea_\perp}{2}\left(\mathbf{E}\left[\mathbf{h}\,\frac{\nabla B}{B}\right]\right) +$$
$$+ \frac{ea_\perp}{2}(\mathbf{Eh})\,(\mathbf{h}\,\mathrm{rot}\,\mathbf{h}) + \frac{ea_\parallel v_\parallel}{2v_\perp}(\mathbf{E}\,[\mathbf{h}\cdot(\mathbf{h}\nabla)\,\mathbf{h}]). \qquad (8.3)$$

To smooth the expression $v_\parallel p_\perp \mathbf{n}_1(\mathbf{h}\nabla)\mathbf{h}$ we write it in the form

$$v_\parallel p_\perp \mathbf{n}_1(\mathbf{h}\nabla)\,\mathbf{h} = \widetilde{v_\parallel(0)}\,\widetilde{p_\perp(0)}\,\mathbf{n}_1^0\left(\widetilde{\mathbf{h}(0)}\,\nabla\right)\widetilde{\mathbf{h}(0)} +$$
$$+ \delta p_\parallel v_\perp \mathbf{n}_1(\mathbf{h}\nabla)\,\mathbf{h} + \delta p_\perp v_\parallel \mathbf{n}_1(\mathbf{h}\nabla)\,\mathbf{h} - v_\parallel v_\perp \mathbf{n}_1 \delta m\,(\mathbf{h}\nabla)\,\mathbf{h} + \qquad (8.4)$$
$$+ v_\parallel p_\perp \delta\mathbf{n}_1(\mathbf{h}\nabla)\,\mathbf{h} + v_\parallel p_\perp \mathbf{n}_1(\delta\mathbf{h}\nabla)\,\mathbf{h} + v_\parallel p_\perp \mathbf{n}_1(\mathbf{h}\nabla)\,\delta\mathbf{h},$$

where $\delta p_\parallel$, $\delta p_\perp$, δm and $\delta\mathbf{h}$ are determined by Eqs. (7.16), (7.18), (7.21), and (7.22). Making use of these relations it is easy to show that

$$\overline{\delta p_\perp v_\parallel \mathbf{n}_1(\mathbf{h}\nabla)\,\mathbf{h}} = \frac{ev_\parallel}{2\omega}(\mathbf{h}\,[\mathbf{E}\cdot(\mathbf{h}\nabla)\,\mathbf{h}]) = \frac{ea_\parallel}{2}(\mathbf{E}\,[\mathbf{h}\cdot(\mathbf{h}\nabla)\,\mathbf{h}]);$$

$$\overline{-v_\parallel v_\perp \delta m \mathbf{n}_1(\mathbf{h}\nabla)\,\mathbf{h}} = -\frac{ea_\parallel}{2}\left(\frac{v_\perp}{c}\right)^2(\mathbf{E}\,[\mathbf{h}\cdot(\mathbf{h}\nabla)\,\mathbf{h}]);$$

$$\overline{v_\parallel p_\perp \delta\mathbf{n}_1(\mathbf{h}\nabla)\,\mathbf{h}} = \overline{v_\parallel p_\perp \alpha\mathbf{n}_2(\mathbf{h}\nabla)\,\mathbf{h}} =$$
$$= \frac{ea_\parallel}{2}\left(1 + \frac{v_\perp^2}{c^2}\right)(\mathbf{E}\,[\mathbf{h}\cdot(\mathbf{h}\nabla)\,\mathbf{h}]) - \frac{a_\parallel p_\perp v_\perp}{2B}(\nabla B\,[\mathbf{h}\cdot(\mathbf{h}\nabla)\,\mathbf{h}]);$$

$$\overline{v_\parallel p_\perp \mathbf{n}_1\cdot(\delta\mathbf{h}\nabla)\,\mathbf{h}} = -\frac{a_\parallel p_\perp v_\perp}{2}(\mathbf{h}\,\mathrm{rot}\,\mathbf{h})\,\mathrm{div}\,\mathbf{h};$$

$$\overline{v_\parallel p_\perp \mathbf{n}_1\cdot(\mathbf{h}\nabla)\,\delta\mathbf{h}} = \frac{a_\parallel p_\perp v_\perp}{2}\{(\mathbf{h}\,\mathrm{rot}\,\mathbf{h})\,\mathrm{div}\,\mathbf{h} - \mathbf{h}\,\mathrm{rot}\,(\mathbf{h}\nabla)\,\mathbf{h}\}.$$

The remaining (first) two terms on the right side of Eq. (8.4) vanish when smoothed. Finally,

$$\overline{v_{\parallel} p_{\perp} \mathbf{n}_1 \cdot (\mathbf{h}\nabla)\,\mathbf{h}} = e a_{\parallel} \left(\mathbf{E}\,[\mathbf{h}\cdot(\mathbf{h}\nabla)\,\mathbf{h}]\right) - $$

$$- \frac{a_{\parallel} p_{\perp} v_{\perp}}{2B} \left(\nabla B\,[\mathbf{h}\cdot(\mathbf{h}\nabla)\,\mathbf{h}]\right) - \frac{a_{\parallel} p_{\perp} v_{\perp}}{2}\,\mathbf{h}\,\mathrm{rot}\,(\mathbf{h}\nabla)\,\mathbf{h}. \tag{8.5}$$

Similarly

$$\overline{- v_{\parallel} p_{\parallel} \mathbf{n}_1 \cdot (\mathbf{h}\nabla)\,\mathbf{h}} = - \frac{e a_{\parallel} v_{\parallel}}{2 v_{\perp}} \left(\mathbf{E}\,[\mathbf{h}\cdot(\mathbf{h}\nabla)\,\mathbf{h}]\right) +$$

$$+ \frac{a_{\parallel} v_{\parallel} p_{\perp}}{2B} \left(\nabla B\,[\mathbf{h}\cdot(\mathbf{h}\nabla)\,\mathbf{h}]\right) + \frac{a_{\parallel} p_{\perp} v_{\parallel}}{2}\,\mathbf{h}\cdot\mathrm{rot}\,(\mathbf{h}\nabla)\,\mathbf{h}. \tag{8.6}$$

It is now necessary to smooth the two expressions $v_{\perp} p_{\parallel} \mathbf{n}_1 \cdot (\mathbf{n}_1\nabla)\,\mathbf{h}$ and $v_{\perp} p_{\perp} \mathbf{n}_1 \cdot (\mathbf{n}_1\nabla)\,\mathbf{h}$. We have

$$v_{\perp} p_{\parallel} \mathbf{n}_1 \cdot (\mathbf{n}_1\nabla)\,\mathbf{h} = \widetilde{v_{\perp}(0)}\;\widetilde{p_{\parallel}(0)}\,\mathbf{n}_1^0 \cdot (\mathbf{n}_1^0\nabla)\,\mathbf{h} +$$

$$+ \delta p_{\parallel} v_{\perp} \mathbf{n}_1 \cdot (\mathbf{n}_1\nabla)\,\mathbf{h} + \delta p_{\perp} v_{\parallel} \mathbf{n}_1 \cdot (\mathbf{n}_1\nabla)\,\mathbf{h} - v_{\perp} v_{\parallel}\,\delta m \mathbf{n}_1 \cdot (\mathbf{n}_1\nabla)\,\mathbf{h} +$$

$$+ v_{\perp} p_{\parallel} \left\{\delta \mathbf{n}_1 \cdot (\mathbf{n}_1\nabla)\,\mathbf{h} + \mathbf{n}_1 \cdot (\delta \mathbf{n}_1\nabla)\,\mathbf{h}\right\} +$$

$$+ v_{\perp} p_{\perp} \mathbf{n}_1 \cdot (\mathbf{n}_1\nabla)\,\delta\mathbf{h} \tag{8.7}$$

With the exception of the first term all terms on the right vanish when smoothed. The first term is written in the form

$$\widetilde{v_{\perp}(0)}\;\widetilde{p_{\parallel}(0)}\,\mathbf{n}_1^0 \cdot (\mathbf{n}_1^0\nabla)\,\mathbf{h} =$$

$$= \widetilde{v_{\perp}(0)}\;\widetilde{p_{\parallel}(0)}\,\mathbf{n}_1^0 \cdot (\mathbf{n}_1^0\nabla)\,\widetilde{\mathbf{h}(0)} + v_{\perp} p_{\perp} \mathbf{n}_1 \cdot (\mathbf{n}_1\nabla)\,\delta\mathbf{h}.$$

Averaging in the sense of Eq. (4.3) for t = 0 we find

$$\widetilde{\widetilde{v_{\perp}(0)}\,\widetilde{p_{\parallel}(0)}\,\mathbf{n}_1^0 \cdot (\mathbf{n}_1^0\nabla)\,\mathbf{h}} = \frac{1}{2}\,\widetilde{v_{\perp}(0)}\;\widetilde{p_{\parallel}(0)}\,\mathrm{div}\,\widetilde{\mathbf{h}(0)}.$$

By virtue of the arbitrary choice of the time origin the value of the argument can be replaced by an arbitrary value of t. Furthermore, $\widetilde{v_{\perp}(t)}$, $\widetilde{p_{\parallel}(t)}$, and $\widetilde{\mathbf{h}(t)}$ differ from $\overline{v_{\perp}(t)}$, $\overline{p_{\parallel}(t)}$, and $\overline{\mathbf{h}(t)}$ by rapidly varying terms of second order. To the same degree of accuracy $\overline{\mathbf{h}(t)}$ coincides with $\mathbf{h}_0(t)$, the value of the unit vector **h** at the location of the guiding center. Hence

$$\overline{v_{\perp} p_{\parallel} \mathbf{n}_1 \cdot (\mathbf{n}_1\nabla)\,\mathbf{h}} = \frac{1}{2}\,\overline{v_{\perp} p_{\parallel}}\,\mathrm{div}\,\mathbf{h}_0. \tag{8.8}$$

Similarly

$$\overline{v_\perp p_\perp \mathbf{n}_1 \cdot (\mathbf{n}_1 \nabla) \mathbf{h}} = \frac{1}{2} \bar{v}_\perp \bar{p}_\perp \operatorname{div} \mathbf{h}_0 . \tag{8.9}$$

2. By smoothing Eqs. (5.3) we obtain the required equations

$$\dot{\bar{p}}_\parallel = e(\mathbf{E}_0 \mathbf{h}_0) + \frac{1}{2} \bar{v}_\perp \bar{p}_\perp \operatorname{div} \mathbf{h}_0 + e\bar{a}_\parallel (\mathbf{E}_0 [\mathbf{h}_0 \cdot (\mathbf{h}_0 \nabla) \mathbf{h}_0]) -$$

$$- \frac{\bar{a}_\parallel \bar{p}_\perp \bar{v}_\perp}{2} \left(\frac{\nabla B_0}{B_0} [\mathbf{h}_0 \cdot (\mathbf{h}_0 \nabla) \mathbf{h}_0] \right) - \frac{\bar{a}_\parallel \bar{p}_\perp \bar{v}_\perp}{2} \mathbf{h}_0 \operatorname{rot} (\mathbf{h}_0 \nabla) \mathbf{h}_0 ; \tag{8.10}$$

$$\dot{\bar{p}}_\perp = - \frac{1}{2} \bar{v}_\perp \bar{p}_\parallel \operatorname{div} \mathbf{h}_0 - \frac{e\bar{a}_\perp}{2} (\mathbf{h}_0 \operatorname{rot} \mathbf{E}_0) + \frac{e\bar{a}_\perp}{2} \left(\mathbf{E}_0 \left[\mathbf{h}_0 \frac{\nabla B_0}{B_0} \right] \right) +$$

$$+ \frac{e\bar{a}_\perp}{2} (\mathbf{E}_0 \mathbf{h}_0)(\mathbf{h}_0 \operatorname{rot} \mathbf{h}_0) + \frac{\bar{a}_\parallel \bar{v}_\parallel \bar{p}_\perp}{2} \left(\frac{\nabla B_0}{B_0} [\mathbf{h}_0 \cdot (\mathbf{h}_0 \nabla) \mathbf{h}_0] \right) +$$

$$+ \frac{1}{2} \bar{a}_\parallel \bar{p}_\perp \bar{v}_\parallel \mathbf{h}_0 \operatorname{rot} (\mathbf{h}_0 \nabla) \mathbf{h}_0 . \tag{8.11}$$

In these equations all fields refer to the guiding center and we have used the smoothed values $\bar{p}_\parallel$, $\bar{p}_\perp$, $\bar{v}_\parallel$, and $\bar{v}_\perp$ everywhere. Obviously this distinction is important only in first-order terms. There is no need to make a distinction between $\bar{p}_\parallel$ and $p_\parallel$, $\mathbf{B}_0$ and $\mathbf{B}$, etc., in second-order terms. These equations differ from Eqs. (6.2) and (6.3) only in notation. The changes in notation have been discussed in subsection 3 of §5 (p.39).

3. In the derivation of the system of drift equations it has been assumed that the transverse particle velocity $v_\perp$ (and its transverse momentum) are not too small. This condition must be satisfied if the drift term in Eq. (7.23) is to be large compared with the second term. The second term $p_\perp$ appears in the denominator and if $p_\perp$ is very small this term may be greater than the first, and the net effect is as though the magnetic field $\mathbf{B}$ were not large. If $\mathbf{n}_2$ is written in the form $\mathbf{n}_2 = [\mathbf{h}\mathbf{n}_1]$ it is evident that the following inequality must be satisfied if the derivation given above is to hold:

$$p_\perp \gg \left| \frac{1}{\omega} \left\{ e(\mathbf{E}\mathbf{n}_2) - p_\parallel \left(\mathbf{n}_2 \frac{d\mathbf{h}}{dt} \right) \right\} \right| . \tag{8.12}$$

The case

$$p_\perp \lesssim \left| \frac{1}{\omega} \left\{ e(\mathbf{E}\mathbf{n}_2) - p_\parallel \left(\mathbf{n}_2 \frac{d\mathbf{h}}{dt} \right) \right\} \right| \tag{8.13}$$

requires special analysis but it is evident that the drift equations also apply in this case. The point here is that $p_\perp$ is a first-order quantity when (8.13) is satisfied. Thus, Eq. (2.21) can be simplified as shown at the end of §2, and can be written

$$\dot{\mathbf{R}} = \bar{v}_{\|} \mathbf{h}_0 + \frac{c}{B_0^2} [\mathbf{E}_0 \mathbf{B}_0] + \bar{v}_{\|} \bar{a}_{\|} [\mathbf{h}_0 \cdot (\mathbf{h}_0 \nabla) \mathbf{h}_0]. \tag{8.14}$$

The transverse velocity does not appear in this equation and hence it is sufficient to obtain an equation for $\dot{\bar{p}}_{\|}$ alone. It is evident from Eq. (8.10) that this equation must be of the form

$$\dot{\bar{p}}_{\|} = e (\mathbf{E}_0 \mathbf{h}_0) + e\bar{a}_{\|} \mathbf{E}_0 [\mathbf{h}_0 \cdot (\mathbf{h}_0 \nabla) \mathbf{h}_0]. \tag{8.15}$$

The problem thus reduces to the proof of Eq. (8.15) when Eq. (8.13) is satisfied. If this condition is satisfied the last two terms in the first equation of (5.3) can be neglected, since they become third-order quantities, and the formula is now written in the form

$$\dot{p}_{\|} = e (\mathbf{E}\mathbf{h}) + v_{\|} \mathbf{p}_\perp \cdot (\mathbf{h}\nabla) \mathbf{h}. \tag{8.16}$$

When the smoothing operation is applied the first term on the right side becomes $e(\mathbf{E}_0\mathbf{h}_0)$. In order to smooth the second term $p_\perp$ must be found to a first approximation. Differentiating $\mathbf{p}_\perp = \mathbf{p} - p_{\|}\mathbf{h}$ with respect to time and neglecting second-order terms we have

$$\frac{d\mathbf{p}_\perp}{dt} = e\left\{\mathbf{E}_\perp + \frac{1}{c}[\mathbf{v}_\perp \mathbf{B}]\right\} - p_{\|} v_{\|} (\mathbf{h}\nabla) \mathbf{h}$$

or

$$\frac{d\mathbf{p}_\perp}{dt} = [\boldsymbol{\omega} \mathbf{p}_\perp] + \mathbf{A}, \tag{8.17}$$

where

$$\mathbf{A} = e\mathbf{E}_\perp - p_{\|} v_{\|} (\mathbf{h}\nabla) \mathbf{h}. \tag{8.18}$$

We are interested in the values of $p_\perp$ over small time intervals (the order of the cyclotron period T). The angular velocity $\boldsymbol{\omega}$ and the vector $\mathbf{A}$ can be regarded as constant for time intervals of this kind. It is then a simple matter to solve Eq. (8.17). We can write $\mathbf{p}_\perp = \mathbf{p}_\perp^0 + \mathbf{C}$ where $\mathbf{C}$ is a constant vector which is chosen in such a way that $[\boldsymbol{\omega}\mathbf{C}] + \mathbf{A} = \mathbf{0}$; further, the vector $\mathbf{C}$ is chosen to be perpendicular to ω. Under these conditions

$$\mathbf{C} = \frac{1}{\omega^2}[\boldsymbol{\omega}\mathbf{A}],$$

$$\frac{d\mathbf{p}^0_\perp}{dt} = [\boldsymbol{\omega}\mathbf{p}^0_\perp].$$

Thus

$$\mathbf{p}_\perp = \mathbf{p}^0_\perp + \frac{1}{\omega^2}[\boldsymbol{\omega}\mathbf{A}], \tag{8.19}$$

where $\mathbf{p}^0_\perp$ is a vector of fixed length that rotates uniformly with a fixed angular velocity $\boldsymbol{\omega}$ and is taken to be perpendicular to the magnetic field $\mathbf{B}$. This term is not important when substituted in Eq. (8.16) since the term it gives rise to vanishes upon smoothing. Hence, when smoothed, the second term in Eq. (8.16) becomes

$$\frac{v_\parallel}{\omega^2}[\boldsymbol{\omega}\mathbf{A}]\cdot(\mathbf{h}\nabla)\,\mathbf{h} = -\frac{mcv_\parallel}{B}[\mathbf{h}\mathbf{E}]\cdot(\mathbf{h}\nabla)\,\mathbf{h} = ea_\parallel \mathbf{E}\,[\mathbf{h}\cdot(\mathbf{h}\nabla)\,\mathbf{h}],$$

which verifies Eq. (8.15).

§ 9. Another Approach to the Equation of Motion of the Guiding Center

The methods developed in the preceding sections can be used to approach the equation of motion of the guiding center from another point of view. In this approach the notion of a guiding center is not used. Instead one tries to find the smoothed velocity of the particle itself. Since all of the expressions required for the solution of the problem in this formulation have been presented it will be useful to present this other approach. To avoid unnecessary complications we limit ourselves to the nonrelativistic case. The calculations are somewhat longer in the relativistic case although there are no new fundamental difficulties. We first find the smoothed particle momentum. This quantity is then divided by the particle mass to obtain the smoothed velocity. The smoothing operation is carried out at time $t = 0$. Since the time origin can be chosen arbitrarily no limitation is imposed on the results.

Writing the particle momentum in the form

$$\mathbf{p} = p_\parallel \mathbf{h} + p_\perp \mathbf{n}_1, \tag{9.1}$$

we introduce Eqs. (7.21), (7.22), (7.18), and (7.24). Retaining first-order terms we have

$$\mathbf{p} = \widetilde{p_{\parallel}(0)\,\mathbf{h}(0)} + \mathbf{h}\delta p_{\parallel} + p_{\parallel}\delta\mathbf{h} + \widetilde{p_{\perp}(0)}\,\mathbf{n}_1^0 + \delta p_{\perp}\mathbf{n}_1 + p_{\perp}\delta\mathbf{n}_1. \tag{9.2}$$

When the smoothing operation is carried out the first term on the right side becomes $\bar{p}_{\parallel}\mathbf{h}$. The terms $\mathbf{h}\delta p_{\parallel}$ and $p_{\parallel}\widetilde{\delta\mathbf{h}}$ vanish upon averaging. In accordance with the definition $\delta p_{\parallel} = p_{\parallel} - p_{\parallel}(0)$, we find on averaging that $\widetilde{\delta p_{\parallel}} = 0$ in the approximation used. Similarly $\widetilde{\delta\mathbf{h}} = 0$. The term $\widetilde{p_{\perp}(0)}\,\mathbf{n}_1^0$ also vanishes on averaging since $\mathbf{n}_1^0$ is a uniformly rotating unit vector. Thus it is only necessary to smooth the terms $\delta p_{\perp}\mathbf{n}_1$ and $p_{\perp}\delta\mathbf{n}_1$. When Eq. (7.22) is used the first of these becomes

$$\delta p_{\perp}\mathbf{n}_1 = -\frac{e}{\omega}(\mathbf{E}\mathbf{n}_2)\,\mathbf{n}_1 + \frac{v_{\parallel}p_{\parallel}}{\omega}(\mathbf{n}_2\cdot(\mathbf{h}\nabla)\,\mathbf{h})\,\mathbf{n}_1 + \frac{v_{\perp}p_{\parallel}}{2\omega}(\mathbf{n}_2\cdot(\mathbf{n}_1\nabla)\,\mathbf{h})\,\mathbf{n}_1 - \frac{v_{\perp}p_{\parallel}}{4\omega}(\mathbf{h}\operatorname{rot}\mathbf{h})\,\mathbf{n}_1 - \frac{v_{\perp}p_{\parallel}}{2}\operatorname{div}\mathbf{h}t\mathbf{n}_1.$$

The third term on the right side vanishes on averaging because the function $\mathbf{n}_2\cdot(\mathbf{n}_1\nabla)\mathbf{h}$ is orthogonal with respect to the function $\mathbf{n}_1 = \mathbf{i}\cos\omega t + \mathbf{j}\sin\omega t$ over a cyclotron period by virtue of Eq. (7.13). The last two terms also vanish upon smoothing; also $\overline{\mathbf{n}_1(t)} = 0$ by virtue of Eq. (7.45). Hence, smoothing the first two terms by means of Eq. (2.14) we have

$$\overline{\delta p_{\perp}\mathbf{n}_1} = \frac{e}{2\omega}[\mathbf{h}\mathbf{E}] - \frac{v_{\parallel}p_{\parallel}}{2\omega}[\mathbf{h}\cdot(\mathbf{h}\nabla)\,\mathbf{h}].$$

Further, using Eqs. (7.28) and (7.32) in the nonrelativistic approximation

$$p_{\perp}\delta\mathbf{n}_1 = \frac{e}{\omega}(\mathbf{E}\mathbf{n}_1)\,\mathbf{n}_2 + \frac{ev_{\perp}^2}{c\omega^2}(\mathbf{n}_1\nabla B)\,\mathbf{n}_2 - \frac{v_{\parallel}p_{\parallel}}{\omega}(\mathbf{n}_1\cdot(\mathbf{h}\nabla)\,\mathbf{h})\,\mathbf{n}_2 - \frac{v_{\parallel}p_{\perp}}{2\omega}(\mathbf{n}_1\cdot(\mathbf{n}_1\nabla)\,\mathbf{h})\,\mathbf{n}_2 + p_{\perp}(at^2 + bt + d)\,\mathbf{n}_2 - p_{\perp}v_{\parallel}t\,(\mathbf{n}_1(\mathbf{h}\nabla)\,\mathbf{h})\,\mathbf{h} + \frac{p_{\perp}v_{\perp}}{\omega}(\mathbf{n}_1\cdot(\mathbf{n}_2\nabla)\,\mathbf{h})\,\mathbf{h}.$$

Whence, by smoothing we find

$$\overline{p\delta\mathbf{n}_1} = \frac{e}{2\omega}[\mathbf{h}\mathbf{E}] + \frac{ev_{\perp}^2}{2c\omega^2}[\mathbf{h}\nabla B] - \frac{v_{\parallel}p_{\parallel}}{2\omega}[\mathbf{h}\cdot(\mathbf{h}\nabla)\,\mathbf{h}] - \frac{p_{\perp}v_{\perp}}{2\omega}(\mathbf{h}\operatorname{rot}\mathbf{h})\mathbf{h}.$$

Now, taking account of Eqs. (1.12), (1.21), and (1.22) it is easy to show that

$$\bar{\mathbf{p}} = \left[\bar{p}_{\parallel} + \frac{1}{2}\bar{p}_{\perp}\bar{a}_{\perp}(\mathbf{h}\,\mathrm{rot}\,\mathbf{h})\right]\bar{\mathbf{h}} + \frac{mc}{\bar{B}^2}\left[\bar{\mathbf{E}}\,\bar{\mathbf{B}}\right] +$$

$$+\frac{1}{2}\bar{p}_{\perp}\bar{a}_{\perp}\left[\bar{\mathbf{h}}\cdot\frac{\nabla\bar{B}}{\bar{B}}\right] + \bar{p}_{\parallel}\bar{a}_{\parallel}\left[\bar{\mathbf{h}}\cdot(\bar{\mathbf{h}}\nabla)\,\bar{\mathbf{h}}\right]. \tag{9.3}$$

When divided by m this expression becomes Eq. (2.21) as it should.

§ 10. Examples

1. The fact that the quantity $p^2_\perp/B$ is an adiabatic invariant can be understood from the following simple example. Suppose that a particle moves in a uniform but time-varying magnetic field. Let the particle velocity be perpendicular to the magnetic field. In a constant magnetic field the particle would move with constant velocity along a Larmor circle with radius given by Eq. (1.21). If the magnetic field changes slowly in time the trajectory described by the particle in the course of the cyclotron period will approximate a circle. The radius of the circle can be found if the centrifugal force $mv^2_\perp/a_\perp$ is equated to the force exerted on the particle by the magnetic field $(e/c)v_\perp B$. For simplicity we shall consider nonrelativistic motion. Then

$$a_\perp = \frac{mv_\perp c}{eB} = \frac{cp_\perp}{eB} \tag{10.1}$$

in accordance with Eq. (1.21). The Larmor radius $a_\perp$ varies slowly in time. The transverse momentum $p_\perp$ will also vary slowly because the varying magnetic field induces an electric field which has a tangential component along the particle trajectory E_s. The rate-of-change of the transverse momentum $p_\perp$ is given by

$$\dot{p}_\perp = eE_s. \tag{10.2}$$

Here, in general, E_s varies slowly in time and changes in this component over times of the order of the cyclotron period can be neglected. Furthermore, in view of the small deviation of the particle trajectory from a Larmor circle (in Fig. 9 the latter is shown dotted) E_s can be replaced by the projection of the vector E in the direction of the tangent to the circle.

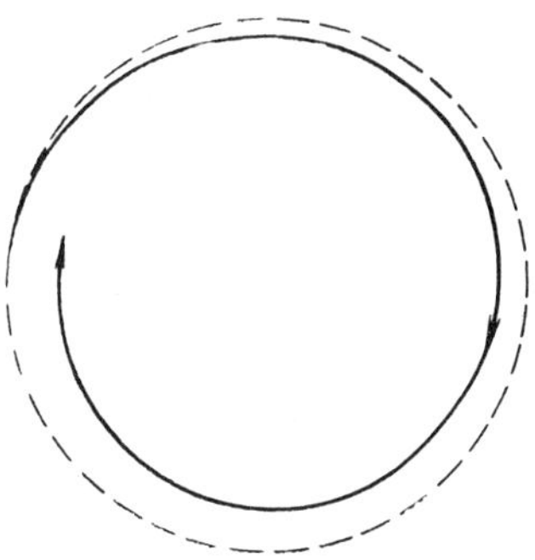

Fig. 9

Then E_s is determined by the equation

$$\oint E_s ds = -\frac{1}{c} \cdot \frac{d\Phi}{dt} = -\frac{\pi a_\perp^2}{c} \cdot \frac{dB}{dt},$$

which yields

$$E_s = -\frac{a_\perp}{2c} \cdot \frac{dB}{dt} = -\frac{p_\perp}{2eB} \cdot \frac{dB}{dt}. \qquad (10.3)$$

As a result Eq. (10.2) becomes

$$\frac{dp_\perp}{dt} = -\frac{p_\perp}{2B} \cdot \frac{dB}{dt}. \qquad (10.4)$$

Integrating this equation we find

$$\frac{p_\perp^2}{B} = \text{const.} \qquad (10.5)$$

We now consider the case of a constant, but inhomogeneous magnetic field. Assume for simplicity that the guiding center of the particle moves in the direction of one of the magnetic lines of force. In this case the mechanism responsible for the change in the momenta $P_\parallel$ and $P_\perp$ is somewhat different. The magnetic field exerts a force $\mathbf{F} = \frac{e}{c}[\mathbf{vB}] = \frac{eB}{c}[\mathbf{vh}]$ on the particle. This force has a component $F_{h_0} = \frac{eB}{c}[\mathbf{vh}]\,\mathbf{h}_0 = \frac{eB}{c}[\mathbf{hh}_0]\,\mathbf{v}$ along $\mathbf{h}_0$ because in general the angle between $\mathbf{h}$ and $\mathbf{h}_0$ is different from zero. This component will change the longitudinal momentum $P_{\parallel}$. By virtue of the conservation of energy $P^2_{\parallel} + P^2_{\perp}$ = const, so that the transverse momentum $P_{\perp}$ must also change.

The discussion leading to the derivation of Eq. (10.5) applies in this case. It also applies in the case in which an inhomogeneous magnetic field changes in time. The only requirement is that at the time being considered the guiding center must move along one of the magnetic lines of force, which is assumed to be rectilinear. To verify this statement we take a reference system in which the guiding center is at rest at the time of interest. The particle trajectory will not be a closed line in this reference system because the longitudinal force component F_{h_0} produces a longitudinal velocity. But the velocity increment is small over a cyclotron period and its square can be neglected. We can also neglect the fact that the particle trajectory does not close after a cyclotron period; the change in magnetic flux as a consequence of the motion of the Larmor circle along the magnetic line of force is also neglected. All changes in magnetic flux in the reference system being considered occur only by virtue of changes in the magnetic field in time so that the discussion leading to Eq. (10.5) applies here.

2. In certain cases the integral in (10.5) is an exact integral of the motion rather than an adiabatic integral, for instance, in the trivial case of motion of a particle in a constant uniform magnetic field. Let us now consider a nontrivial case.

Assume that the electric field **E** is radial, i.e., directed outward from a fixed center O. In all other respects **E** can be arbitrary. Suppose that a point magnetic pole is placed at O and that this pole also produces a radial magnetic field that does not change in time. Let O be the origin of coordinates. The moment of the force e**E** with respect to the point O is zero and the moment equation can be written

$$\frac{d}{dt}[\mathbf{rp}] = \frac{e}{c}[\mathbf{r}[\mathbf{vB}]]$$

or, since **r** and **B** are collinear,

$$\frac{d}{dt}[\mathbf{rp}_{\perp}] = \frac{eBr}{c}\mathbf{v}_{\perp}. \qquad (10.6)$$

Noting that

$$\frac{d}{dt}\left(\frac{\mathbf{r}}{r}\right) = \frac{1}{r}\dot{\mathbf{r}} - \frac{\mathbf{r}}{r^2}\dot{r} = \frac{1}{r}\mathbf{v}_{\perp},$$

we write Eq. (10.6) in the form

$$\frac{d}{dt}\left[\mathbf{r}\mathbf{p}_\perp\right] = \frac{eBr^2}{c}\frac{d}{dt}\left(\frac{\mathbf{r}}{r}\right). \tag{10.7}$$

In the case of a Coulomb magnetic field Br^2 and eBr^2/c are constants. Denoting the last constant by A and integrating Eq. (10.7) we have

$$\left[\mathbf{r}\mathbf{p}_\perp\right] + A\frac{\mathbf{r}}{r} = \mathbf{C} = \text{const}, \tag{10.8}$$

where **C** is a constant of integration. Taking the scalar product of **r** with Eq. (10.8) we have

$$Ar = (\mathbf{C}\mathbf{r}). \tag{10.9}$$

In Eq. (10.8) the $A\mathbf{r}/r$ term is now moved to the right side and the square is completed. Using Eq. (10.9) we have

$$r^2p_\perp^2 = C^2 - A^2 = \text{const}. \tag{10.10}$$

For a Coulomb field $B = \text{const}/r^2$ so that Eq. (10.10) becomes

$$\frac{p_\perp^2}{B} = \text{const}. \tag{10.11}$$

Thus, in this case the quantity in (10.11) is an exact integral of the motion. This result is not of great importance because it is impossible to produce a Coulomb magnetic field.

3. The adiabatic invariance of the quanity $p_\perp^2/B$ is also responsible for the reflection of a particle from a region of strong magnetic field. Assume that the magnetic field is constant in time and let the particle move along a line of magnetic force in the direction of increasing magnetic field. The angle between the direction of the particle velocity and the magnetic line of force is denoted by ϑ. Then $p_\| = p\cos\vartheta$ and $p_\perp = p\sin\vartheta$. The total particle momentum p remains constant by virtue of the energy equation. However, the transverse momentum $p_\perp$ must increase in accordance with the relation $p_\perp^2/B = \text{const}$. For this reason the longitudinal momentum $p_\|$ must decrease. This result also follows from Eq. (5.21), or from the more exact equation (6.21). Equation (5.21) shows that on the average a retarding force acts along the line of force; this retarding force equals the projection of $-\mu\nabla B$ in the direction of the magnetic field and is directed against ∇B, thus retarding the particle motion.

As the particle moves into the region of strong magnetic field there may be a point M on the magnetic line of force at which the longitudinal momentum of the particle goes to zero so that the transverse momentum becomes equal to the total momentum. At this point $p\cos\vartheta = 0$, $p\sin\vartheta = p$, i.e., $\vartheta = \pi/2$. Hence, denoting the magnetic field strength at M by B_M we can write

$$\frac{p_\perp^2}{B} = \frac{p^2\sin^2\vartheta}{B} = \frac{p^2}{B_M},$$

whence

$$\sin\vartheta = \sqrt{\frac{B}{B_M}}. \tag{10.12}$$

Having reached the point M the particle cannot move further in the direction of increasing magnetic field because the adiabatic invariance of $p_\perp^2/B$ means that its transverse momentum $p_\perp$ would have to be greater than p, which would violate the conservation of energy. Hence, the particle is reflected at M and starts to move in the opposite direction. The effect is completely analogous to the optical phenomenon known as total internal reflection. The region of strong magnetic field is essentially a mirror as far as particles impinging upon it are concerned. Such regions are known as magnetic mirrors or magnetic "stoppers." If $\sin\vartheta > \sqrt{B/B_M}$, the particle does not reach point M, but is reflected earlier. If $\sin\vartheta < \sqrt{B/B_M}$ the particle is reflected beyond M. Such a particle is either reflected at some other point M', at which $\sin\vartheta = \sqrt{B/B_{M'}}$, or is not reflected and continues to move along the line of force.

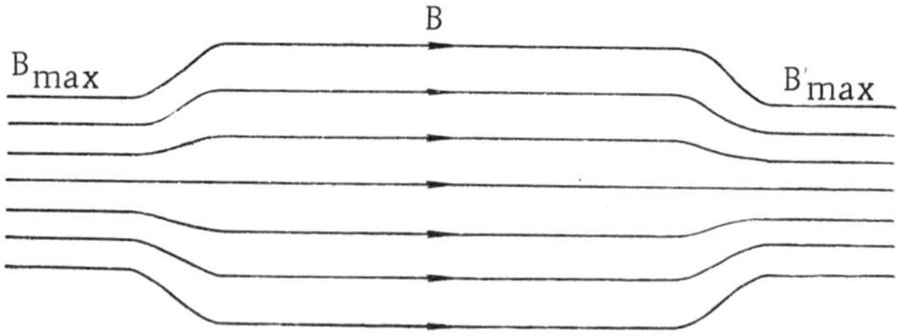

Fig. 10

4. The reflection of particles from magnetic mirrors is the basis for various devices that are used as magnetic traps, i. e., devices in which charged particles are confined by magnetic fields. Systems designed according to this principle belong to the class of so-called adiabatic traps, since their operation depends on the adiabatic invariance of $p^2_{\perp}/B$. One of the simplest devices of this kind was proposed by Budker [8] and independently by York [17]; this is a trap with an axisymmetric magnetic field. It is a cylindrical tube located in a solenoid that produces a strong uniform magnetic field **B** parallel to the axis of the trap. At the ends of the tube there are additional windings that increase the magnetic field in these regions. A schematic diagram of the lines of force in such a system is shown in Fig. 10, which represents a cross section of the trap in the plane passing through the axis. The strong magnetic field **B** forces the particle to move in a Larmor circle of small radius, preventing particle escape to the side walls. The particles are reflected from the region of strong magnetic field. We denote by B_{max} the maximum value of the magnetic field at the ends of the trap. If ϑ is the angle formed by the particle velocity vector and the direction of the magnetic field at the center of the trap (where the field is uniform) the particle will be reflected from the magnetic mirrors if $\sin\vartheta > \sqrt{B/B_{max}}$. However, if $\sin\vartheta < \sqrt{B/B_{max}}$ the magnetic mirrors cannot contain the particle and such particles escape. The adiabatic Budker system cannot contain all particles. There is an escape cone $\vartheta = \vartheta_0$, where ϑ_0 is determined by the relation

$$\sin\vartheta_0 = \sqrt{\frac{B}{B_{max}}}. \quad (10.13)$$

If the direction of the particle velocity lies outside the escape cone ($\vartheta > \vartheta_0$) the particle is contained by the trap. If it lies inside the escape cone ($\vartheta < \vartheta_0$) the particle escapes from the trap.

It is easy to compute the reflection coefficient R [5] for an isotropic particle velocity distribution; this quantity is defined as the ratio of the number of particles reflected from the magnetic mirror in a given time to the total number of particles incident on the mirror in the same time. Assume that the absolute values of the velocities of all particles are the same and let n be the number of particles per cubic centimeter. For an isotropic velocity distribution the total number of particles incident on a square centimeter of mirror surface per second is $\frac{1}{4}nv$. The total number of particles reflected from a square centimeter of mirror surface per second is

$$\frac{nv}{2}\int_{\vartheta_0}^{\frac{\pi}{2}}\cos\vartheta\sin\vartheta\,d\vartheta=\frac{nv}{4}\cos^2\vartheta_0.$$

The reflection coefficient is then given by

$$R=\cos^2\vartheta_0=1-\frac{B}{B_{max}}. \qquad (10.14)$$

This coefficient is independent of the velocity v so that Eq. (10.14) applies for any isotropic velocity distribution.

The particle experiences a drift in the region of inhomogeneous magnetic field. According to Eq. (5.11) the drift velocity is

$$\mathbf{w}=-\frac{1}{\omega\varrho}\left(v_{\parallel}^2+\frac{v_{\perp}^2}{2}\right)\mathbf{b}, \qquad (10.15)$$

because **E** = 0 in the case being considered and it is assumed that there is no current **j** in the trap. The drift thus occurs along the binormal **b** and consequently forces the particle to gyrate around the axis of the trap. For this reason the drift is called the azimuthal drift. The vector **b** changes direction at a point of discontinuity or twist of the magnetic line of force. Similarly, the azimuthal drift changes direction at a point of discontinuity of the magnetic line of force.

5. Let us assume now that the magnetic mirror moves slowly with a constant velocity u in the direction of the magnetic lines of force. In the Budker system this situation can be realized by moving the auxiliary winding that produces the strong magnetic field at the end of the trap.

Consider the reflection of particles from a slowly moving magnetic mirror. By virtue of the adiabatic invariance of $p_{\perp}^2/B$ the transverse momentum of the particle is not changed after reflection from the mirror because the particle enters the same uniform magnetic field in which it was located before reflection. However, the longitudinal momentum and the longitudinal velocity are changed on reflection from a moving mirror. It is a simple matter to solve this problem in the coordinate system in which the magnetic mirror is at rest. In this system the incident particle is reflected with exactly the same longitudinal velocity it had before reflection. Thus, in the original reference system, after reflection the longitudinal velocity of the particle is changed by twice the velocity of the moving mirror (for simplicity we treat nonrelativistic motion). If the particle and mirror move toward each other the longitudinal velocity of the particle is increased by $2|u|$; however, if the particle moves in the same direction as the mirror the longitudinal velocity of the particle is reduced by the same amount $2|u|$.

Let us now assume that the particle and mirror move toward each-other. In each reflection the kinetic energy associated with the longitudinal motion of the particle is increased by an amount

$$\frac{m(v_{\parallel} + 2u)^2}{2} - \frac{mv_{\parallel}^2}{2} = 2muv_{\parallel}.$$

(We neglect quadratic terms in u.) The kinetic energy associated with the transverse motion of the particle is not changed on reflection. Let n be the number of particles per cubic centimeter having a longitudinal velocity $v_{\parallel}$. Half of these move toward the mirror and the other half away from the mirror. Assume that the magnetic mirror is strong enough that all particles are reflected. If S is the area of the mirror, then $\frac{1}{2} Snv_{\parallel}$ particles are reflected in one second. The increase in the longitudinal kinetic energy $\mathcal{E}_{\parallel}$ of the particles in the system is then

$$\frac{d\mathcal{E}_{\parallel}}{dt} = 2muv_{\parallel} \cdot \frac{1}{2} Snv_{\parallel} = 2\frac{\mathcal{E}_{\parallel}}{V} Su,$$

where V is the volume. Since $Su = -dV/dt$, this equation becomes

$$\frac{d\mathcal{E}_{\parallel}}{\mathcal{E}_{\parallel}} + 2\frac{dV}{V} = 0 \qquad (10.16)$$

and after integration we have

$$\mathcal{E}_{\parallel} V^2 = \text{const.} \qquad (10.17)$$

The quantity $v_{\parallel}$ does not appear explicitly anywhere; hence the assumption that $v_{\parallel}$ is the same for all particles, which we have used in deriving Eq. (10.17), is not important. The relation in (10.17) can be written in another way through the use of a longitudinal kinetic temperature $T_{\parallel}$, which is proportional to the mean kinetic energy associated with the longitudinal motion of the particles. Thus

$$T_{\parallel} V^2 = \text{const} \tag{10.18}$$

or

$$\frac{T_{\parallel}}{n^2} = \text{const.} \tag{10.19}$$

This is the equation of an adiabatic gas with adiabaticity index (specific heat ratio) $\gamma = 3$. This value of γ results because the gas model we have adopted allows no energy exchange between the longitudinal and transverse degrees of freedom; the gas is one-dimensional, that is to say, it acts like a gas whose particles have only one degree of freedom ($N = 1$). In general, the adiabaticity index is given by

$$\gamma = \frac{2 + N}{N}. \tag{10.20}$$

If it is assumed that the isotropic velocity distribution is restored continuously as a result of collisions or any other mechanism the mean longitudinal kinetic energy $\mathcal{E}_{\parallel}$ is related to the total kinetic energy $\mathcal{E}$ by the expression $\mathcal{E}_{\parallel} = {}^1/_3\, \mathcal{E}$ and Eq. (10.16) is replaced by

$$\frac{d\mathcal{E}}{\mathcal{E}} + \frac{2}{3} \cdot \frac{dV}{V} = 0.$$

This leads to an adiabaticity index $\gamma = {}^5/_3$ as it should for a monatomic gas.

6. The example we have just considered is of importance in the theory of cosmic rays. A cosmic-ray theory must provide a mechanism by which charged particles can be accelerated in interstellar space. Acceleration by electrostatic fields is evidently not a feasible explanation since the high conductivity of the ionized gas in stellar and interstellar clouds limits the values such fields can reach. For this reason the suggestion has been advanced that the acceleration is due to time-varying magnetic fields. According to a mechanism proposed by Fermi [9] the charged particle moves in a magnetic field between two clouds of interstellar material. If it is assumed that the magnetic field in the clouds is greater than in the space between the clouds the particle can become trapped in the same way as in the Budker adiabatic trap. Those particles will be trapped whose velocity vectors make a relatively large angle with respect to the magnetic field. If it is assumed that the clouds approach each other the charged particle acquires energy in each reflection since the moving cloud acts as a moving magnetic mirror.

This acceleration mechanism has an important limit, however. As $v_{\parallel}$ increases the angle ϑ is reduced and the particle finally escapes so that the ratio of total energy to transverse energy can only increase to some well defined limit that depends on the effective reflection coefficient of the clouds acting as magnetic mirrors. Furthermore, the transverse velocity cannot increase as long as the magnetic field B between the clouds remains fixed since $p^2_{\perp}/B$ and thus $p_{\perp}$ remain constant in the absence of collisions and other perturbing factors. In order to achieve continuous particle acceleration it is thus necessary to assume that collisions or some other mechanism continuously restore the isotropic velocity distribution that is disturbed as a result of particle reflections from the clouds; in this way particles can again be trapped and accelerated. However, collisions become less and less effective as the particles acquire higher energies. Fermi proposed that the isotropic distribution of particle velocities in interstellar space is restored as a result of shock waves or plasma oscillations.

7. Let us assume now that the configuration of magnetic lines in an adiabatic trap such as that proposed by Budker remains unchanged but that the magnitude of the magnetic field is a function of time. We shall consider the motion of the guiding center of the particle using Eq. (5.11) [10]. The first term $v_{\parallel}\mathbf{h}$ on the right side of this equation gives the velocity of the guiding center along the magnetic line of force, a quantity that is of no interest here. The third term $-(1/\omega\rho)(v^2_{\parallel} + v^2_{\perp}/2)\mathbf{b}$ corresponds to the so-called azimuthal drift, i.e., the motion around a circle with center at axis of the system; this motion is in the direction of the binormal to the line of force and is also not of interest. The last term in Eq. (5.11) vanishes because there are no currents ($\mathbf{j} = 0$). Even if there is current flow the analysis given below still applies without change. All that is required is that the radial component of the current density must vanish; any parallel component $j_{\parallel}$ or azimuthal component produces motion along the magnetic field or an azimuthal drift, both of which are not of interest. The only remaining term is the second term, $(c/B^2)[\mathbf{EB}]$, which describes the electric drift. We concentrate our attention on this term. This drift, as we shall

now show, causes the guiding center of the particle to move toward the axis of the trap if the magnetic field increases in time, and causes it to move away from the axis if the magnetic decreases in time.

Assume that the dimensions of the region of uniform magnetic field are large compared with the regions occupied by the magnetic mirrors. We can then neglect processes that occur inside the magnetic mirrors. The mirrors are regarded simply as a means of reflecting particles. We can then assume that the time-varying magnetic field is uniform. The electric field **E** arises by virtue of the fact that the magnetic field **B** varies in time. It is evident from symmetry considerations that the electric force lines will be concentric circles with centers on the axis. Hence the velocity associated with the electric drift $(c/B^2)[\mathbf{EB}]$ is in the radial direction, that is to say, it must be toward or away from the axis. It is then easy to show, using the general rules for determining the direction of an electric field **E** produced by electromagnetic induction, that when **B** increases in time the velocity is directed toward the axis of the trap and that when **B** decreases the velocity is directed away from the axis. The magnitude of the field **E** can be determined easily using the rules for electromagnetic induction. Denote by r the distance of the guiding center of the particle from the axis and apply the circulation theorem for **E**, taking as the path of integration a circle of radius r with center on the axis in the plane perpendicular to the axis. Then

$$|2\pi r E| = \left|\frac{1}{c}\frac{d\Phi}{dt}\right|,$$

where $\Phi = \pi r^2 B$ is the magnetic flux that cuts the area bounded by the circle.

Thus

$$E = \frac{r}{2c}\left|\frac{dB}{dt}\right|,$$

and the velocity associated with the electric drift is

$$\dot{r} = -\frac{c}{B}E = -\frac{r}{2B}\frac{dB}{dt},$$

which, upon integration, yields

$$\pi r^2 B \equiv \Phi = \text{const.} \qquad (10.21)$$

The result that has been obtained can be given another interpretation which is associated with the general principles of magnetohydrodynamics. In this case we assume that the trap contains many particles (volume density n) rather than a single particle. The density is small enough, however, so that interactions between particles can be neglected. The particles can then be treated independently and the motion of each particle can be described using the results obtained for an individual particle. When the magnetic field changes, the value of r (distance to the axis) for each particle changes (more precisely, the value for the guiding center changes). We consider particles which, at a given instant of time, are located on a circle whose center lies on the axis. When the magnetic field changes this circle is deformed but the magnetic flux that cuts it remains unchanged.

Comparing Eq. (10.21) with Eq. (5.17) we note that the distance of a particle from the axis r changes with changing magnetic field in accordance with the same rule that describes the change in Larmor radius $a_\perp$. The increasing magnetic field results in an acceleration of the particles around the Larmor circle, i. e., an increase in the transverse velocity $v_\perp$. As the magnetic mirrors move together the longitudinal velocity $v_\|$ increases. The total particle velocity increases, thus causing the trapped plasma to become hotter. The increase in field **B** simultaneously produces a contraction of plasma toward the axis.

8. An increase in magnetic field with no change in the configuration of lines of force causes contraction of the plasma in the longitudinal direction as well as in the transverse direction. This effect can be understood from an examination of the motion of an individual particle. In a fixed magnetic field a particle in a Budker adiabatic trap will execute longitudinal oscillations between the magnetic mirrors. The positions of the reflection points in the regions of the magnetic mirrors depend on the ratio of transverse particle velocity to longitudinal velocity ($v_\perp/v_\|$) at any fixed point on the magnetic line of force. As such a fixed point we may arbitrarily choose the point lying in the plane of the transverse cross section of the system passing through its center. The larger the indicated velocity ratio the closer the reflection points will be to the center, thus making the amplitude of the longitudinal oscillations smaller, as we have seen. But, a simple increase in magnetic field strength with no change in the geometry of the lines of force increases the transverse velocity $v_\perp$ leaving the longitudinal velocity $v_\parallel$ unchanged. This causes the ratio $v_\perp/v_\parallel$ to become larger; in turn the amplitude of the longitudinal oscillations is reduced and the plasma contracts in the longitudinal direction.

The following simple example [10] serves to illustrate this effect. Let us assume that the magnetic field at the axis of the system is

$$B(z,\ t) = B_0(t) + \frac{1}{2} k(t) z^2,$$

where $B_0(t)$ and k(t) are slowly varying functions of time. The increment in these functions over a longitudinal-oscillation period is assumed to be small. The z axis is taken along the axis of the trap, and the origin of coordinates is taken at the center. The equation describing the longitudinal oscillations of the particle along the z axis can be obtained from Eq. (6.21), and is of the form

$$\ddot{z} + \Omega^2(t) z = 0, \tag{10.22}$$

where $\Omega(t)$ is a slowly varying function given by

$$\Omega(t) = \sqrt{\frac{\mu k}{m}}.$$

We assume that the function k(t) is essentially positive so that the frequency $\Omega(t)$ is real.

The solution of Eq. (10.22) is sought in the form

$$z = ae^{i\varphi},$$

where a and φ are real functions of the time and it is assumed that the first is a slowly varying function. Substituting in Eq. (10.22) and separating real and imaginary parts we have

$$a\dot{\varphi}^2 - \ddot{a} = a\Omega^2,$$

$$2\dot{a}\dot{\varphi} + a\ddot{\varphi} \equiv \frac{1}{a}\frac{d}{dt}(a^2\dot{\varphi}) = 0.$$

The second derivative of the slowly varying amplitude a can be neglected in the first equation and we find that $\dot{\varphi} = \pm\,\Omega$; using this result in the second equation we have

$$a^2\Omega = \text{const.} \tag{10.23}$$

Whence we conclude that the quantity $a^2\Omega$ is an adiabatic invariant. We now turn to the real form of the solution, which can be written

$$z = a\cos\int\Omega\,(t)\,dt. \tag{10.24}$$

The solution is in the form of a "harmonic" oscillation with slowly varying amplitude and frequency. Since the magnetic moment μ is also an adiabatic invariant, as k increases the frequency Ω also increases. Hence we conclude from Eq. (10.23) that the amplitude of the oscillations is reduced. This effect is then responsible for the contraction of the plasma in the longitudinal direction.

9. The magnetic field around the earth can be regarded as a large trap for charged particles of cosmic origin. In this field the smoothed motion of the charged particle is along the magnetic line of force. Superimposed on it is the drift motion toward the east or to the west in the direction of the geomagnetic parallel. The lines of force of the earth's magnetic field come together near the magnetic poles of the earth. Hence, charged particles moving along the magnetic lines of force can experience reflection near these poles and the latter play the role of magnetic mirrors. The particle will execute oscillatory motion between the north and south magnetic poles of the earth, as in a magnetic mirror system. Investigations carried out with artificial earth satellites and rockets have actually shown that the earth's magnetic field forms an effective magnetic mirror system for charged particles that are produced by various nuclear processess in the space surrounding the earth. This work is described, for example, in review papers by S. N. Vernov and A. E. Chudakov [11] and by Van Allen [12] who give detailed bibliographies. We shall limit ourselves here to a brief discussion of the results of this work.

Around the earth there are two spatially separated regions (belts) of high-intensity corpuscular radiation. The outer belt, consisting of electrons, starts in the equatorial plane at a distance of about 20,000 km from the center of the earth and extends to a distance of about 60,000 km. The boundaries of the belt are fixed by the appropriate force lines of the earth's magnetic field. In the range of geomagnetic latitude 55 - 70° the outer belt is observed at relatively low altitudes (300 - 1500 km above the earth's surface). Moving away from the earth along a line of force a sharp increase in the intensity of the corpuscular radiation is observed. This then appears to be experimental verification of the existence, around the earth, of a magnetic trap that contains charged particles. The electrons in the outer belt can be divided into two energy classes. The energies in the first class are typically several tens of kilo-electron volts. The maximum flux of electrons with energy greater than 20 keV is approximately 10^9 $cm^{-2} \cdot sec^{-1} \cdot sterad^{-1}$. The energy of the electrons in the second class is of the order of 1 MeV. The maximum flux of electrons of this class is approximately 10^5 $cm^{-2} \cdot sec^{-1} \cdot sterad^{-1}$.

The inner belt, which consists primarily of protons with energies of approximately 100 MeV, starts at a height of approximately 600 km in the equatorial plane of the western hemisphere and extends to several earth radii. The boundary of the inner belt is the line of force emanating from the earth at a geomagnetic latitude of 35°. The proton flux in the inner belt is approximately 10^2 $cm^{-2} \cdot sec^{-1} \cdot sterad^{-1}$. In addition to containing protons of high energy the inner belt also contains low energy particles which are evidently electrons.

Corpuscular radiation is also observed between these two belts. However the electron and proton fluxes in these intermediate regions are approximately three orders of magnitude smaller than in the inner and outer belts.

It is not difficult to determine the point at which a charged particle undergoes reflection in the earth's magnetic field. The earth's field can be approximated by the field of a point magnetic dipole located near the center of the earth. We denote the magnetic moment of this dipole by **M**. The dipole magnetic field is given by the familiar expression

$$\mathbf{B} = \frac{3\,(\mathbf{Mr})}{r^5}\mathbf{r} - \frac{\mathbf{M}}{r^3}, \tag{10.25}$$

whence

$$B = \frac{M}{r^3}\sqrt{3\sin^2\lambda + 1}, \tag{10.26}$$

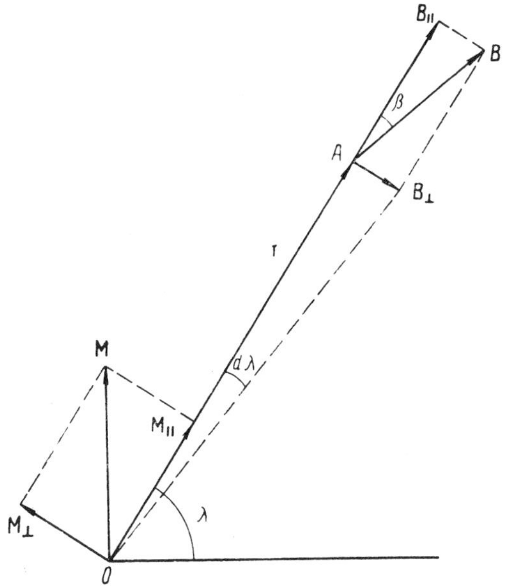

Fig. 11

where λ is the geomagnetic latitude. It is easy to find the equation for the lines of force of the dipole. The vector **M** (Fig. 11) is resolved into two components: $\mathbf{M}_{\parallel}$, parallel to the radius vector **r**, and $\mathbf{M}_{\perp}$, perpendicular to this vector. At the point of observation A the first component gives a field $\mathbf{B}_{\parallel} = 2\mathbf{M}_{\parallel}/r^3$ and the second a field $\mathbf{B}_{\perp} = -\mathbf{M}_{\perp}/r^3$. Hence the angle β between the radius vector **r** and the line of force is given by

$$\tan\beta = \frac{B_{\perp}}{B_{\parallel}} = \frac{M_{\perp}}{2M_{\parallel}} = \frac{1}{2}\cot\lambda.$$

The projection of an infinitesimally small portion of the line of force in the direction of the vector $B_{\perp}$ can, on the one hand, be given by $dr\tan\beta = (dr/2)\cot\lambda$, and on the other, by $-rd\lambda$. Thus

$$\frac{dr}{2}\cot\lambda = -rd\lambda,$$

and we obtain the equation for the line of force

$$r = r_e\cos^2\lambda, \qquad (10.27)$$

where the constant r_e has the meaning of the length of the radius vector $\mathbf{r}$ in the equatorial plane, i. e., at $\lambda = 0$.

Let ϑ_e be the angle between the direction of motion of the particle and the line of force in the equatorial plane. Then the value of the field B at the point at which the particle experiences reflection can be found from Eq. (10.12) by the substitution $B \rightarrow B_e$, $B_M \rightarrow B$. Thus

$$\sin^2 \vartheta_e = \frac{B_e}{B}.$$

Eliminating B_e and B by means of Eq. (10.26) and taking account of Eq. (10.27) we have

$$\sin^2 \vartheta_e = \frac{\cos^6 \lambda}{\sqrt{3 \sin^2 \lambda + 1}}. \tag{10.28}$$

This formula together with Eq. (10.27) then represent the solution to the problem.

10. In conclusion we consider two examples in which the trajectory of a particle in a magnetic field can be determined exactly. We can then compare the results of the exact calculations with the results obtained in the drift approximation.

Assume a constant magnetic field perpendicular to the plane of the page (Fig. 12) and let the field strength B depend only on r, the distance from a fixed point O. A charged particle moves in the plane of the figure and it is required to find its trajectory.

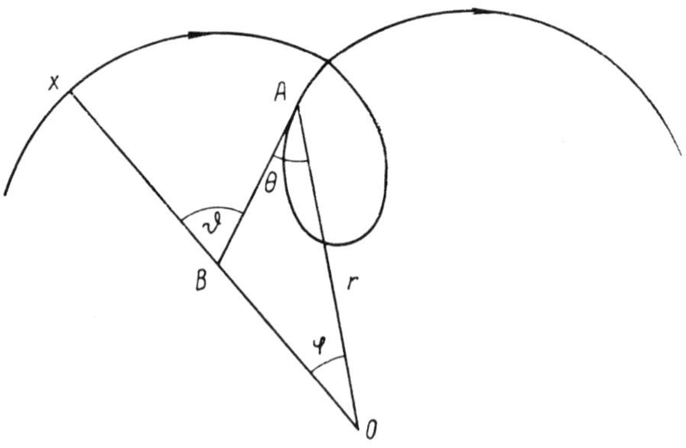

Fig. 12

We take the point O to be the origin of a polar coordinate system with polar axis Ox. The position of a point can be characterized by r, the distance from the origin O, and the polar angle φ. Denote by ϑ the angle between the polar axis Ox and the tangent to the particle trajectory BA. The radius of curvature of the trajectory a is given by Eq. (1.21) and depends only on r for a given particle velocity. By the definition of curvature,

$$\frac{d\vartheta}{ds} = \frac{1}{a} = \frac{eB}{cp}, \qquad (10.29)$$

where ds is an element of length of the trajectory. The angle between the radius vector OA and the tangent to the trajectory BA is denoted by Θ Thus

$$\vartheta = \Theta + \varphi, \qquad (10.30)$$

$$dr = ds \cos \Theta, \qquad (10.31)$$

and Eq. (10.29) assumes the form

$$\cos \Theta \frac{d\Theta}{dr} + \cos \Theta \frac{d\varphi}{dr} = \frac{1}{a}. \qquad (10.32)$$

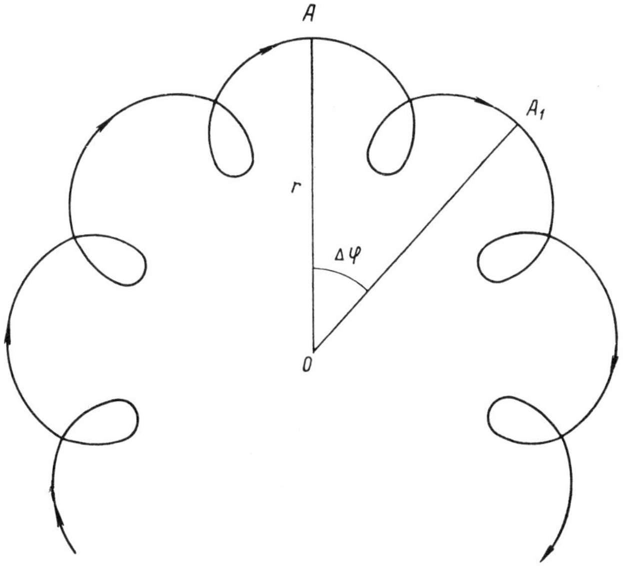

Fig. 13

This equation is supplemented by the equation

$$r\,\frac{d\varphi}{dr}=\tan\Theta, \tag{10.33}$$

which follows directly from Fig. 12. By means of this relation Eq. (10.32) can be transformed to read

$$d\,(r\sin\Theta)=\frac{r}{a}\,dr. \tag{10.34}$$

The right side contains the known function r; hence, integrating Eq. (10.34) we have

$$\sin\Theta=\frac{1}{r}\int_{r_{\max}}^{r}\frac{r}{a}\,dr. \tag{10.35}$$

The quantity φ is then determined from Eq. (10.33):

$$\varphi=\int_{r_{\max}}^{r}\frac{\tan\Theta}{r}\,dr. \tag{10.36}$$

We take the polar axis to be the direction of one of the maximum radius vectors of the points on the trajectory. Equations (10.29) and (10.35) determine the trajectory in parametric form. The form of the trajectory is given in Fig. 13.

The case in which B = const/r is a simple one. In this case a/r is a constant that we denote by α. Eliminating r from Eqs. (10.32) and (10.33) we then have

$$d\Theta+d\varphi=\frac{1}{\alpha}\cdot\frac{d\varphi}{\sin\Theta}$$

or

$$d\varphi=\frac{\alpha\sin\Theta\,d\Theta}{1-\alpha\sin\Theta}. \tag{10.37}$$

This equation can be used to determine the "drift angle" $\Delta\varphi$, i. e., the angular distance between two neighboring extrema on the particle trajectory (cf. Fig. 13). The drift angle is evidently given by

$$\Delta\varphi = \alpha \int_{\frac{\pi}{2}}^{\frac{\pi}{2}+2\pi} \frac{\sin\Theta\, d\Theta}{1-\alpha\sin\Theta} = 2\pi\left(\frac{1}{\sqrt{1-\alpha^2}}-1\right). \quad (10.38)$$

Now let us compute the drift angle in the drift approximation. According to Eq. (5.5) the drift velocity $\omega = (1/2B)\, va\, |dB/dr|$. Since $B \sim 1/r$ then $\omega = (v/2)(a/r) = (v/2)\,\alpha$. In a cyclotron period $T = 2\pi/\omega$ the guiding center of the particle is displaced by $\omega T = \pi(v/\omega)\,\alpha = \pi a\alpha$. This corresponds to an angular displacement or drift angle

$$\Delta\varphi = \pi\alpha\,\frac{a}{r} = \pi\alpha^2. \quad (10.39)$$

However, this expression can be obtained from the exact expression (10.38) by expanding $1/\sqrt{1-\alpha^2}$ and neglecting terms of fourth order and higher in α. Thus, Eq. (10.39) is accurate to terms of order α^4.

11. Assume now that the magnetic field is perpendicular to the plane of the figure (Fig. 14), and that it varies linearly in the y direction in such a way that the field vanishes along the x axis. Let grad B be in the direction of negative y. Then

$$\frac{1}{a} = \frac{eB}{cp} = -\frac{1}{A^2}\,y, \quad (10.40)$$

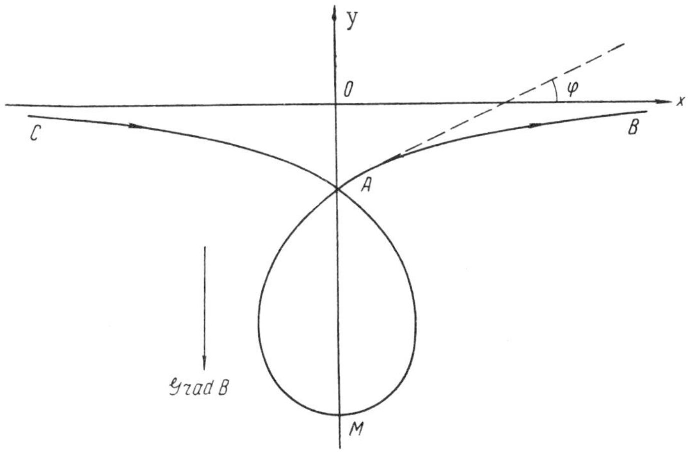

Fig. 14

where A is some constant. We denote by φ the angle between the direction of the tangent to the particle trajectory and the positive x axis. Then, from the definition of curvature

$$\frac{d\varphi}{ds} = -\frac{1}{a} = \frac{1}{A^2} y.$$

Using the relations $dx = ds \cos\varphi$ and $dy = ds \sin\varphi$ we obtain the two equations:

$$\begin{aligned} y\,dx &= A^2 \cos\varphi\, d\varphi, \\ y\,dy &= A^2 \sin\varphi\, d\varphi. \end{aligned} \tag{10.41}$$

The second of these can be integrated immediately and yields

$$y^2 = -2A^2 \cos\varphi + \text{const}.$$

We shall consider a particular case which can be integrated easily, taking the const such that $y = 0$ when $\varphi = 0$. Thus, writing const $= 2A^2$, we have

$$y = 2A \sin\frac{\varphi}{2}. \tag{10.42}$$

Substituting this expression in the first equation in (10.41) we can reduce it to the form

$$dx = \frac{A}{2} \frac{\cos\varphi}{\sin\frac{\varphi}{2}} d\varphi = \frac{A}{2} \frac{d\varphi}{\sin\frac{\varphi}{2}} - A \sin\frac{\varphi}{2}\, d\varphi.$$

Integrating we find

$$x = A \ln\tan\frac{\varphi}{4} + 2A \cos\frac{\varphi}{2}. \tag{10.43}$$

The constant of integration is chosen in such a way that the abscissa x vanishes when $\varphi = \pi$ (the point M on the trajectory).

Equations (10.42) and (10.43) are the equations of the trajectory in parametric form. The trajectory has only one loop and goes to infinity at both ends. The x axis is an *asymptote* of the trajectory. Thus, in general the particle motion in the case at hand is entirely different from that which would be given by drift theory. This result can be understood since the particle moves in a region of *weak* magnetic field (the field B vanishes at the x axis).

We may note that the problem just treated is mathematically identical with that of determining the shape of a surface of a liquid when it is subject to the force of gravity and to surface tension when an infinitely long heavy plate that is not wetted by the liquid is placed on the liquid surface [13, 18]. The cross section of this surface in the vertical plane perpendicular to the length of the plate reproduces each of the infinite petals MAB and MAC of the particle trajectory for a given depth of submersion.

§ 11. Drift Integrals of the Motion in Constant Electric and Magnetic Fields

1. The drift equations of motion (6.10), (6.11), and (6.12) always have one integral which is the adiabatic invariant

$$\frac{P_\perp^2}{B} \equiv I_\perp = \text{const.} \tag{11.1}$$

If the electric and magnetic fields are constant in time it is possible to write an additional integral, the energy integral. In this case the electric field **E** is derivable from a potential, and can be written in the form $\mathbf{E} = -\text{grad}\,\varphi(\text{r})$. Equation (6.13) then becomes

$$\frac{d}{dt}(mc^2) = -e(\dot{\mathbf{R}}\nabla\varphi) = -e(\dot{\mathbf{R}}\nabla)\varphi = -e\frac{d\varphi}{dt},$$

Here, all quantities are functions of the radius vector **R** of the guiding center of a particle, i. e., they refer to points on the trajectory of this center. Since **R** in turn depends on t, in the final analysis these can be regarded as functions of t alone. Integrating the last equation we obtain the energy integral

$$mc^2 + e\varphi = \mathcal{E} = \text{const}, \tag{11.2}$$

which uniquely determines the particle mass m at each point of the trajectory of the guiding center. Similarly, Eq. (11.1) determines the transverse momentum $P_\perp$ uniquely at the points of the same trajectory. Thus, by virtue of Eq. (1.4) we determine the total momentum P uniquely as well as the longitudinal component $P_\parallel = \sqrt{P^2 - P_\perp^2}$:

$$P_\parallel^2 = (mc)^2 - (m_0c)^2 - I_\perp B. \tag{11.3}$$

Now let us formulate the problem differently, going from the motion of an individual particle to an analysis of the motion of an ensemble of noninteracting identical particles with the same values of $\mathscr{E}$ and $I_\perp$. With respect to this ensemble the quantities m, $P_\parallel$, $P_\perp$ as well as $V_\parallel$, $V_\perp$, $a_\parallel$, and $a_\perp$ are specified not only along the trajectory of the guiding center of the individual particle, but over the entire space. The equation of motion of the individual particle is found by substituting the values of $V_\parallel$, $V_\perp$, $a_\parallel$, and $a_\perp$ in Eq. (6.10). We write this equation in the form obtained by Morozov and Solov'ev[14] which is also useful for the basic results presented later in this section. We have

$$\text{rot}\,(P_\parallel \mathbf{h}) = P_\parallel\,\text{rot}\,\mathbf{h} + [\nabla P_\parallel \mathbf{h}].$$

From Eq. (11.3)

$$\nabla P_\parallel = \frac{e}{V_\parallel}\mathbf{E} - \frac{I_\perp}{2P_\parallel}\nabla B.$$

Hence

$$\text{rot}\,(P_\parallel \mathbf{h}) = P_\parallel\,\text{rot}\,\mathbf{h} + \frac{e}{V_\parallel}[\mathbf{E}\mathbf{h}] + \frac{I_\perp}{2P_\parallel}[\mathbf{h}\nabla B].$$

Making use of this relation we write Eq. (6.10) in the form

$$\dot{\mathbf{R}} = \frac{V_\parallel}{B}\left\{\mathbf{B} + \frac{e}{c}\,\text{rot}\,(P_\parallel \mathbf{h}) - \frac{cP_\parallel}{e}(\mathbf{h}\,\text{rot}\,\mathbf{h})\,\mathbf{h}\right\}. \qquad (11.4)$$

This is an ordinary vector differential equation. When **E** and **B** are independent of time the entire system of equations of the drift approximation reduces to this equation. It is a first-order equation. Hence, the motion of the guiding center of an individual particle is determined uniquely by its position at the initial time, which can be chosen arbitrarily.

2. We assume that **h** rot **h** = 0. Then since **B** rot **h** = **h** rot **B**, this condition is equivalent to **h** rot **B** = 0 or (**hj**) = 0. Thus we imply that the longitudinal component of the current density $\mathbf{j}_\parallel$ vanishes. We now introduce the vector potential **A** associated with the magnetic field. Then **B** = rot **A** and Eq. (11.4) assumes the form

$$\dot{\mathbf{R}} = \frac{V_\parallel}{B}\,\text{rot}\,\mathbf{A}^*, \qquad (11.5)$$

where

$$\mathbf{A}^* = \mathbf{A} + \frac{c}{e} P_{\parallel} \mathbf{h}. \tag{11.6}$$

The vector

$$\mathbf{B}^* = \mathbf{B} + \frac{c}{e} \operatorname{rot} (P_{\parallel} \mathbf{h}) \tag{11.7}$$

can be regarded as some kind of a fictitious magnetic field and $\mathbf{A}^*$ as its vector potential. It is evident from Eq. (11.5) that the guiding center of the particle always moves along the line of force of this "magnetic field."

Taking the vector product of Eq. (11.5) with $\mathbf{B}^*$ we have

$$[\dot{\mathbf{R}}\mathbf{B}^*] = 0. \tag{11.8}$$

Formally, this equation coincides with the equation of motion of a particle of zero mass in a magnetic field $\mathbf{B}^*$ and can be written in the Lagrangian form

$$\frac{d}{dt}\frac{\partial L}{\partial \dot{q}_i} - \frac{\partial L}{\partial q_i} = 0 \tag{11.9}$$

with the Lagrangian

$$L = (\mathbf{A}^* \dot{\mathbf{R}}), \tag{11.10}$$

which is a function of the generalized coordinates q_i of the guiding center and the corresponding generalized velocities. If any coordinate q_i is cyclic, i.e., if $\partial L/\partial q_i = 0$, the corresponding generalized momentum is a constant, that is to say, it is an integral of the motion. Thus, the integrals of the drift equations can be found using the symmetry of the problem.

We consider three kinds of symmetry.

a. Translational Symmetry. In this case the magnetic field and the electric potential φ are independent of one of the Cartesian coordinates, say z:

$$\mathbf{B} = \mathbf{B}(x, y), \quad \varphi = \varphi(x, y).$$

The vector potential **A** can be chosen in such a way as to also be independent of z. By virtue of Eqs. (11.2) and (11.6) the vector $\mathbf{A}^*$ is also independent of z. Hence the coordinate z does not appear in the Lagrangian

$$L = (\mathbf{A}^*\dot{\mathbf{R}}) = \dot{x}\mathbf{A}_x^* + \dot{y}\mathbf{A}_y^* + \dot{z}\mathbf{A}_z^*,$$

and we obtain the integral of the motion

$$\frac{\partial L}{\partial \dot{z}} = \mathbf{A}_z^* = \text{const.} \qquad (11.11)$$

b. Axial Symmetry. The position of a point in space is specified by the cylindrical coordinates z, r, and α. In the case of axial symmetry the components B_z, B_r, and B_α of the vector **B** and the scalar potential φ depend only on z and r but are independent of α. Hence the vector potential **A** and the vector potential $\mathbf{A}^*$ can be chosen in such a way that the components A_z, A_r, and A_α and A_z^*, A_r^*, and A_α^* are also independent of α. The coordinate α then does not appear in the Lagrangian

$$L = \dot{z}A_z^* + \dot{r}A_r^* + \dot{\alpha}rA_\alpha^*, \qquad (11.12)$$

i.e., this coordinate is cyclic and we obtain the following integral of the motion:

$$\frac{\partial L}{\partial \dot{\alpha}} = rA_\alpha^* = \text{const.} \qquad (11.13)$$

Let us apply this result to the motion of a charged particle in the magnetic field of a dipole. This question has already been considered in subsection 9 of the preceding section. The magnetic field of the dipole can be described by the vector potential $\mathbf{A} = [\mathbf{MR}]/R^3$. It only has the azimuthal component A_α. Both the dipole and the vector $\mathbf{A}^* = \mathbf{A} + (c/e)P_{\parallel}\mathbf{h}$ exhibit axial symmetry and the integral in (11.13) applies. In the case at hand $A_\alpha^* = A_\alpha = (M/R^2)\cos\lambda$, $r = R\cos\lambda$, and the integral in (11.13) becomes

$$\frac{\cos^2\lambda}{R} = \text{const},$$

i.e., the equation for the line of force.

c. Helical Symmetry. As before the position of a point in space is specified by the cylindrical coordinates r, z, and α. In the case of helical symmetry the components B_r, B_z, and B_α and the potential φ at points r_1, z_1, α_1 and r_2, z_2, α_2 coincide if

$$r_1 = r_2, \qquad \frac{\alpha_1 - \alpha_2}{2\pi} = \frac{z_1 - z_2}{b},$$

where b is the pitch of the helix. Writing this condition in the form

$$\alpha_1 - \frac{2\pi z_1}{b} = \alpha_2 - \frac{2\pi z_2}{b},$$

we conclude that in the case of helical symmetry B_r, B_z, B_α, and φ depend only on r and $\alpha - 2\pi z/b$. The vector potential **A** and consequently the vector $\mathbf{A}^*$ can be chosen in such a way that their components in the cylindrical coordinate system A_r, A_z, A_α, A_r^*, A_z^*, A_α^*, depend on the same arguments. We now introduce the generalized coordinates

$$r, \quad q_1 = \alpha - \frac{2\pi z}{b}, \qquad q_2 = \alpha + \frac{2\pi z}{b}.$$

In these coordinates the Lagrangian (11.12) can be written in the form

$$L = \dot{r} A_r^* - \frac{b}{4\pi}\left(A_z^* - \frac{2\pi r}{b} A_\alpha^*\right)\dot{q}_1 + \frac{b}{4\pi}\left(A_z^* + \frac{2\pi r}{b} A_\alpha^*\right)\dot{q}_2,$$

and is independent of q_2. Hence we obtain the integral

$$\frac{4\pi}{b}\frac{\partial L}{\partial \dot{q}_2} = A_z^* + \frac{2\pi r}{b} A_\alpha^* = \text{const}. \qquad (11.14)$$

3. Morozov and Solov'ev [14] limited themselves to the case in which **h** rot **h** = 0. We now ask whether it is possible to generalize their results to the case in which this condition is not satisfied. The right side of Eq. (11.4) contains a known vector function. Let us denote this vector function by **C(R)**. An arbitrary vector, say **C(R)**, can be written **C** = $[1/f(\mathbf{R})]$ rot **F(R)**. Actually, $f(\mathbf{R})$ can be taken as the solution of the equation

$$\operatorname{div}(f\mathbf{C}) = \mathbf{C}\operatorname{grad} f + f\operatorname{div}\mathbf{C} = 0. \qquad (11.15)$$

Then, writing **C** in the form **C** = $[1/f(\mathbf{R})]\,\mathbf{D}(\mathbf{R})$ we find that div **D** = 0 so that **D** = rot **F**. Hence Eq. (11.14) becomes

$$f(\mathbf{R})\,\dot{\mathbf{R}} = \operatorname{rot}\mathbf{F}(\mathbf{R}), \qquad (11.16)$$

whence

$$[\dot{\mathbf{R}} \operatorname{rot} \mathbf{F}(\mathbf{R})] = 0. \tag{11.17}$$

The last equation can be written in Lagrangian form (11.9) using the Lagrangian L = (**FR**). Consequently, all the results obtained above also apply in the case in which $\mathbf{h} \operatorname{rot} \mathbf{h} \neq 0$ so long as $\mathbf{A}^*$ is replaced by **F**. In this case, when the integrals of motion are obtained from the symmetry of the problem it is necessary to take that solution $f(\mathbf{R})$ of Eq. (11.15) and that vector $\mathbf{F}(\mathbf{R})$ which have the same symmetry. The problem is reduced to the integration of a partial differential equation (11.15). In practice this reduction is not very useful since general methods for the solution of equations such as (11.15) are not available.

§ 12. Liouville Theorem in the Drift Approximation

1. In the drift approximation the motion of a particle is characterized by five variables: the three coordinates of the guiding center x, y, z and the two momenta $P_{\parallel}$ and $P_{\perp}$. In place of the momenta $P_{\parallel}$ and $P_{\perp}$ we can use $p_{\parallel}$ and $p_{\perp}$, which are related to $P_{\parallel}$ and $P_{\perp}$ by Eq. (6.4). In this section we will first use the variables $p_{\parallel}$ and $p_{\perp}$. Then Eqs. (6.1), (6.2), and (6.3) are the equations of motion in the drift approximation. Using the identity $(\mathbf{h}\nabla)\mathbf{h} = -[\mathbf{h} \operatorname{rot} \mathbf{h}]$ we write this equation in the form

$$\dot{\mathbf{R}} = \left[v_{\parallel} + \frac{cp_{\perp}^2}{2meB}(\mathbf{h} \operatorname{rot} \mathbf{h})\right]\mathbf{h} + \frac{c}{B}[\mathbf{E}\mathbf{h}] + \\ + \frac{cp_{\perp}^2}{2meB^2}[\mathbf{h}\nabla B] + \frac{cp_{\parallel}^2}{meB}\operatorname{rot}\mathbf{h} - \frac{cp_{\parallel}^2}{meB}(\mathbf{h} \operatorname{rot} \mathbf{h})\,\mathbf{h}; \tag{12.1}$$

$$\dot{p}_{\parallel} = e(\mathbf{E}\mathbf{h}) + \frac{p_{\perp}^2}{2m}\operatorname{div}\mathbf{h} + \frac{cp_{\parallel}}{B}(\mathbf{E} \operatorname{rot} \mathbf{h}) - \frac{cp_{\parallel}}{B}(\mathbf{E}\mathbf{h})(\mathbf{h} \operatorname{rot} \mathbf{h}) - \\ - \frac{cp_{\parallel}p_{\perp}^2}{2meB}(\nabla B \operatorname{rot} \mathbf{h}) + \frac{cp_{\parallel}p_{\perp}^2}{2meB^2}(\nabla B\,\mathbf{h})(\mathbf{h} \operatorname{rot} \mathbf{h}) + \frac{cp_{\parallel}p_{\perp}^2}{2meB}\mathbf{h} \operatorname{rot}[\mathbf{h} \operatorname{rot} \mathbf{h}]; \tag{12.2}$$

$$\frac{dp_{\perp}^2}{dt} = -\frac{p_{\parallel}p_{\perp}^2}{m}\operatorname{div}\mathbf{h} - \frac{cp_{\perp}^2}{B}(\mathbf{h} \operatorname{rot} \mathbf{E}) + \frac{cp_{\perp}^2}{B^2}([\mathbf{h}\nabla B]\,\mathbf{E}) + \\ + \frac{cp_{\perp}^2}{B}(\mathbf{E}\mathbf{h})(\mathbf{h} \operatorname{rot} \mathbf{h}) + \frac{cp_{\parallel}^2 p_{\perp}^2}{meB^2}(\nabla B \operatorname{rot} \mathbf{h}) - \frac{cp_{\parallel}^2 p_{\perp}^2}{meB^2}(\mathbf{h}\nabla B)(\mathbf{h} \operatorname{rot} \mathbf{h}) - \\ - \frac{cp_{\parallel}^2 p_{\perp}^2}{meB}\mathbf{h} \operatorname{rot}[\mathbf{h} \operatorname{rot} \mathbf{h}]. \tag{12.3}$$

The mass m is a function of the momenta $p_{\parallel}$ and $p_{\perp}$ and by virtue of Eq. (1.4) is given by

$$(mc)^2 = (m_0c)^2 + p_{\parallel}^2 + p_{\perp}^2. \tag{12.4}$$

From this we find

$$\frac{\partial m}{\partial p_{\parallel}} = \frac{v_{\parallel}}{c^2}, \qquad \frac{\partial m}{\partial p_{\perp}} = \frac{v_{\perp}}{c^2}. \tag{12.5}$$

Let us imagine a very large number (going over to a continuum in the limit) of noninteracting identical particles; the state of each particle is described by five variables in the drift approximation: the three rectangular coordinates x, y, z of the guiding center and the two momenta $p_{\parallel}$ and $p_{\perp}$. Let x^0, y^0, z^0, $p^0_{\parallel}$, and $p^0_{\perp}$ be the initial values of these variables, which occupy some region D^0. The values of x, y, z, $p_{\parallel}$, and $p_{\perp}$ at any other instant of time t are then determined by the equations of motion (12.1), (12.2), and (12.3) and will occupy the well defined region D^t which evolves from the motion of the region D^0. Assume that there exists a function $G(x, y, z, p_{\parallel}, p_{\perp})$ such that the following equality is satisfied for any time t:

$$\int_{D^0} G\left(x^0, y^0, z^0, p^0_{\parallel}, p^0_{\perp}\right) dx^0 dy^0 dz^0 dp^0_{\parallel} dp^0_{\perp} = \\ = \int_{D^t} G\left(x, y, z, p_{\parallel}, p_{\perp}\right) dx\, dy\, dz\, dp_{\parallel} dp_{\perp}, \tag{12.6}$$

where the second region is not the initial volume D^0. An integral such as (12.6) having this property is called an i n t e g r a l i n v a r i a n t and the quantity $d\Gamma = G dx dy dz dp_{\parallel} dp_{\perp}$ may be called the elementary volume in the five-dimensional space x, y, z, $p_{\parallel}$, and $p_{\perp}$. We now assert that for the variables that have been taken we can write $G = p_{\perp}$. The point here is that using Eq. (12.5) and the identity

$$(\mathbf{h}\operatorname{rot}\mathbf{h})\operatorname{div}\mathbf{h} + \mathbf{h}\operatorname{grad}(\mathbf{h}\operatorname{rot}\mathbf{h}) + \mathbf{h}\operatorname{rot}[\mathbf{h}\operatorname{rot}\mathbf{h}] = 0, \tag{12.7}$$

by simple differentiation it is easy to show from Eqs. (12.1), (12.2), and (12.3)

$$\operatorname{div}_r \dot{R} + \frac{\partial \dot{p}_{\parallel}}{\partial p_{\parallel}} + \frac{\partial}{\partial p_{\perp}^2}\left(\frac{dp_{\perp}^2}{dt}\right) = 0. \tag{12.8}$$

whence, on the basis of the well-known Poincaré theorem [15], we conclude that the integral

$$\int_{Dt} dx\, dy\, dz\, dp_{\parallel}\, dp_{\perp}^2 = 2\int_{D^t} p_{\perp} dx\, dy\, dz\, dp_{\parallel}\, dp_{\perp} \tag{12.9}$$

is an integral invariant. This statement can be regarded as the Liouville theorem in the drift approximation. Consequently we can write $G = p_{\perp}$ and the role of the volume element is played by the quantity

$$d\Gamma = p_{\perp} dx\, dy\, dz\, dp_{\parallel}\, dp_{\perp}. \tag{12.10}$$

2. The Liouville theorem can also be formulated quite easily using the variables x, y, z, $P_{\parallel}$, and $P_{\perp}$. For this purpose we use the Jacobian for substitution of variables in multiple integrals. It is easy to obtain the appropriate Jacobian from (6.4) and (6.20)

$$\frac{\partial(x,\, y,\, z,\, P_{\parallel},\, P_{\perp})}{\partial(x,\, y,\, z,\, p_{\parallel},\, p_{\perp})} = \frac{\partial(P_{\parallel},\, P_{\perp})}{\partial(p_{\parallel},\, p_{\perp})} = 1 + \frac{a_{\perp}^2}{2}(\mathbf{h}\operatorname{rot}\mathbf{h})^2 = 1$$

because second-order quantities can be neglected in the approximation used here. Hence, for the variables x, y, z, $P_{\parallel}$, and $P_{\perp}$ the role of the volume element is played by the quantity

$$d\Gamma = \left[P_{\perp} + \frac{1}{2}P_{\parallel}a_{\perp}(\mathbf{h}\operatorname{rot}\mathbf{h})\right] dx\, dy\, dz\, dP_{\parallel}\, dP_{\perp}, \tag{12.11}$$

while the integral invariant is the integral

$$\int \left[P_{\perp} + \frac{1}{2}P_{\parallel}a_{\perp}(\mathbf{h}\operatorname{rot}\mathbf{h})\right] dx\, dy\, dz\, dP_{\parallel}\, dP_{\perp}, \tag{12.12}$$

taken over the volume occupied by exactly the same phase points moving in a phase space x, y, z, $P_{\parallel}$, and $P_{\perp}$ in accordance with the drift equations of motion (6.10), (6.11), and (6.12). The invariance of the integral (12.12) then essentially represents the Liouville theorem in the drift approximation. We see that in the variables x, y, z, $P_{\parallel}$, and $P_{\perp}$,

$$G = P_{\perp} + \frac{1}{2}P_{\parallel}a_{\perp}(\mathbf{h}\operatorname{rot}\mathbf{h}). \tag{12.13}$$

3. The Liouville theorem can be used to derive equations which must be satisfied by the *distribution function* in the space of the variables x, y, z, $p_{\parallel}$, and $p_{\perp}$ or the variables x, y, z, $P_{\parallel}$, and $P_{\perp}$. Assume for example that we have a fully ionized plasma consisting of electrons and positively charged ions located in a combined electric and magnetic field. In general it can contain positive ions of various kinds. Consider the behavior of particles of one kind. *In the drift approximation we can introduce the distribution function* $f(x, y, z, p_{\parallel}, p_{\perp})$ *defined in such a way that* $f(x, y, z, p_{\parallel}, p_{\perp})d\Gamma$ *gives the mean number of particles of the kind being considered for which the coordinates of the guiding center lie between* x *and* x + dx, y *and* y + dy, z *and* z + dz, *while the momenta* $p_{\parallel}$ *and* $p_{\perp}$ *lie between* $p_{\parallel}$ *and* $p_{\parallel} + dp_{\parallel}$, $p_{\perp}$ *and* $p_{\perp} + dp_{\perp}$ *(obviously, in place of* $p_{\parallel}$ *and* $p_{\perp}$ *we could also use* $P_{\parallel}$ *and* $P_{\perp}$*).* The interaction of particles between themselves and with particles of other kinds can be taken into account by introducing a *self-consistent field,* that is, an electromagnetic field excited by both external sources and by macroscopic space charges and currents in the plasma itself. This procedure takes care of *remote* particle interactions but does not consider close interactions. Interactions at *short* distances imply that the Coulomb attraction or repulsion can operate. This interaction is in the nature of a *collision.* If collisions are neglected the motion of each plasma particle can be described by Eqs. (6.1), (6.2), and (6.3) or Eqs. (6.10), (6.11), and (6.12) in the drift approximation. In this approximation the distribution function f must satisfy the equation

$$\frac{d}{dt}(f d\Gamma) = 0,$$

which expresses the *conservation of the number of particles.* By virtue of Liouville's theorem $d\Gamma$ = const so that this equation can be written in the form

$$\frac{df}{dt} = \frac{\partial f}{\partial t} + \dot{\mathbf{R}} \operatorname{grad}_{\mathbf{r}} f + \frac{\partial f}{\partial p_{\parallel}} \dot{p}_{\parallel} + \frac{\partial f}{\partial p_{\perp}} \dot{p}_{\perp} = 0, \qquad (12.14)$$

where the derivatives $\dot{\mathbf{R}}$, $\dot{p}_{\parallel}$, and $\dot{p}_{\perp}$ are given by Eqs. (6.1)-(6.3). In this case **E** and **B** are taken to mean the *self-consistent* electric and magnetic fields. In those cases in which collisions between particles cannot be neglected Eq. (12.14) must contain an additional term that expresses the change in the distribution function caused by *collisions.*

It should be emphasized that the distribution function f that we have introduced does not refer to the particles themselves but to the distribution of guiding centers.

§ 13. Extension of Drift Theory to the Case of Strong Transverse Electric Fields

1. Drift theory can be extended to the case in which the electric field contains a strong component perpendicular to the magnetic field. For this purpose we transform to a *moving* coordinate system in which the electric and magnetic fields are *parallel* to each other (in particular the electric field can vanish). The velocity **w** of the moving system is chosen in such a way that it is *perpendicular* to the vectors **E** and **B**. The fields **E'** and **B'** in the new coordinate system are then given by

$$\mathbf{E}' = \frac{\mathbf{E} + \frac{1}{c}[\mathbf{wB}]}{\sqrt{1 - \frac{w^2}{c^2}}}; \quad \mathbf{B}' = \frac{\mathbf{B} - \frac{1}{c}[\mathbf{wE}]}{\sqrt{1 - \frac{w^2}{c^2}}}. \tag{13.1}$$

The velocity **w** can be found from the condition that the vectors **E'** and **B'** must be collinear:

$$\mathbf{E} + \frac{1}{c}[\mathbf{wB}] = \alpha\left\{\mathbf{B} - \frac{1}{c}[\mathbf{w\,E}]\right\},$$

where α is a scalar. Taking the vector product of the last equation with **B** and making use of the fact that $(\mathbf{wB}) = (\mathbf{wE}) = 0$ we have

$$[\mathbf{EB}] - \frac{B^2}{c}\mathbf{w} = \frac{\alpha}{c}(\mathbf{BE})\,\mathbf{w},$$

while scalar multiplication by **E** yields

$$\alpha\,(\mathbf{BE}) = E^2 - \frac{1}{c}([\mathbf{EB}]\,\mathbf{w}).$$

Eliminating $\alpha(\mathbf{BE})$ from the last two equations we have

$$\mathbf{w} = c\,\frac{1 + \frac{w^2}{c^2}}{B^2 + E^2}\,[\mathbf{EB}], \tag{13.2}$$

that is to say, we have a quadratic equation for determining the velocity w. It is easy to show that the roots of this equation are real and that the product of the roots is c^2. Hence, one root is always greater than c while one is always smaller. Obviously the smaller root should be taken. Whence it follows that the coordinate system with the required properties exists and is unique.

We now wish to write an equation of motion for the particle as expressed in the moving coordinate system chosen by the method indicated above. In addition to containing the electric and magnetic forces this equation will also contain inertial forces. In the new coordinate system the electric field **E'** will only have a component in the direction of the magnetic field **B'**. If this component and the inertial forces can be regarded as first-order quantities, we can formulate a drift theory in the moving coordinate system in exactly the same way as in the earlier sections. Then there only remains the inverse transformation to the original "fixed" reference system, a purely kinematic problem.

2. In order to eliminate unnecessary complications in the calculations we shall consider the nonrelativistic case and the Bogolyubov-Zubarev approximation. We then can neglect quantities of order $(w/c)^2$ and $(E/B)^2$. As before we take the electric field to be small compared with the magnetic field. However the field **E** is not treated as a first-order quantity. The first-order quantities are now the longitudinal components of the field **E** in the direction of the magnetic field and the spatial derivatives of the field **B**. In this approximation

$$\mathbf{w} = c\,\frac{[\mathbf{EB}]}{B^2}, \qquad (13.3)$$

$$\mathbf{E}' = \mathbf{E} + \frac{1}{c}[\mathbf{wB}] = \frac{(\mathbf{EB})}{B^2}\,\mathbf{B} = (\mathbf{Eh})\,\mathbf{h}, \qquad (13.4)$$

$$\mathbf{B}' = \mathbf{B} - \frac{1}{c}[\mathbf{wE}] = \mathbf{B}, \qquad (13.5)$$

that is to say, in transforming to the new coordinate system the magnetic field can be regarded as unchanged. However, the electric field **E'** only has a component along the magnetic field. As we have indicated, this component can be regarded as a first-order quantity.

In the moving coordinate system Eq. (1.2) becomes

$$\dot{\mathbf{p}}' = e\left(\mathbf{E}' - \frac{m}{e}\dot{\mathbf{w}}\right) + \frac{e}{c}[\mathbf{v}'\mathbf{B}], \tag{13.6}$$

where $\mathbf{v}'$ and $\mathbf{p}'$ are the particle velocity and momentum in the moving coordinate system. In a formal sense this equation is the same as Eq. (1.2). However, the role of the electric field is now played by the vector $\mathbf{E}'-(m/e)\dot{\mathbf{w}}$, which is treated as a first-order quantity. Hence, in the moving coordinate system we can introduce a guiding center whose coordinates are determined by a formula analogous to Eq. (1.17) so that the motion can be smoothed. The smoothed velocity of the guiding center with respect to the moving coordinate system can be obtained from Eq. (5.5) if $\mathbf{E}$ is replaced by $\mathbf{E}'-(m/e)\dot{\mathbf{w}}$; $v_\perp$ by $v'_\perp$; and $v_\parallel$ by $v'_\parallel$ (the last quantity is obviously equal to $v_\parallel$). By $v'_\perp$ and $v'_\parallel$ we are to understand the smoothed values of the transverse and longitudinal velocities of the particle in the moving coordinate system. In making the transformation to the fixed coordinate system the smoothed velocity of the guiding center found in this way must be supplemented by the velocity $\mathbf{w}$. As a result, the smoothed velocity of the guiding center in the fixed coordinate system is

$$\dot{\mathbf{R}} = v_\parallel \mathbf{h} + \frac{c}{B^2}[\mathbf{EB}] - \frac{cm}{eB^2}\left[\dot{\mathbf{w}}\mathbf{B}\right] + \frac{v'_\perp a_\perp}{2}\left[\mathbf{h}\frac{\nabla B}{B}\right] + \\ + v_\parallel a_\parallel [\mathbf{h}\cdot(\mathbf{h}\nabla)\,\mathbf{h}]. \tag{13.7}$$

This expression differs from Eq. (5.5) in the presence of the additional term $-(cm/eB^2)[\dot{\mathbf{w}}\mathbf{B}]$. This term can be interpreted as the drift due to the effect of the inertial force $-m\dot{\mathbf{w}}$. In this case by $\dot{\mathbf{w}}$ we are to understand the smoothed value of the appropriate derivative, specifically:

$$\dot{\mathbf{w}} = \frac{\partial \mathbf{w}}{\partial t} + (\dot{\mathbf{R}}\nabla)\,\mathbf{w}. \tag{13.8}$$

In the Bogolyubov-Zubarev approximation the equations for $\dot{p}_\parallel = m\dot{v}_\parallel$ and $\dot{p}_\perp = m\dot{v}_\perp$ are obtained from Eqs. (5.6) and (5.7) by the same substitution as used above. As a result we obtain

$$\dot{p}_\parallel = e(\mathbf{E}'\mathbf{h}) - m(\dot{\mathbf{w}}\mathbf{h}) + \frac{1}{2}p'_\perp v'_\perp \operatorname{div}\mathbf{h}, \tag{13.9}$$

$$\dot{p}'_\perp = -\frac{1}{2}p_\parallel v'_\perp \operatorname{div}\mathbf{h}. \tag{13.10}$$

Equation (5.15) becomes

$$\frac{p_\perp'^2}{B} = \text{const} \tag{13.11}$$

and shows that $p_\perp'^2/B$ is the adiabatic invariant.

Equation (5.13) becomes

$$\frac{d}{dt}\left(\frac{mv'^2}{2}\right) = e(\mathbf{E}'\mathbf{v}_\parallel) - m(\dot{\mathbf{w}}\mathbf{v}_\parallel). \tag{13.12}$$

The physical significance of the additional term $m(\dot{\mathbf{w}}\mathbf{v}_\parallel)$ is quite clear: in the moving coordinate system work is done not only by the electric field but by the inertial force $m\dot{\mathbf{w}}$ as well.

LITERATURE CITED

1. H. Alfvén, Cosmical Electrodynamics, Oxford, The Clarendon Press, 1953.
2. N. N. Bogolyubov and D. N. Zubarev, Ukr. matem. zhurn. (Ukrainian Mathematical Journal) 7, 5 (1955).
3. Bogolyubov and Mitropolskii, Asymptotic Methods in the Theory of Nonlinear Oscillations, (translated from the Russian) Gordon and Breach, New York, 1961.
4. G. Hellwig, Z. Naturforsch. 10a, 508 (1955).
5. S. Boguslavskii, Electron Trajectories in Electromagnetic Fields (in Russian), Moscow, 1929, also: Selected Works in Physics (in Russian) Fizmatgiz, Moscow, 1961.
6. L. Spitzer, Jr., Physics of Fully Ionized Gases, Interscience, New York, 1962.
7. S. I. Braginskii, Ukr. matem. zhurn. (Ukrainian Mathematical Journal) 8, 119 (1956).
8. G. I. Budker, Plasma Physics and the Problem of Controlled Thermonuclear Reactions (translated from the Russian) Pergamon Press, New York, 1959, Vol. III.
9. E. Fermi, Astrophys. J. 119, 1 (1954).
10. L. A. Artsimovich, Controlled Thermonuclear Reactions (translated from the Russian) Gordon and Breach, New York, 1965.
11. S. N. Vernov and A. E. Chudakov, Usp. Fiz. Nauk 70, 585 (1960), Soviet Phys. Uspekhi 3, 230 (1960).
12. J. van Allen, Usp. Fiz. Nauk 70, 715 (1960).
13. Ginzburg, Levin, Rabinovich, Sivukhin, and Chetverikova, Problem Set for the General Course in Physics (in Russian) Fizmatgiz, 1960, 2nd ed. Chap. 2. Problems 848, 849.
14. A. I. Morozov and L. S. Solov'ev, DAN 128, 506 (1959), Soviet Phys. Doklady 4, 1031 (1959).
15. E. Goursat, A Course in Mathematical Analysis, Dover, New York, 1959.
16. M. Kruskal, Proc. 3rd International Conference on Ionization Phenomena, Venice 1957, p. 562.
17. A. Bishop, Project Sherwood, Doubleday and Co., New York, 1960.
18. G. Kirchhoff, Mechanics (in Russian) Academy of Sciences Press (USSR), 1962 (Lecture 14).

PARTICLE INTERACTIONS IN A FULLY IONIZED PLASMA

B. A. Trubnikov

In this review we shall consider the kinetic effects that derive from particle interactions in a fully ionized homogeneous gas. The emphasis is placed on maximum simplicity and clarity of development. Our approach is based on a relatively novel and systematic use of special potential functions and electrostatic analogies; this approach makes it possible to write many of the required relations in simple form and frequently facilitates the deriviation of the required results.

The motion of test particles in a plasma is considered in detail in Part I of this review and a nonrigorous derivation of the kinetic equation is given in Part II. Part III is concerned with the analysis of certain kinetic effects in a plasma.

I. TEST PARTICLES IN A PLASMA

§ 1. Force of Friction Due to Scattering in a Coulomb Field

We begin by considering the following simple problem, which will be useful below in the derivation of the kinetic equation.

Suppose that a uniform plane flux of point particles of type β with mass m and charge e_β from infinity is incident on a fixed point charge e_α; the incident particles have a velocity **u** and the number of incident particles per unit volume is n_β. We wish to determine the average force **F** exerted on the fixed charge e_α by the incident particles (Fig. 1).

It is assumed that any given instant of time the charge e_α interacts with only one (β) particle in the flux. This is really a statement of the "binary-collision" approximation.

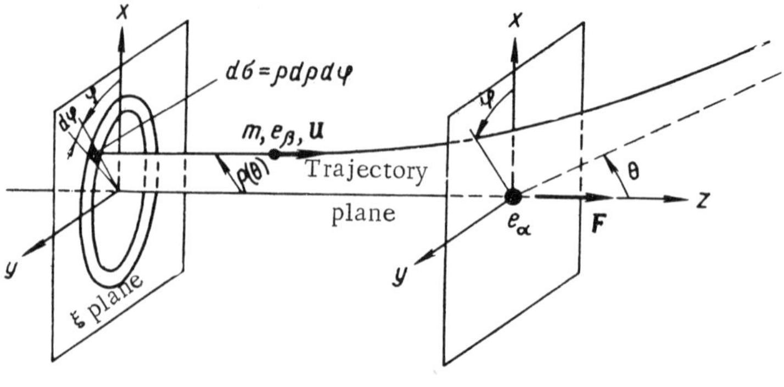

Fig. 1

The motion of a particle in a fixed Coulomb field is assumed to be known to the reader and we shall only state the required results here. Because the force is a central force the motion of one particle can always be regarded as a planar. This particle describes a hyperbola and the scattering angle θ is related to the impact parameter ρ (Fig. 1) by

$$\tan\frac{\theta}{2}=\frac{\varrho_{\perp}}{\varrho}, \tag{1.1}$$

where

$$\varrho_{\perp}=\frac{e_{\alpha}e_{\beta}}{mu^2}.$$

Here $\rho_{\perp}$ is the value of the impact parameter for which the particle is deflected through a right angle: $\theta = \pi/2$ $[\tan(\pi/4) = 1]$. The scattering cross section is given by the familiar Rutherford formula.

It is clear from symmetry considerations that the force **F** can only be directed along the velocity of the incoming particle **u**. We introduce a coordinate system x, y, z with z axis in the direction of **u** (Fig. 1). Since action must equal reaction the force **F** is equal (with reversed sign) to the force exerted by the fixed charge e_{α} on the flux of incoming (β) particles. This latter force can be determined easily since it is equal to the change per unit time of the total momentum of the particles in the incident flux. Thus

$$\mathbf{F}=-\frac{d}{dt}\sum_{\beta}\mathbf{p}^{\beta}=-\frac{\mathbf{u}}{u}m\frac{d}{dt}\left(\sum_{\beta}u_z^{\beta}\right). \tag{1.2}$$

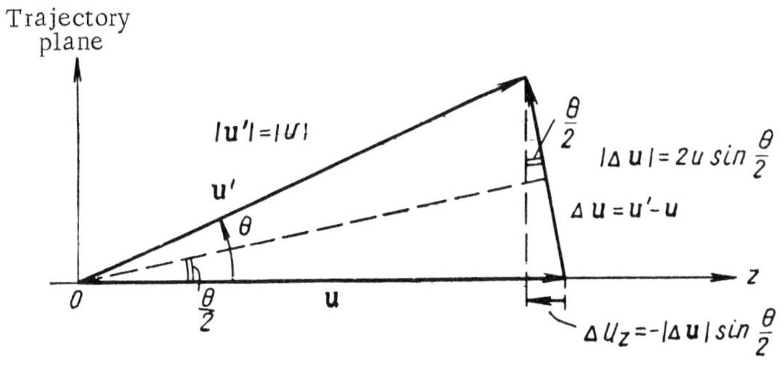

Fig. 2

Since a collision with a fixed scattering center implies an elastic collision, the velocity of the (β) particle can only change in direction as a result of the collision; the absolute magnitude remains unchanged.

It is evident from Fig. 2, in which **u'** denotes the velocity of the (β) particle after the collision, that the change in the z projection of the velocity of the particle is

$$\Delta u_z^\beta = -2u\sin^2\frac{\theta}{2} = -2u\frac{\varrho_\perp^2}{\varrho_\perp^2+\varrho^2}. \tag{1.3}$$

Here we have used the relation between the scattering angle θ and the impact parameter ρ given in Eq. (1.1).

The number of (β) particles passing through an elementary area $d\sigma = \rho d\rho d\varphi$ in the plane ξ perpendicular to the z axis (Fig. 1) per unit time is $n_\beta u d\sigma$. Multiplying this quantity by $\Delta p_z^\beta = m\Delta u_z^\beta$ and integrating over the entire ξ plane we find the change per unit time of the total momentum of the particles in the incident flux, thereby obtaining the force **F**:

$$\mathbf{F} = -\frac{\mathbf{u}}{u}\int\limits_\xi (m\Delta u_z^\beta)(n_\beta u d\sigma) = \frac{\mathbf{u}}{u}(m2u\varrho_\perp^2 n_\beta u 2\pi)\int\limits_0^\infty \frac{\varrho d\varrho}{\varrho^2+\varrho_\perp^2}. \tag{1.4}$$

The integral that appears here diverges logarithmically at large values of the impact parameter.

To obtain a finite value for the force **F** we must assume that the integration in Eq. (1.4) extends out to some finite ρ_{max} such that $\rho_{max} \gg \rho_\perp$.

Then

$$\lambda = \int_0^{\varrho_{max}} \frac{\varrho d\varrho}{\varrho_\perp^2 + \varrho^2} = \ln \frac{\sqrt{\varrho_{max}^2 + \varrho_\perp^2}}{\varrho_\perp} \cong \ln\left(\frac{\varrho_{max}}{\varrho_\perp}\right). \quad (1.5)$$

Finally, substituting $\rho_\perp = e_\alpha e_\beta/mu^2$ in Eqs. (1.4) and (1.5) we obtain the following expression for **F**:

$$\mathbf{F} = \lambda \frac{4\pi}{m} e_\alpha^2 e_\beta^2 n_\beta \frac{\mathbf{u}}{u^3}, \quad (1.6)$$

where

$$\lambda = \ln\left[\frac{\varrho_{max}}{e_\alpha e_\beta/mu^2}\right]. \quad (1.7)$$

§ 2. Coulomb Logarithm and the Role of Remote Interactions

The quantity λ is known as the Coulomb logarithm and its value is determined by the choice of ρ_{max}. In a fully ionized neutral plasma consisting of ions and electrons ρ_{max} is usually taken to be equal to the so-called Debye radius D, which is defined as follows.

Select a particular charged particle α and examine the distribution of the other charges in the field due to this particle. The electrostatic potential φ must satisfy Poisson's equation in the immediate vicinity of the selected particle:

$$\Delta\varphi = \frac{1}{r}\frac{d^2}{dr^2}(r\varphi) = -4\pi e\,(Zn_i - n_e). \quad (2.1)$$

Here, Ze is the charge of the ion while n_i and n_e are the ion and electron densities; in thermodynamic equilibrium in a potential field $\varphi(r)$ these densities satisfy the Boltzmann relations:

$$\left.\begin{aligned} n_i &= n_i^0 \exp\left[-\frac{Ze\varphi}{T_i}\right], \\ n_e &= n_e^0 \exp\left[\frac{e\varphi}{T_e}\right]. \end{aligned}\right\} \quad (2.2)$$

(To obtain a general result we assume that the temperatures T_i and T_e are different.) The constants multiplying the exponentials are taken to be the mean particle densities in the plasma n_i^0 and n_e^0 because at large distances from the selected particle (where $\varphi \to 0$) the densities n_i and n_e must approach the average value. Expanding the exponentials in Eq. (2.2) and substituting the results in Eq. (2.1), taking account of the fact that the plasma is neutral ($Zn_i^0 = n_e^0$), we obtain the following equation for $\varphi(r)$:

$$\frac{1}{r}(r\varphi)'' = -4\pi e\left[Zn_i^0\left(1 - \frac{Ze\varphi}{T_i}\right) - n_e^0\left(1 + \frac{e\varphi}{T_e}\right)\right] = \frac{\varphi}{D^2}, \tag{2.3}$$

where

$$D = \sqrt{\frac{T_e T_i/4\pi\,|e_e e_i|}{n_i^0 T_i + n_e^0 T_e}}. \tag{2.4}$$

The quantity D has the dimension of length and is called the Debye radius. The solution of Eq. (2.3) is the function

$$\varphi(r) = \frac{e_\alpha}{r}\exp\left(-\frac{r}{D}\right); \tag{2.5}$$

at small distances ($r < D$) this function becomes the pure Coulomb potential of the particle being considered and at large distances (larger than D) it becomes exponentially small. Thus, under actual conditions in a neutral plasma close to a state of thermodynamic equilibrium the Coulomb field of the individual charge is cut off (shielded) at a distances of order D; as a practical matter, it may be assumed that the particles do not interact, and do not undergo scattering, in collisions characterized by an impact parameter greater than D. Thus, it is natural to use the Debye radius D as ρ_{max} in the Coulomb logarithm λ. It should be noted, however, that the Debye shielding is not established instantaneously. Oscillations of the space charge in a plasma are characterized by the plasma frequency $\omega_0 = \sqrt{4\pi n e^2/m_e}$ so that the time required to establish the shielding is of order

$$\tau_{sh} \sim \frac{1}{\omega_0} \sim \frac{D}{v_{T,e}} \tag{2.6}$$

($v_{T,e} \sim \sqrt{T_e/m_e}$ is the electron thermal velocity). It is assumed everywhere in what follows that the Debye shielding has been established; hence, our analysis applies only to slow processes, i. e., those with characteristic times much greater than τ_{sh} the period of the plasma oscillations.

If the plasma is not in equilibrium the notion of a cutoff for λ becomes somewhat ambiguous and the value of λ can be indicated only to within an accuracy of a factor of the order of unity under the logarithm sign. Under these conditions it is not very useful to substitute the exact value of the parameter $\rho_\perp$ in λ. Inasmuch as the logarithm is a slowly varying function it is usually adequate to take some mean value $\rho_\perp$, replacing mu^2 by $(3/2)(T_\alpha + T_\beta)$. Values of λ for an electron-proton plasma with equal T_i and T_e are given, for example, in Spitzer [2].

Let us now consider a numerical example. Take $T_i = T_e = 1$ keV ($\sim 10^7$ °K); $n_e = n_i = 10^{15}$ cm^{-3}; $Z = 1$.

Then

$$D = \sqrt{\frac{T}{8\pi n e^2}} = 0.5\cdot 10^{-3}\ \text{cm},$$

$$\varrho_\perp = \frac{e^2}{3T} = 0.5\cdot 10^{-10}\ \text{cm},$$

and, correspondingly,

$$\frac{D}{\varrho_\perp} = 10^7,$$

$$\lambda = \ln\frac{D}{\varrho_\perp} \cong 16.$$

These numbers are typical of the values encountered in problems in controlled fusion and lead to the following conclusion, which is of fundamental importance. In remote interactions ($\rho \gg \rho_\perp$) particles are scattered at small angles [cf. Eq. (1.1)]:

$$\theta = 2\varrho_\perp/\varrho \ll 1.$$

The value $\rho_{min} = 2\rho_\perp$ essentially separates the close interactions from the remote interactions. We then find that

$$\lambda = \int\limits_0^{\varrho_{max}} \frac{\varrho\, d\varrho}{\varrho^2 + \varrho_\perp^2} = \lambda_n + \lambda_f$$

where

$$\lambda_n = \int_0^{\varrho_{min}=2\varrho_\perp} \frac{\varrho d\varrho}{\varrho^2 + \varrho_\perp^2} = \ln\sqrt{5} \sim 1;$$

$$\lambda_f = \int_{\varrho_{min}}^{\varrho_{max}} \frac{\varrho d\varrho}{\varrho^2 + \varrho_\perp^2} \approx \ln\frac{\varrho_{max}}{\varrho_{min}} \gg 1. \qquad (2.7)$$

Returning to Eq. (1.6) it is evident that the force **F** exerted on a charged particle α by the particle β which is incident on it can be divided into two parts:

$$F = (\lambda_n + \lambda_f)\,\mathrm{const} = F_n + F_f \qquad (2.8)$$

where $\mathbf{F}_{n.p.}$ is the force due to incoming particles that pass near the target while $F_{d.p.}$ is the force due to distant particles; in accordance with Eq.(2.7) when $\lambda \gg 1$

$$\frac{F_f}{F_n} \approx \frac{\lambda_f}{\lambda_n} \approx \lambda \gg 1. \qquad (2.9)$$

Thus, the total contribution of remote interactions in the interaction of charged plasma particles is found to be approximately λ times greater than that due to near interactions. Hence, when $\lambda \gg 1$, to logarithmic accuracy we can, in general, neglect near interactions, this important feature is a consequence of the long-range nature of the Coulomb force, which falls off approximately as r^{-2}. If the range of the interparticle force were shorter the remote interactions would not play such an important role.

§ 3. Average Force Acting on a Particle in a Plasma

Let us now consider a problem that is closer to the true physical situation. We wish to find the average force acting on a charged particle α moving with a velocity **v** through a medium consisting of charged particles β whose velocity distribution is described by an arbitrary function $f_\beta(\mathbf{v}')$ (such that $\int f_\beta(\mathbf{v}')d\mathbf{v}' = n_\beta$ the density of (β) particles). If only two-particle interactions are considered the force $\mathbf{F}_\alpha$ will be made up of the forces experienced by the particle α as a result of its collisions with individual (β) particles. We isolate from the ensemble of (β) particles an elementary flux of particles moving with velocity **v'**. The particle density in this flux is

$$dn_\beta(\mathbf{v}') = f_\beta(\mathbf{v}')\,d\mathbf{v}'[\mathrm{cm}^{-3}]. \tag{3.1}$$

Now consider the interaction of the test particle α with one of the (β) particles of the selected class. The motions of these two particles are described by the equations

$$\left.\begin{aligned} m_\alpha \ddot{\mathbf{r}}_\alpha &= e_\alpha e_\beta \frac{\mathbf{r}_\alpha - \mathbf{r}_\beta}{|\mathbf{r}_\alpha - \mathbf{r}_\beta|^3}, \\ m_\beta \ddot{\mathbf{r}}_\beta &= e_\alpha e_\beta \frac{\mathbf{r}_\beta - \mathbf{r}_\alpha}{|\mathbf{r}_\beta - \mathbf{r}_\alpha|^3}. \end{aligned}\right\} \tag{3.2}$$

It is a well-known result of classical mechanics that the motion of two interacting particles can be described most conveniently by introducing the center-of-mass coordinates and the relative distance between the particles:

$$\left.\begin{aligned} \mathbf{R} &= \frac{m_\alpha \mathbf{r}_\alpha + m_\beta \mathbf{r}_\beta}{m_\alpha + m_\beta}, \\ \mathbf{r} &= \mathbf{r}_\alpha - \mathbf{r}_\beta. \end{aligned}\right\} \tag{3.3}$$

The original coordinates can be expressed in terms of the center-of-mass coordinates by the relations

$$\left.\begin{aligned} \mathbf{r}_\alpha &= \mathbf{R} + \frac{m_\beta}{m_\alpha + m_\beta}\mathbf{r}, \\ \mathbf{r}_\beta &= \mathbf{R} - \frac{m_\alpha}{m_\alpha + m_\beta}\mathbf{r}. \end{aligned}\right\} \tag{3.4}$$

Substituting these expressions in Eq. (3.2), we obtain an equation for the motion of the center of mass $\ddot{\mathbf{R}} = 0$ whence

$$\dot{\mathbf{R}} = \mathbf{V} = \mathrm{const}, \tag{3.5}$$

corresponding to equilibrium translational motion, and an equation for the relative motion

$$m_{\alpha\beta}\ddot{\mathbf{r}} = e_\alpha e_\beta \frac{\mathbf{r}}{r^3}, \tag{3.6}$$

where

$$m_{\alpha\beta} = \frac{m_\alpha m_\beta}{m_\alpha + m_\beta},$$

which describes the motion of a fictitious particle with reduced mass $m_{\alpha\beta}$ in the fixed Coulomb field.

This last relation makes it possible to exploit the results of the problem solved earlier in which we have treated the force acting on a fixed scattering center.

Multiplying the first equation in (3.4) by m_α and differentiating twice with respect to time taking account of Eq. (3.5) we have

$$m_\alpha \ddot{\mathbf{r}}_\alpha = m_\alpha \ddot{\mathbf{R}} + m_{\alpha\beta}\ddot{\mathbf{r}} = m_{\alpha\beta}\ddot{\mathbf{r}}. \tag{3.7}$$

Thus, the force acting on particle α in a given interaction is equal to the force that would be exerted on a particle with the reduced mass which, in turn, is equal to the force exerted on the fixed center with sign reversed. The "reduced-mass" particles are incident on this fictitious fixed center with velocity

$$\dot{\mathbf{r}} = \dot{\mathbf{r}}_\alpha - \dot{\mathbf{r}}_\beta = \mathbf{v} - \mathbf{v}'. \tag{3.8}$$

Hence, if the following substitutions are made in Eq. (1.6):

$$m \to m_{\alpha\beta}, \quad n_\beta \to dn_\beta(\mathbf{v}') \quad \text{and} \quad \mathbf{u} \to \mathbf{v} - \mathbf{v}', \tag{3.9}$$

we can find the force exerted on the fixed center by the elementary flux of particles with velocity $\mathbf{v}'$ that has been selected:

$$d\mathbf{F} = \lambda \frac{4\pi}{m_{\alpha\beta}} e_\alpha^2 e_\beta^2 \frac{\mathbf{v} - \mathbf{v}'}{|\mathbf{v} - \mathbf{v}'|^3} f_\beta(\mathbf{v}')\, d\mathbf{v}'. \tag{3.10}$$

Integrating over all fluxes dn_β and substituting a minus sign in front, we obtain the average force acting on a particle of type α moving with velocity $\mathbf{v}'$ through a medium of (β) particles:

$$\mathbf{F}_\alpha(\mathbf{v}) = -\int d\mathbf{F} = -\lambda \frac{4\pi}{m_{\alpha\beta}} e_\alpha^2 e_\beta^2 \int \frac{\mathbf{v} - \mathbf{v}'}{|\mathbf{v} - \mathbf{v}'|^3} f_\beta(\mathbf{v}')\, d\mathbf{v}'. \tag{3.11}$$

Here and below we shall understand λ to mean the approximate mean value

$$\lambda = \ln \frac{D}{<\varrho_{\perp}>}, \tag{3.12}$$

where

$$<\varrho_{\perp}> = \frac{e_{\alpha}e_{\beta}}{m_{\alpha\beta}\,|\mathbf{v}-\mathbf{v}'|^2} \approx \frac{e_{\alpha}e_{\beta}}{\frac{3}{2}(T_{\alpha}+T_{\beta})}$$

[D is the Debye radius, cf. Eq. (2.4)].

It is both interesting and instructive to note that the integral over velocity space has exactly the same form as that obtained in problems in electrostatics in which it is required to find the electric field produced by a system of charges distributed continuously in coordinate space with a density $\rho(\mathbf{r}) = f_{\beta}(\mathbf{r})$:

$$\mathbf{E}(\mathbf{r}) = \int \frac{\mathbf{r}-\mathbf{r}'}{|\mathbf{r}-\mathbf{r}'|^3}\,\varrho(\mathbf{r}')\,dV' = -\operatorname{grad}_r \varphi_e(\mathbf{r}). \tag{3.13}$$

Here the potential $\varphi_e(\mathbf{r})$ satisfies Poisson's equation $\Delta_r\varphi_e = -4\pi\rho$ and is given by

$$\varphi_e(\mathbf{r}) = \int \frac{\varrho(\mathbf{r}')\,dV'}{|\mathbf{r}-\mathbf{r}'|}. \tag{3.14}$$

With this useful analogy in mind we now introduce a formal "potential" function $\varphi_{\beta}(\mathbf{v})$ which is defined in such a way that

$$\left.\begin{aligned} \Delta_v\varphi_{\beta} &= f_{\beta}, \\ \varphi_{\beta}(\mathbf{v}) &= -\frac{1}{4\pi}\int \frac{f_{\beta}(\mathbf{v}')\,d\mathbf{v}'}{|\mathbf{v}-\mathbf{v}'|}, \end{aligned}\right\} \tag{3.15}$$

that is to say, this function plays the role of the electrostatic potential φ_e (the factor $1/4\pi$, as in the case of rationalized electromagnetic units, is omitted for convenience). The force $\mathbf{F}_{\alpha}(\mathbf{v})$ acting on the test particle α is then found from Eq. (3.11) and is expressed in terms of φ_{β} by the relation

$$\mathbf{F}_{\alpha}(\mathbf{v}) = -\lambda\,\frac{m_{\alpha}+m_{\beta}}{m_{\alpha}m_{\beta}}\,(4\pi e_{\alpha}e_{\beta})^2\,\nabla_v\varphi_{\beta}(\mathbf{v})\,; \tag{3.16}$$

in many cases the answer can be written by direct analogy with the electrostatic problem. Various applications of this formula are given in Part III of the present review.

§ 4. Test Particles in a Plasma

Using the force found in §3 and the equation of motion

$$m_\alpha \frac{\overline{d\mathbf{v}}}{dt} = \mathbf{F}_\alpha(\mathbf{v}) \tag{4.1}$$

it is possible to find the average change in the particle velocity as a function of time. However, the equation that is obtained does not by any means give an adequate description of the motion of the test particle in the plasma.

This motion can be analyzed conveniently by introducing the so-called "velocity" space; in this "velocity" space the three coordinate axes are used to plot the velocity components v_x, v_y, v_z (Fig. 3). If the test particle (α) has a velocity $\mathbf{v}$ at a given instant of time we say that the particle is located at the point $\mathbf{v}$ in velocity space.

As the particle velocity changes its position in velocity space changes accordingly (either continuously or discontinuously). In the general case these displacements will be extremely complicated and intricate (Fig. 3).

It is obviously impossible to trace the motion of a single particle, and in any case it would be difficult to analyze this motion in terms of a general law; for this reason we are forced to a statistical description of the motion.

In the statistical description we assume that instead of containing a single test particle the plasma contains a large number N (which becomes infinite in the limit) of test particles (α) which have the same velocity $\mathbf{v}_0$ at $t_0 = 0$. This collection of many absolutely identical objects is called an ensemble in statistics.

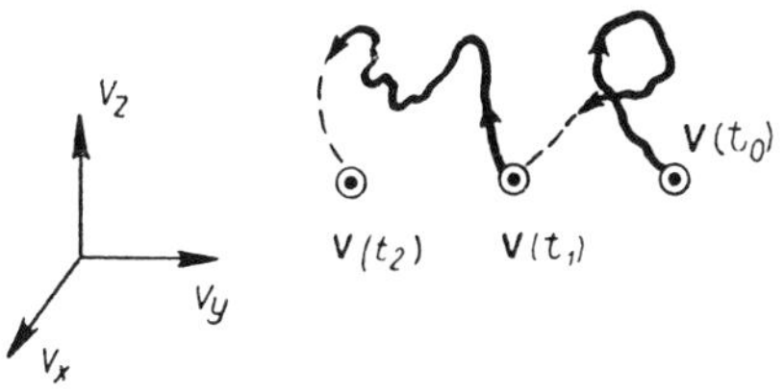

Fig. 3

The ensemble of test particles we have selected is equivalent to a plane flux of N particles of type α in an infinite uniform medium of field particles β. At time $t_0 = 0$ all N test particles in the flux are concentrated at point $\mathbf{v}_0$ in velocity space. To be explicit we may imagine that these particles form a spherically symmetric cloud of very small dimensions (consequently, high density) located at point $\mathbf{v}_0$. At subsequent times this cloud will spread, changing both its shape and dimensions. The qualitative behavior of a cloud of test particles in velocity space can be depicted as in Fig. 4.

Let us now find quantities suitable for a complete description of this process.

The position of the cloud at any instant of time is obviously characterized by the coordinates of the center of gravity

$$\overline{v_i(t)} = \frac{1}{N}\sum_{\nu=1}^{N} v_i^{(\nu)}(t); \qquad i = x, y, z, \tag{4.2}$$

where the summation is taken over all N particles in the cloud. Thus, this quantity is simply the mean velocity of the particles in the cloud.

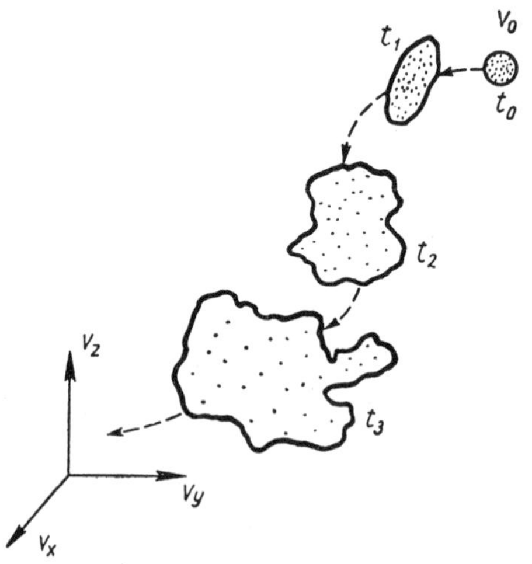

Fig. 4

On this basis displacements of the cloud as a whole are given by the derivative $d[\overline{v_i(t)}]/dt$.

Now we wish to find quantities that will characterize the dimensions and shape of the cloud, that is to say, its expansion in various directions. It is well known that in the one-dimensional case the spreading of a quantity x can be characterized by the so-called mean-square deviation

$$\overline{(\Delta x)^2} = \overline{(x - \overline{x})^2} = \overline{x^2} - \overline{x}^2. \tag{4.3}$$

Direct generalization of this quantity to our three-dimensional case must obviously result in a symmetric tensor of second rank:

$$\overline{\Delta v_i \Delta v_j} = \overline{(v - \overline{v})_i (v - \overline{v})_j} = \overline{v_i v_j} - \overline{v}_i \overline{v}_j . \tag{4.4}$$

Correspondingly, the rate-of-change of the dimensions and shape of the cloud will be determined by the time derivative of this tensor $d(\overline{\Delta v_i \Delta v_j})/dt$.

Generalizing on the basis of the two quantities that have been introduced to characterize the state of a cloud we postulate that a complete description, i. e., the specification of the distribution of test particles in velocity space, requires an infinite number of tensor quantities

$$\overline{v_i}, \quad \overline{v_i v_j}, \quad \overline{v_i v_j v_k}, \quad \overline{v_i v_j v_k v_l}, \ldots \tag{4.5}$$

or associated tensors defined by relations such as (4.4)

$$\overline{v}_i, \quad \overline{\Delta v_i \Delta v_j}, \quad \overline{\Delta v_i \Delta v_j \Delta v_k}, \ldots \tag{4.6}$$

The bar above a quantity here denotes an average over an ensemble of test particles in velocity space, that is to say, for any function $w(\mathbf{v})$ that depends on the velocity $\mathbf{v}$, the bar denotes the operation

$$\overline{w} = \frac{1}{N} \sum_{\nu=1}^{N} w(\mathbf{v}^{(\nu)}). \tag{4.7}$$

Quantities such as the tensors in (4.5) or (4.6) are called moments and are used frequently in physics for the description of various distributions. For example, the familiar multipole expansion of the electric potential (dipole, quadrupole, octupole etc.) in electrostatics is nothing more than the application of the notion of moments to the description of the distribution of a system of electric charges in coordinate space. Thus, just as a system of electric charges distributed in space can be described completely in terms of the moments characteristic of the distribution (dipole, quadrupole, etc., including moments up to those of infinite order), in the present case the distribution in velocity space can be specified completely if all of the characteristic moments are known.

Similarly, a complete description of the spreading of the cloud of test particles requires that the time rate of change of each of the moments be known:

$$\frac{d}{dt}\bar{v}_i, \quad \frac{d}{dt}\overline{\Delta v_i \Delta v_j}, \quad \frac{d}{dt}\overline{\Delta v_i \Delta v_j \Delta v_k}\ , \text{ etc.,} \tag{4.8}$$

We compute these derivatives for the initial time $t_0 = 0$, when all of the test particles in the cloud are located at the point $\mathbf{v}_0$ in velocity space.

§ 5. Rate of Change of the Moments

We note that the first derivative $d\bar{v}_i/dt$ is essentially the mean acceleration of the test particle α due to the average force exerted on this particle as a result of collisions with particles in the medium. We have computed this force earlier so that the first quantity in the sequence (4.8) is already known. However, to be consistent we shall carry out the calculation in parallel for the time derivatives of the moments of order I, II, and III in (4.8).

Let us introduce the notation α/β which means that a given quanity refers to the scattering of a test particle α in a medium made up of field particles β. Inasmuch as the time derivative of a quantity is the change in this quantity per unit time we can now describe the quantities in (4.8) by the more convenient notation

$$< v_i >^{\alpha/\beta}, \quad < \Delta v_i \Delta v_j >^{\alpha/\beta}, \quad < \Delta v_i \Delta v_j \Delta v_k >^{\alpha/\beta}, \text{ etc.,} \tag{5.1}$$

regarding these as the change per unit time of the corresponding moments. The further calculations are analogous to those carried out in §§ 1 and 3 where we determined the forces acting on a test particle α.

As in Eq. (3.1) the aggregate of field particles β is represented as a superposition of elementary plane fluxes. The spatial density of one elementary flux, in which the particles move with velocity $\mathbf{v}'$, is

$$dn_\beta = dn_\beta(\mathbf{v}') = f_\beta(\mathbf{v}')\, d\mathbf{v}' \ \text{cm}^{-3}. \tag{5.2}$$

Let us consider the collision of a test particle α having a velocity $\mathbf{v}$ with one of the particles β of this flux. The center-of-mass coordinate $\mathbf{R}$ and the relative radius vector $\mathbf{r}$ are used in accordance with Eq. (3.3). Making use of the first equation in (3.4) we can express the change in the velocity of particle α caused by collisions in terms of the velocity change of a fictitious particle with reduced mass

$$\mathbf{v}_\alpha = \dot{\mathbf{R}} + \frac{m_\beta}{m_\alpha + m_\beta}\mathbf{u},$$

whence

$$\Delta\mathbf{v}_\alpha = \frac{m_{\alpha\beta}}{m_\alpha}\Delta\mathbf{u}, \tag{5.3}$$

since the velocity of the center of mass $\dot{\mathbf{R}}$ is not changed in the collision. Thus, the problem is again reduced to the scattering of a flux of particles of reduced mass on a fixed center.

At time $t = 0$, for which we are computing the derivatives of all of the moments (5.1), it is obvious that $\overline{v}_i|_{t=0} = v_i^0$. It is also clear that in taking the average over test particles in the ensemble [(Eqs. (4.2) and (4.7)] the summation reduces to a summation over all particles in the flux incident on a fixed scattering center. The number of particles moving through an area $d\sigma = \rho d\rho d\varphi$ in the ξ plane (cf. Fig. 1) in unit time is determined by the density of the selected flux and is given by

$$dn_\beta(\mathbf{v}')\,|\mathbf{u}|\,d\sigma = f_\beta(\mathbf{v}')\, d\mathbf{v}' u\, d\sigma. \tag{5.4}$$

We multiply this number by the components of the vector $\Delta\mathbf{v}_\alpha = (m_{\alpha\beta}/m_\alpha)\Delta\mathbf{u}$, integrate over the entire ξ plane, as in the derivation of Eq. (1.4), and then integrate over the elementary fluxes as in Eq. (3.11); in this way we find

$$< \Delta v_i >^{\alpha/\beta} = \int f_\beta(\mathbf{v}')\, w_i d\mathbf{v}', \tag{5.5}$$

where

$$w_i = \frac{m_{\alpha\beta}}{m_\alpha}\int_\xi \Delta u_i u\, d\sigma;$$

$$\left.\begin{aligned} &< \Delta v_i \Delta v_j >^{\alpha/\beta} = \int f_\beta(\mathbf{v}')\, w_{ij} d\mathbf{v}', \\ \text{and}\quad & w_{ij} = \left(\frac{m_{\alpha\beta}}{m_\alpha}\right)^2 \int_\xi \Delta u_i \Delta u_j u d\sigma; \\ &< \Delta v_i \Delta v_j \Delta v_k >^{\alpha/\beta} = \int f_\beta(\mathbf{v}')\, w_{ijk} d\mathbf{v}', \\ \text{and}\quad & w_{ijk} = \left(\frac{m_{\alpha\beta}}{m_\alpha}\right)^3 \int_\xi \Delta u_i \Delta u_j \Delta u_k u d\sigma. \end{aligned}\right\} \quad (5.5)$$

The change per unit time for the higher moments is computed in the same way. The quantities w_i, w_{ij}, and w_{ijk}, etc., are then tensors of the corresponding rank. The only vector on which these can depend is the relative velocity vector $\mathbf{u} = \mathbf{v} - \mathbf{v}'$; hence, from considerations of tensor dimensionality we can write

$$\left.\begin{aligned} w_i = \frac{u_i}{u} A, \quad w_{ij} = \delta_{ij} B + \frac{u_i u_j}{u^2} C, \\ w_{ijk} = \left(\frac{u_i}{u}\delta_{jk} + \frac{u_j}{u}\delta_{ik} + \frac{u_k}{u}\delta_{ji}\right) D + \frac{u_i u_j u_k}{u^3} E. \end{aligned}\right\} \quad (5.6)$$

It should be noted that other combinations of the required tensor dimensionality cannot be formed from components of the vector $\mathbf{u}$ and any single tensor. The quantities A, B, C, D, E are scalars and it is convenient to compute them in the coordinate system in which the z axis is along $\mathbf{u}$, as in Fig. 1. It is evident from Fig. 2 that in this system

$$\left.\begin{aligned} \Delta u_x = u \sin\theta \cos\varphi, \quad \Delta u_y = u \sin\theta \sin\varphi, \\ \Delta u_z = -u(1 - \cos\theta). \end{aligned}\right\} \quad (5.7)$$

Applying these general expressions to the case at hand, the Coulomb interaction, for which [cf. Eq. (1.1)]

$$\tan\frac{\theta}{2} = \frac{\varrho_\perp}{\varrho}, \quad (5.8)$$

where

$$\varrho_\perp = \frac{e_\alpha e_\beta}{m_{\alpha\beta} u^2},$$

we have

$$\left.\begin{aligned} \Delta u_x &= 2u \sin\frac{\theta}{2}\cos\frac{\theta}{2}\cos\varphi = 2u\frac{\varrho\varrho_\perp}{\varrho^2+\varrho_\perp^2}\cos\varphi; \\ \Delta u_y &= 2u\frac{\varrho\varrho_\perp}{\varrho^2+\varrho_\perp^2}\sin\varphi; \qquad \Delta u_z = -2u\frac{\varrho_\perp^2}{\varrho^2+\varrho_\perp^2}. \end{aligned}\right\} \tag{5.9}$$

In our coordinate system the vector w_i has only a z component, which is equal to A. From Eqs. (5.5), (5.6), and (5.9) we then find

$$A = \frac{m_{\alpha\beta}}{m_\alpha}\int_\xi \Delta u_z u d\sigma = -\frac{1+\frac{m_\alpha}{m_\beta}}{4\pi u^2}\left(\frac{4\pi e_\alpha e_\beta}{m_\alpha}\right)^2\int_0^{\varrho_{\max}}\frac{\varrho d\varrho}{\varrho^2+\varrho_\perp^2} \tag{5.10}$$

The divergent integral that appears here is cut off at $\rho_{\max} = D$ and is denoted by λ (cf. §§1 and 2).

The tensor w_{ij} is diagonal in our coordinate system [cf. Eqs. (5.5) and (5.6)]:

$$w_{ij} = \begin{pmatrix} B & 0 & 0 \\ 0 & B & 0 \\ 0 & 0 & B+C \end{pmatrix}, \tag{5.11}$$

where

$$B = w_{xx} = \left(\frac{m_{\alpha\beta}}{m_\alpha}\right)^2\int(\Delta u_x)^2 u d\sigma;$$

$$B + C = w_{zz} = \left(\frac{m_{\alpha\beta}}{m_\alpha}\right)^2\int(\Delta u_z)^2 u d\sigma.$$

Thus, substituting Δu_i from Eq. (5.9) we have

$$B = \left(\frac{m_{\alpha\beta}}{m_\alpha}\right)^2\int_\xi\left(2u\frac{\varrho\varrho_\perp}{\varrho_\perp^2+\varrho^2}\cos\varphi\right)^2 u\varrho d\varrho d\varphi = \frac{1}{4\pi u}\left(\frac{4\pi e_\alpha e_\beta}{m_\alpha}\right)^2\int_0^{\varrho_{\max}}\frac{\varrho^3 d\varrho}{(\varrho^2+\varrho_\perp^2)^2}. \tag{5.12}$$

This integral also diverges logarithmically and differs by a quantity of order unity from the integral in Eq. (5.10), which we have provisionally denoted by the symbol λ:

$$\int_0^{\varrho_{max}} \frac{\varrho^3 d\varrho}{\left(\varrho^2+\varrho_\perp^2\right)^2} = -\frac{1}{2} + \int_0^{\varrho_{max}} \frac{\varrho d\varrho}{\varrho^2+\varrho_\perp^2} = \lambda - \frac{1}{2}. \quad (5.13)$$

Inasmuch as λ is determined to within an accuracy of order unity the difference between these two integrals can be neglected.

The B + C = w_{zz} integral does not diverge and is λ times smaller than the divergent w_{xx}. When $\lambda \gg 1$ the quantity w_{zz} can be set equal to zero. Taking account of the considerations given above we finally obtain

$$w_i = \frac{u_i}{u} A = -\left(1+\frac{m_\alpha}{m_\beta}\right) L^{\alpha/\beta} \frac{u_i}{4\pi u^3}; \quad (5.14)$$

while the tensor w_{ij} (taking w_{zz} = B + C = 0) is

$$w_{ij} = \left(\delta_{ij} - \frac{u_i u_j}{u^2}\right) B = L^{\alpha/\beta}\left(\delta_{ij} - \frac{u_i u_j}{u^2}\right)\frac{1}{4\pi u}, \quad (5.15)$$

where, for brevity, we have used the notation $L^{\alpha/\beta} = \lambda(4\pi e_\alpha e_\beta/m_\alpha)^2$.

§ 6. Characteristic Features of the Coulomb Interaction. The Potential Functions ψ and φ

If we were to compute the third-rank tensor (w_{ijk}) and the tensors of higher order it would turn out that all of these contain integrals that do not diverge; indeed, they converge at distances of order $\rho_\perp$ since $\rho_\perp$ is the only parameter in integrals of this type. Consequently, the magnitudes of these quantities are determined by close collisions, in contrast with the logarithmically diverging integrals in w_i and w_{ij}, in which the basic contributions are due to remote collisions. Since the procedure for cutting off the divergent integrals has been introduced on the basis of external considerations, in a formal sense the convergent integrals can be regarded as negligibly small compared with the divergent integrals. If the actual cutoff at ρ_{max} = D is used the convergent integrals are smaller than the logarithmically divergent integrals by a factor of λ.

Thus, although the sequence $\langle \Delta v_i \rangle^{\alpha/\beta}$, $\langle \Delta v_i \Delta v_j \rangle^{\alpha/\beta}$, $\langle \Delta v_i \Delta v_j \Delta v_k \rangle^{\alpha/\beta}$, etc., is formally required to describe the spreading of the cloud of test particles in velocity space we see that in the Coulomb case the only important terms are the first and second

$$\left.\begin{aligned} <\Delta v_i>^{\alpha/\beta} &= -\left(1+\frac{m_\alpha}{m_\beta}\right) L^{\alpha/\beta}\frac{1}{4\pi}\int \frac{u_i}{u^3} f_\beta(\mathbf{v}')\,d\mathbf{v}'; \\ &(\mathbf{u}=\mathbf{v}-\mathbf{v}'); \\ <\Delta v_i \Delta v_j>^{\alpha/\beta} &= L^{\alpha/\beta}\frac{1}{4\pi}\int\left(\frac{\delta_{ij}}{u}-\frac{u_i u_j}{u^3}\right) f_\beta(\mathbf{v}')\,d\mathbf{v}'. \end{aligned}\right\} \quad (6.1)$$

These expressions have been obtained by substituting w_i and w_{ij} from Eqs. (5.14) and (5.15) in Eq. (5.5). The other rates of change of the moments, the third $<\Delta v_i \Delta v_j \Delta v_k>^{\alpha/\beta}$ and higher, are smaller by a factor of λ and can be neglected when $\lambda \gg 1$.*

This circumstance represents an extremely important feature of the Coulomb interaction and serves to distinguish it from all other interactions which fall off more rapidly. Specifically, the possibility of neglecting the third $<\Delta v_i \Delta v_j \Delta v_k>$ and higher moments means that the motion of Coulomb particles can be visualized as a diffusion process in velocity space; this result will be used in a subsequent part of this review in the derivation of the kinetic equation. We should also point out that the approximation in which only the first $<\Delta v_i>$ and second $<\Delta v_i \Delta v_j>$ moments are considered (neglecting the higher orders), is called the Fokker-Planck approximation. Spitzer [2] calls $<\Delta v_i>$ and $<\Delta v_i \Delta v_j>$ diffusion coefficients.

To close this section we now write Eq. (6.1) in a more convenient form.

Using the relations

$$\left.\begin{aligned} \frac{\partial^2 |\mathbf{u}|}{\partial v_i \partial v_j} &= \frac{\delta_{ij}}{u} - \frac{u_i u_j}{u^3} \\ \frac{\partial}{\partial v_i}\frac{1}{u} &= -\frac{u_i}{u^3}, \end{aligned}\right\} \quad (6.2)$$

*The moments of different order, for example the second $<\Delta v_i \Delta v_j>$ and third $<\Delta v_i \Delta v_j \Delta v_k>$, have different dimensionality and can only be compared in terms of dimensionless units, for example by measuring the velocity in units of $\sqrt{T/m}$.

where $\mathbf{u} = \mathbf{v} - \mathbf{v}'$, Eq. (6.1) can be written

$$\left.\begin{aligned} \langle\Delta v_i\rangle^{\alpha/\beta} &= \left(1+\frac{m_\alpha}{m_\beta}\right) L^{\alpha/\beta}\frac{\partial}{\partial v_i}\left(\frac{1}{4\pi}\int\frac{f_\beta(\mathbf{v}')}{|\mathbf{v}-\mathbf{v}'|}\,d\mathbf{v}'\right); \\ \langle\Delta v_i\Delta v_j\rangle^{\alpha/\beta} &= L^{\alpha/\beta}\frac{\partial^2}{\partial v_i\partial v_j}\left(\frac{1}{4\pi}\int|\mathbf{v}-\mathbf{v}'|\,f_\beta(\mathbf{v}')\,d\mathbf{v}'.\right. \end{aligned}\right\} \tag{6.3}$$

It is then obvious that two "potential" functions can be introduced to describe the distribution of β particles:*

$$\left.\begin{aligned} \psi_\beta(\mathbf{v}) &= -\frac{1}{8\pi}\int|\mathbf{v}-\mathbf{v}'|\,f_\beta(\mathbf{v}')\,d\mathbf{v}', \\ \varphi_\beta &= -\frac{1}{4\pi}\int\frac{f_\beta(\mathbf{v}')}{|\mathbf{v}-\mathbf{v}'|}\,d\mathbf{v}'. \end{aligned}\right\} \tag{6.4}$$

The coefficients in these expressions are chosen to obtain the following simple relations between the functions ψ_β and φ_β and the distribution function f_β:†

$$\Delta\psi_\beta = \varphi_\beta, \quad \Delta\Delta\psi_\beta = \Delta\varphi_\beta = f_\beta, \tag{6.5}$$

whose validity is easily established from

$$\Delta_v|\mathbf{v}-\mathbf{v}'| = \frac{2}{|\mathbf{v}-\mathbf{v}'|};\ \Delta_v\frac{1}{|\mathbf{v}-\mathbf{v}'|} = -4\pi\delta(\mathbf{v}-\mathbf{v}'). \tag{6.6}$$

---

*Potential functions of this kind were introduced in 1957 in a paper by Rosenbluth et al. [3] and independently, somewhat later, in [4]. The functions g and h introduced by Rosenbluth et al. [3] can be expressed in terms of our potential functions by means of the relations

$$g(\mathbf{v}) = -8\pi\sum_\beta\psi_\beta(\mathbf{v})\ \text{and}\ h_\alpha(\mathbf{v}) = -4\pi\sum_\beta\left(1+\frac{m_\alpha}{m_\beta}\right)\varphi_\beta(\mathbf{v}),$$

and are in fact less convenient than our "individual" functions ψ_β and φ_β which refer to particles of one kind β.

†Here, the symbol Δ denotes the Laplacian operator in velocity space; in the formulas for $\langle\Delta v_i\rangle$ and $\langle\Delta v_i\Delta v_j\rangle$ the symbol Δ denotes an increment: $\Delta\mathbf{v} = \mathbf{v}' - \mathbf{v}$.

Using the potential functions ψ_β and φ_β in Eq. (6.3) finally we have

$$\left.\begin{aligned} <\Delta v_i>^{\alpha/\beta} &= -\left(1+\frac{m_\alpha}{m_\beta}\right) L^{\alpha/\beta}\frac{\partial\varphi_\beta}{\partial v_i}; \\ <\Delta v_i \Delta v_j>^{\alpha/\beta} &= -2L^{\alpha/\beta}\frac{\partial^2\psi_\beta}{\partial v_i \partial v_j}. \end{aligned}\right\} \tag{6.7}$$

In addition, it follows from Eq. (6.5) that

$$<\Delta v_k \Delta v_k>^{\alpha/\beta} = -2L^{\alpha/\beta}\Delta_v\psi_\beta = -2L^{\alpha/\beta}\varphi_\beta, \tag{6.8}$$

where, in accordance with the usual rule in tensor calculations, a repeated subscript (k) indicates summation over k = x, y, z.

Equations (6.7) and (6.8) yield the relation

$$\begin{aligned} <\Delta v_i>^{\alpha/\beta} &= \frac{1+\dfrac{m_\alpha}{m_\beta}}{2}\frac{\partial}{\partial v_i}<\Delta v_k \Delta v_k>^{\alpha/\beta} = \\ &= \frac{1+\dfrac{m_\alpha}{m_\beta}}{2}\frac{\partial}{\partial v_k}<\Delta v_i \Delta v_k>^{\alpha/\beta}. \end{aligned} \tag{6.9}$$

Thus, recalling the physical meaning of $<\Delta v_i>$ and $<\Delta v_i \Delta v_k>$ we may say that the velocity of a cloud of test particles as a whole in velocity space is related to the rate of expansion in all directions.

In conclusion we note that the relations that have been obtained can be used to determine the mean rate of momentum loss of a test particle α moving through a medium of (β) particles:

$$\frac{d\mathbf{p}_\alpha}{dt} = m_\alpha <\Delta \mathbf{v}>^{\alpha/\beta} = -m_\alpha\left(1+\frac{m_\alpha}{m_\beta}\right) L^{\alpha/\beta}\nabla_v\varphi_\beta; \tag{6.10}$$

the energy loss rate can also be found:

$$\frac{d\varepsilon_\alpha}{dt} = \frac{m_\alpha}{2}\frac{d}{dt}\overline{v_i v_i} = m_\alpha\left(\frac{1}{2}<\Delta v_i \Delta v_i> + v_i <\Delta v_i>\right). \tag{6.11}$$

Here we have used the relation

$$\overline{\Delta v_i \Delta v_i} = \overline{v_i v_i} - \overline{v}_i \overline{v}_i. \tag{6.12}$$

Substituting Eqs. (6.7) and (6.8) in Eq. (6.11) we have

$$\frac{d\varepsilon_\alpha}{dt} = -m_\alpha L^{\alpha/\beta}\left[\varphi_\beta + \left(1 + \frac{m_\alpha}{m_\beta}\right)(\mathbf{v}\nabla\varphi_\beta)\right]. \qquad (6.13)$$

Applications of Eqs. (6.10) and (6.13) are described in Part III.

§ 7. Use of the Scattering Cross Sections

In the kinetic theory of gases particle collisions are conveniently described by means of the so-called cross sections. In the case of short-range forces, for example those that operate between neutral molecules, the cross section for elastic scattering is given approximately by

$$\sigma = \pi d^2 \text{ cm}^2, \qquad (7.1)$$

where d is the effective diameter of the molecule.

This cross section has the dimensions of area and is sometimes called the scattering cross section. The quantity

$$\sqrt{\sigma} = f \text{ cm} \qquad (7.2)$$

has the dimensions of length and is called the scattering amplitude. Any molecule moving through a gas over a path Δx must collide with all of the molecules whose centers lie within a cylinder of height Δx and base area $\pi d^2 = \sigma$. If the density of the gas is n the number of such molecules is $\Delta x \sigma n$. The mean free path l is a segment of the path Δx in which the molecule experiences one collision:

$$l\sigma n = 1,$$

whence

$$l = \frac{1}{n\sigma}. \qquad (7.3)$$

The time between two successive collisions is

$$\tau = \frac{l}{v} = \frac{1}{nv\sigma}, \qquad (7.4)$$

where v is the velocity (usually the thermal velocity) of the particles being considered.

The quantities that have been defined, the cross section, the mean free path, and the mean free time τ (in plasma physics the latter is usually called the relaxation time) are convenient parameters for characterizing various processes that occur in a gas. For example, a knowledge of these quantities is sufficient to estimate the diffusion coefficient, viscosity, and thermal conductivity, which are really the particle density flux, the momentum density flux, and the energy density flux due to collisions in the gas:

$$\left.\begin{aligned} i &= -D\frac{dn}{dx}, \\ \pi_{xy} &= -\eta\frac{\partial v_y}{\partial x}, \\ q &= -\varkappa\frac{\partial T}{\partial x}. \end{aligned}\right\} \qquad (7.5)$$

These equations are conventionally called transport equations and the coefficients D, η, and $\varkappa$ are called transport coefficients. The elementary kinetic theory of gases (cf. the review by Braginskii in this volume) shows that these coefficients can be estimated from the relations

$$\left.\begin{aligned} D &\cong lv = \frac{v}{n\sigma}, \\ \eta &\cong mnD = \frac{mv}{\sigma}, \\ \varkappa &\cong nD = \frac{v}{\sigma}, \end{aligned}\right\} \qquad (7.6)$$

where $v = \sqrt{T/m}$ is the thermal velocity of the molecules.

In a more rigorous approach it is found that the detailed analysis of various processes requires the introduction of several cross sections rather than a single cross section; correspondingly, it is necessary to introduce several mean free paths and mean free times. In Part III we shall see that it is necessary to introduce at least three different relaxation times for each particle species in a plasma.

Let us now consider the question of cross sections in somewhat greater detail. The differential scattering cross section is defined by

$$d\sigma = \left(\frac{\varrho(\theta)}{\sin\theta} \frac{d\varrho(\theta)}{d\theta} \right) d\Omega = \varrho\, d\varrho\, d\varphi, \tag{7.7}$$

where $\rho(\theta)$ the impact parameter is regarded as a function of the scattering angle θ in the center-of-mass system. Geometrically the quantity $d\sigma$ represents an elementary area in the plane ξ perpendicular to the velocity associated with the flux of particles incident on the scattering center 0 (cf. Fig. 1). Physically $d\sigma$ is the number of particles scattered per unit time into an angle θ within the elementary solid angle $d\Omega$, divided by the flux of incoming particles. The quantity

$$\sigma = \int d\sigma = \int \left(\frac{d\sigma}{d\Omega} \right) d\Omega \tag{7.8}$$

is called the total scattering cross section. If the interaction potential does not vanish rigorously at all values of the impact parameter greater than some critical value (as is the case, for example, for hard elastic spheres, which do not interact when they are not in contact) the integral in (7.8) diverges and the total scattering section becomes infinite (at least in classical theory; in the quantum-mechanical case the cross section can be finite if the potential falls off rapidly enough). Because it is divergent, the total cross section is obviously not useful in any formula that is used to find the physical properties of a gas. In kinetic theory it is found more useful to introduce quantities of the form

$$\sigma_k = \int (1 - \cos^k \theta)\, d\sigma, \quad k = 1,\ 2,\ 3\ldots \tag{7.9}$$

The first of these,

$$\sigma_1 = \int (1 - \cos\theta)\, d\sigma\ , \tag{7.10}$$

is called the transport cross section (it is also called the diffusion cross section and the slowing-down cross section), a name that arises because the factor $(1 - \cos\theta)$ gives the loss of directed particle velocity in an elastic scattering event (cf. Fig. 2):

$$\Delta u_z = -u\,(1 - \cos\theta) \tag{7.11}$$

[see also Eq. (1.3)]. The second quantity,

$$\sigma_2 = \int (1 - \cos^2\theta)\, d\sigma\ , \tag{7.12}$$

may be conveniently called the "deflection" cross section since the factor $1 - \cos^2\theta = \sin^2\theta$ characterizes the mean-square increment in transverse particle velocity in scattering of a plane flux on a fixed center of force. Chapman and Cowling [5] show that the viscosity and thermal conductivity of a gas are determined by the deflection cross section σ_2: let $\mathbf{g}$ be the relative velocity of two particles measured in units of $\sqrt{2T/\mu}$ so that the Maxwellian distribution of relative velocities is

$$f_{rel}\, d\mathbf{v}_{rel} = \left(\frac{\mu}{2\pi T}\right)^{3/2} \exp\left(-\frac{\mu v^2_{rel}}{2T}\right) d\mathbf{v}_{rel} = \pi^{-3/2} e^{-g^2} d\mathbf{g} \tag{7.13}$$

(here μ is the reduced mass and the normalization $\int f_{rel}\, d\mathbf{v}_{rel} = 1$ is used); then, using the angle brackets < > to denote averages over this distribution we obtain the following formulas [5] for the viscosity and thermal conductivity of a simple gas (this excludes mixtures):

$$\left.\begin{aligned} \eta &= \frac{5}{2}\sqrt{mT} \Big/ \langle g^5\sigma_2\rangle; \\ \varkappa &= \frac{15}{4m}\,\eta. \end{aligned}\right\} \tag{7.14}$$

The slowing-down cross section σ_1 determines the mobility of particles and appears in the diffusion coefficient that describes an inhomogeneous mixture of two gases:

$$D_{12} = \sqrt{\frac{9T}{8\mu_{12}}} \Big/ n\langle g^3\sigma_1\rangle. \tag{7.15}$$

In contrast with Eq. (7.6), which only gives orders of magnitude, Eqs. (7.14) and (7.15) can be used to get quantitative expressions for the transport coefficients.

As an illustration let us consider an example in which the molecules are regarded as hard elastic spheres of diameter d_α (α denotes the particle species). In this case the differential scattering cross section is isotropic in the center-of-mass system and is independent of the relative velocity:

$$\frac{d\sigma}{d\Omega} = \pi\left(\frac{d_\alpha + d_\beta}{2}\right)^2 \Big/ 4\pi\,. \tag{7.16}$$

The slowing-down cross section is

$$\sigma_1 = \int (1 - \cos\theta) \frac{d\sigma}{d\Omega} d\Omega = \pi \left(\frac{d_\alpha + d_\beta}{2} \right)^2,$$

and the diffusion coefficient for a mixture of two gases follows from Eq. (7.15)

$$D_{12} = \sqrt{\frac{9T}{8\mu_{12}}} \Big/ n\sigma_1^{12} \langle g^3 \rangle = \frac{1}{n(d_1 + d_2)^2} \sqrt{\frac{9T}{8\pi\mu_{12}}} . \quad (7.17)$$

Here $n = n_1 + n_2$ is the total density of the gas. The deflection cross section for molecules of one species is

$$\sigma_2 = \int (1 - \cos^2\theta) \frac{d\sigma}{d\Omega} d\Omega = \frac{2}{3} \pi d^2 \quad (7.18)$$

and, in accordance with Eq. (7.14), the viscosity and thermal conductivity for the simple gas (excluding mixtures and assuming an elastic sphere model) are

$$\left. \begin{aligned} \eta &= \frac{5}{2} \sqrt{mT} \Big/ \sigma_2 \langle g^5 \rangle = \frac{5\sqrt{mT}}{16 d^2 \sqrt{\pi}}; \\ \varkappa &= \frac{15\eta}{4m} = \frac{25\sqrt{T/m}}{64 d^2 \sqrt{\pi}} . \end{aligned} \right\} \quad (7.19)$$

In Eqs. (7.17) and (7.19) the mean values $\langle g^n \rangle$ are determined in accordance with Eq. (7.13):

$$\langle g^n \rangle = \pi^{-3/2} \int |\mathbf{g}|^n e^{-g^2} d\mathbf{g} = 2\pi^{-1/2} \int_0^\infty e^{-x} x^{\frac{n+1}{2}} dx = \frac{\frac{n+1}{2}!}{\frac{1}{2}!} . \quad (7.20)$$

We now consider the behavior of a test particle α in a medium of field particles β described by a distribution function $f_\beta(\mathbf{v}_\beta)$; we wish to find the rate-of-change of momentum and energy of the test particle.

The velocity change of the test particle α due to a collision with a (β) particle is related to the change of relative velocity $\mathbf{u}$ by Eq. (5.3):

$$\Delta \mathbf{v}_\alpha = \frac{m_{\alpha\beta}}{m_\alpha} \Delta \mathbf{u}. \quad (7.21)$$

Thus, the momentum and energy increments are

$$\Delta \mathbf{p}_\alpha = m_\alpha \Delta \mathbf{v}_\alpha = m_{\alpha\beta} \Delta \mathbf{u};$$

$$\Delta \varepsilon_\alpha = \frac{m_\alpha}{2}\left[(\mathbf{v} + \Delta \mathbf{v})^2 - \mathbf{v}^2\right] = m_\alpha \left[\mathbf{v}\Delta \mathbf{v} + \frac{1}{2}(\Delta \mathbf{v})^2\right] =$$

$$= m_{\alpha\beta}\left[\mathbf{v}_\alpha \Delta \mathbf{u} + \frac{m_{\alpha\beta}}{2m_\alpha}(\Delta \mathbf{u})^2\right]. \tag{7.22}$$

Since the scattering is elastic the modulus u does not change. Hence

$$(\mathbf{u} + \Delta \mathbf{u})^2 - \mathbf{u}^2 = 2\mathbf{u}\Delta \mathbf{u} + (\Delta \mathbf{u})^2 = 0. \tag{7.23}$$

The energy change is then

$$\Delta \varepsilon_\alpha = m_{\alpha\beta}\left(\mathbf{v}_\alpha - \frac{m_{\alpha\beta}}{m_\alpha}\mathbf{u}\right)\Delta \mathbf{u}. \tag{7.24}$$

Integration over all values of the impact parameter $\rho d\rho d\varphi = d\sigma$ yields

$$\left.\begin{aligned} \int \Delta \mathbf{p}_\alpha d\sigma &= m_{\alpha\beta}\int \Delta \mathbf{u}\, d\sigma; \\ \int \Delta \varepsilon_\alpha\, d\sigma &= m_{\alpha\beta}\left(\mathbf{v}_\alpha - \frac{m_{\alpha\beta}}{m_\alpha}\mathbf{u}\right)\int \Delta \mathbf{u} d\sigma. \end{aligned}\right\} \tag{7.25}$$

In the last integral, taking

$$\begin{aligned} \Delta u_z &= -u\,(1 - \cos\theta), \\ \Delta u_x &= u \sin\theta \cos\varphi, \\ \Delta u_y &= u \sin\theta \sin\varphi, \end{aligned} \tag{7.26}$$

results in

$$\int \Delta \mathbf{u}\, d\sigma = -\mathbf{u}\sigma_1. \tag{7.27}$$

Thus

$$\int \Delta \mathbf{p}_\alpha\, d\sigma = -m_{\alpha\beta}\mathbf{u}\sigma_1;$$

$$\int \Delta \varepsilon_\alpha d\sigma = -m_{\alpha\beta}\left(\mathbf{v}_\alpha \mathbf{u} - \frac{m_{\alpha\beta}}{m_\alpha}\mathbf{u}^2\right)\sigma_1. \tag{7.28}$$

It follows from Eq. (5.4) that the mean rate-of-change of the momentum and energy of the test particle can be obtained by multiplying Eq. (7.28) by $f_\beta u d\mathbf{v}_\beta$ and integrating over all field particles:

$$\left.\begin{aligned} \frac{d\mathbf{p}_\alpha}{dt} &= \int d\mathbf{v}_\beta f_\beta u \int \Delta\mathbf{p}_\alpha d\sigma = -m_{\alpha\beta}\int d\mathbf{v}_\beta f_\beta \sigma_1 |\mathbf{u}|\mathbf{u}; \\ \frac{d\varepsilon_\alpha}{dt} &= \int d\mathbf{v}_\beta f_\beta u \int \Delta\varepsilon_\alpha d\sigma = \\ &= -m_{\alpha/\beta}\mathbf{v}_\alpha \int d\mathbf{v}_\beta f_\beta \sigma_1 |\mathbf{u}|\mathbf{u} + \frac{m^2_{\alpha/\beta}}{m_\alpha}\int d\mathbf{v}_\beta f_\beta \sigma_1 |\mathbf{u}|^3. \end{aligned}\right\} \quad (7.29)$$

These formulas apply for any law of interaction between the particles but become particularly simple for the case of so-called "Maxwellian" molecules, which repel each other with a force inversely proportional to the fifth power of the distance:

$$\mathbf{F} = -\nabla_r U(\mathbf{r}) \sim r^{-5}, \quad (7.30)$$

where

$$U(r) = \gamma/r^4.$$

The simplicity of this particular case arises, as is evident from simple dimensional arguments, from the fact that the dependence of scattering angle θ on impact parameter ρ must be of the form

$$\theta = f(U(\rho)/\varepsilon_{rel}), \quad (7.31)$$

where $U(\rho) = \gamma/\rho^4$ is the interaction potential; $\varepsilon_{rel} = \mu u^2/2$ is the energy associated with the relative motion (μ is the reduced mass); $f(x)$ is a dimensionless function.

The inverse function $\rho(\theta)$ is

$$\rho(\theta) = \rho_\perp g(\theta), \quad (7.32)$$

where $\rho_\perp = (\gamma/\varepsilon_{rel})^{1/4} \sim |\mathbf{u}|^{-1/2}$ and $g(\theta)$ is again a dimensionless function. Consequently the cross section

$$d\sigma = \rho d\rho d\varphi = \rho_\perp^2 h(\theta)\, d\Omega, \quad (7.33)$$

where $h(\theta)$ is a new dimensionless function that will be inversely proportional to the relative velocity: $d\sigma \sim u^{-1}$. In this case the transport cross section σ_1 is inversely proportional to u:

$$\sigma_1 \Big|_{\substack{\text{"Maxwellian"}\\ \text{molecule}}} = \frac{\text{const}}{u}. \tag{7.34}$$

The time between collisions $\tau = 1/n\sigma u$ will, in general, be independent of the energy of the relative motion. Returning to Eq. (7.29) it is evident that both integrals in Eq. (7.29) can be easily computed in general form for Maxwellian molecules (substituting $\sigma_1 = \text{const}/u$):

$$\left.\begin{aligned} \int d\mathbf{v}_\beta f_\beta \sigma_1 |u| \mathbf{u} &= \text{const}\, \mathbf{v}_\alpha n_\beta; \\ \int d\mathbf{v}_\beta f_\beta \sigma_1 |u|^3 &= \text{const}\,(v_\alpha^2 + \langle v_\beta^2 \rangle)\, n_\beta. \end{aligned}\right\} \tag{7.35}$$

(We assume for simplicity that the gas of field particles β is at rest as a whole so that $\int d\mathbf{v}_\beta f_\beta \mathbf{v}_\beta = 0$.) It is evident that in this case the transfer (loss) of momentum and energy of the test particle α is determined solely by the density n_β and the mean energy (temperature) of the field particles β (since $\langle v_\beta^2 \rangle = 3T_\beta/m_\beta$).

Chapman and Cowling [5] show that the kinetic coefficients for Maxwellian molecules can be computed quite easily but we shall not consider these further.

In general the various cross sections σ_k can be used to express the tensors w_i, w_{ij}, w_{ijk}, etc., introduced in §5. For instance, using (7.26), the scalar quantities A, B, C given by Eqs. (5.10) and (5.11) can be written

$$A = \frac{m_{\alpha\beta}}{m_\alpha} \int \Delta u_z u\, d\sigma = -\frac{m_{\alpha\beta}}{m_\alpha} u^2 \sigma_1;$$

$$B = \left(\frac{m_{\alpha\beta}}{m_\alpha}\right)^2 \int (\Delta u_x)^2 u\, d\sigma = \frac{m_{\alpha\beta}^2}{m_\alpha^2} u^3 \frac{\sigma_2}{2};$$

$$B + C = \left(\frac{m_{\alpha\beta}}{m_\alpha}\right)^2 \int (\Delta u_z)^2 u\, d\sigma = \left(\frac{m_{\alpha\beta}}{m_\alpha}\right)^2 u^3 \int (1 - \cos\theta)^2 d\sigma =$$

$$= \frac{m_{\alpha\beta}^2}{m_\alpha^2} u^3 (2\sigma_1 - \sigma_2). \tag{7.36}$$

Substituting these values of A, B, C in Eq. (5.6) we have

$$w_i = -\frac{m_{\alpha\beta}}{m_\alpha} u_i u \sigma_1,$$
$$w_{ij} = \frac{m_{\alpha\beta}^2}{m_\alpha^2} u^3 \left[\delta_{ij}\frac{\sigma_2}{2} + \frac{u_i u_j}{u^2}\left(2\sigma_1 - \frac{3}{2}\sigma_2\right)\right]. \quad (7.37)$$

The tensors of higher rank (w_{ijk}, w_{ijkl}, etc.) will contain the cross sections σ_3, σ_4 and cross sections of still higher order; unfortunately these do not admit of such simple physical meaning as the cross sections σ_1 (slowing-down cross section) and σ_2 (deflection cross section).

Let us again consider the case of Coulomb particles. In this case the differential cross section is given by the well-known Rutherford relation

$$\frac{d\sigma}{d\Omega} = \frac{\varrho(\theta)}{\sin\theta}\frac{d\varrho(\theta)}{d\theta} = \frac{\varrho_\perp^2}{4\sin^4(\theta/2)}, \quad (7.38)$$

where

$$\varrho_\perp = \frac{e_\alpha e_\beta}{\mu u^2},$$

and where we have made use of Eq. (1.1), which relates the impact parameter and the scattering angle

$$\varrho(\theta) = \varrho_1 \cot(\theta/2). \quad (7.39)$$

It is evident that all the "partial" cross sections σ_k diverge logarithmically at small scattering angles, that is to say, at large impact parameters:

$$\sigma_k = \int (1 - \cos^k\theta)\frac{d\sigma}{d\Omega}\,d\Omega \cong \pi(2\varrho_\perp)^2 k \int_{\theta_{min}}^{\pi} \frac{d\theta}{\theta}. \quad (7.40)$$

As we have indicated earlier, the maximum impact parameter in a plasma (at which the particles no longer interact effectively so that scattering can be ignored) can be taken as the Debye radius D. Thus

$$\theta_{min} = 2\varrho_\perp/D, \quad \int_{\theta_{min}}^{\pi}\frac{d\theta}{\theta} = \ln\frac{\pi}{\theta_{min}} \cong \ln\frac{D}{\varrho_\perp} = \lambda, \quad (7.41)$$

and the Coulomb logarithm is recovered. Introducing the notation

$$\sigma_{\text{Coul}}(\mathbf{u}) = \pi\lambda\,(2\varrho_{\perp})^2 = \pi\lambda\left(\frac{e_\alpha e_\beta}{\mu u^2/2}\right)^2, \tag{7.42}$$

we have from Eq. (7.40)

$$\sigma_k\Big|_{\text{plasma}} = k\sigma_{\text{Coul}}(\mathbf{u}). \tag{7.43}$$

In particular, $\sigma_2 = 2\sigma_1$ so that the third equation in (7.36) vanishes: $B + C = 0$. Now substituting

$$\sigma_1 = \sigma_{\text{Coul}}(\mathbf{u}) = \lambda\,\frac{4\pi e_\alpha^2 e_\beta^2}{m_{\alpha\beta}^2}\cdot\frac{1}{u^4} \tag{7.44}$$

in Eq. (7.29) we find the mean change in momentum and energy per unit time of a test particle α moving in a medium of field particles β which interact via the Coulomb interaction (we recall that $\mathbf{u} = \mathbf{v}_\alpha - \mathbf{v}_\beta$):

$$\left.\begin{aligned}\frac{d\mathbf{p}_\alpha}{dt} &= -\lambda\,\frac{4\pi e_\alpha^2 e_\beta^2}{m_{\alpha\beta}}\int\frac{\mathbf{u}}{u^3}\,f_\beta\,d\mathbf{v}_\beta,\\ \frac{d\varepsilon_\alpha}{dt} &= -\lambda\,\frac{4\pi e_\alpha^2 e_\beta^2}{m_{\alpha\beta}}\left[\mathbf{v}_\alpha\int\frac{\mathbf{u}}{u^3}\,f_\beta\,d\mathbf{v}_\beta - \frac{m_{\alpha\beta}}{m_\alpha}\int\frac{1}{u}\,f_\beta\,d\mathbf{v}_\beta\right];\end{aligned}\right\} \tag{7.45}$$

it can be easily shown that this expression coincides with Eqs. (6.10) and (6.13).

By using various qualitative estimates of the energy of the relative motion $\mu u^2/2$ in the expression for $\sigma_{\text{Coul}}(\mathbf{u})$ we can introduce the temperature. Thus, in a plasma the collision cross section can be taken approximately as

$$\sigma_{\text{Coul}} = \pi\left(\frac{e^2}{T}\right)^2\lambda \cong \frac{\lambda e^4}{T^2} \qquad (T = kT^\circ). \tag{7.46}$$

In this case the mean free path l and the time between collisions (the mean relaxation time) are of the following order

$$l = \frac{1}{n\sigma_{\text{Coul}}} = \frac{T^2}{\lambda n e^4};\ \tau = \frac{l}{v} = \frac{\sqrt{m}T^{3/2}}{\lambda n e^4}. \tag{7.47}$$

Thus, for example, it is evident that the mean free paths of ions and electrons will be the same for equal temperatures whereas

$$\tau^{e/e} : \tau^{i/i} \approx \sqrt{m/M}. \tag{7.48}$$

Since the quantities σ_1 and σ_2 are approximately the same the retardation length $l = 1/n\sigma_1$ is approximately equal to the deflection length $l = 1/n\sigma_2$.

It should be kept in mind that a proper estimate of a given process requires the introduction of its own effective cross section, so that several cross sections will be found to be of importance. For example consider the exchange of energy between ions and electrons. For simplicity we shall consider the case in which an electron $m_e = m$ impinges on an ion at rest $m_i = M \gg m$. Then $\mathbf{u} = \mathbf{v}_\alpha$ and

$$m_{ei} = \frac{m_e m_i}{m_e + m_i} \cong m\left(1 - \frac{m}{M}\right). \tag{7.49}$$

From Eq. (7.28) we have

$$\int \Delta\varepsilon_e \, d\sigma = -m_{ei}\left(1 - \frac{m_{ei}}{m_e}\right) u^2\sigma_1 \cong -\varepsilon_e\left(2\frac{m}{M}\sigma_1\right). \tag{7.50}$$

Similarly, in the case in which an ion impinges on an electron at rest

$$\int \Delta\varepsilon_i \, d\sigma = -mu^2\sigma_1 = -\varepsilon_i\left(2\frac{m}{M}\sigma_1\right). \tag{7.51}$$

If an energy-transfer cross section $\sigma_\varepsilon^{\alpha/\beta}$ is introduced using the relation

$$\int \Delta\varepsilon_\alpha \, d\sigma = -\varepsilon_\alpha \sigma_\varepsilon^{\alpha/\beta}, \tag{7.52}$$

then, in order-of-magnitude terms,

$$\sigma_\varepsilon^{e/i} = \sigma_\varepsilon^{i/e} = 2\frac{m}{M}\sigma_1 \cong \left(\frac{m}{M}\right)\frac{\lambda e^4}{T^2}. \tag{7.53}$$

Thus the relative fractional energy transfer in a collision between two particles depends on the mass ratio of the particles: maximum transfer occurs when the masses are equal and the transfer is proportional to $m/M \ll 1$ if the masses are very different. For this reason the energy-transfer cross section is 2m/M times smaller than the slowing-down cross section. The following relation holds between the relaxation times:

$$\tau^{e/e} : \tau^{i/i} : \tau_{\varepsilon}^{e/i} \approx 1 : \sqrt{\frac{M}{m}} : \frac{M}{m} . \qquad (7.54)$$

In Part III we shall be dealing primarily with relaxation times rather than cross sections; the former characterize the durations of various plasma processes directly.

II. KINETIC EQUATION FOR COULOMB PARTICLES

§ 8. Motion of Particles in Phase Space

The statistical description of an ensemble of particles is facilitated by the introduction of a six-dimensional phase space whose axes comprise the three Cartesian coordinates x, y, and z, and the three velocity components v_x, v_y, and v_z (Fig. 5).*

If a given particle is located at a point **r** and has a velocity **v** it is then said to be at the point (**r**, **v**) in phase space.

The number of particles of type α located in the volume element of this space

$$d\Omega^{(6)} = d\mathbf{r}\, d\mathbf{v} = dx\, dy\, dz\, dv_x dv_y dv_z, \qquad (8.1)$$

can be written in the form

$$dN_\alpha = f_\alpha(t, \mathbf{r}, \mathbf{v})\, d\mathbf{r}\, d\mathbf{v}, \qquad (8.2)$$

where f_α characterizes the density distribution of particles of type α in phase space and is usually called the distribution function.

By kinetic equation we shall mean an equation for the function $f_\alpha(t, \mathbf{r}, \mathbf{v})$ that describes the changes in the course of time of the particle

*Phase space is usually taken to mean the space of configuration coordinates and momenta rather than velocities. This difference is unimportant in general; however, the interpretation and manipulation of the potential functions that we have introduced turn out to be much simpler in velocity space and we shall use this space in what follows.

distribution in phase space, that is to say, the distribution over coordinates and velocity.

Although our derivation of this equation is not rigorous, it is hoped that it will be instructive.

Let us consider the motion of particles in phase space.

In the absence of collisions the coordinates and velocities of the particles vary continuously, "from point to point;" correspondingly the "motion" of the particles in phase space is continuous. Under these conditions the function $f_\alpha(t, \mathbf{r}, \mathbf{v})$ satisfies an "equation of continuity"

$$\frac{\partial f_\alpha}{\partial t} + \mathrm{div}_r\,(\mathbf{v} f_\alpha) + \mathrm{div}_v \mathbf{j} = 0, \tag{8.3}$$

where

$$\mathbf{j} = \dot{\mathbf{v}} f_\alpha = \frac{\mathbf{F}_\alpha^{(e)}}{m_\alpha} f_\alpha \tag{8.4}$$

is the flux of α particles in velocity space and $\mathbf{F}_\alpha^{(e)}$ is the external force acting on a particle α.

The equation in (8.3) is analogous to the usual equation of continuity

$$\frac{\partial \varrho}{\partial t} + \mathrm{div}\,\mathbf{j} = 0, \tag{8.5}$$

where

$$\mathbf{j} = \mathbf{v}\varrho,$$

which describes the motion of an arbitrary continuous medium – a liquid or a gas, in the usual three-dimensional coordinate space.

Both of these equations express the conservation of the number of particles; that is to say, both equations state that the number of particles within an arbitrary fixed volume can only change as a result of the passage of particles through the surface that bounds this volume, as shown schematically in Fig. 5.

We now write this condition in the form

$$\frac{d}{dt}\int_{\Omega^{(6)}} f_\alpha \, d\Omega^{(6)} = -\oint j_N^{(6)} d\,\Sigma^{(5)}, \tag{8.6}$$

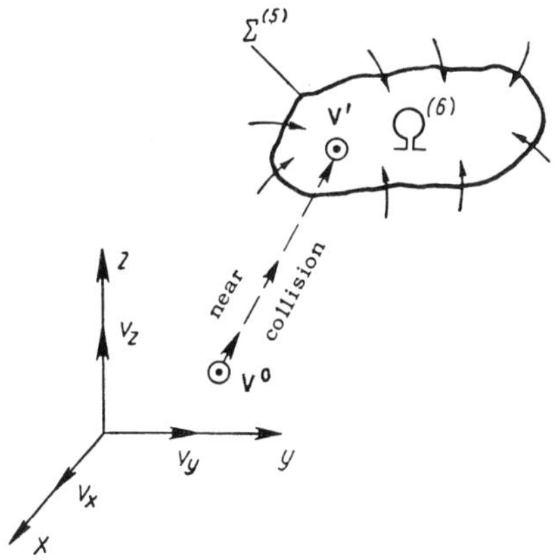

Fig. 5

where $j_N^{(6)}$ is the projection of the six-dimensional flux of (α) particles in the direction of the external normal N to the surface $\Sigma^{(5)}$,and use Gauss' theorem to transform the integral over the normal flux through the closed surface $\Sigma^{(5)}$ into an integral over the six-dimensional divergence in the volume $\Omega^{(6)}$; the result is Eq. (8.3).

The effect of collisions can now be introduced. From a macroscopic point of view the change in the spatial coordinates of a particle during the collision process can always be neglected. Hence, as far as the coordinate part of phase space is concerned the motion of the particles corresponds to a continuous "point-to-point" variation and the second term in the kinetic equation (8.3) $\text{div}_r(\mathbf{v}f_\alpha)$, which describes this motion, remains unchanged.

On the other hand, collisions have a marked effect on the continuity of motion in velocity space. The velocity of a particle can be changed appreciably in a single collision and this change can occur in essentially zero time. Let the velocity of a given particle before and after a collision be denoted by **v** and **v'** respectively; at the instant of the collision the particle is "annihilated" at the point **v** and is "created" at some remote point **v'** without passing through the intermediate points in velocity space. Examination of Fig. 5, in which the dashed line is such a transitition $\mathbf{v} \rightarrow \mathbf{v}'$, shows that particles can appear within the selected volume $\Omega^{(6)}$ without having passed through the bounding surface $\Sigma^{(5)}$. Thus, in general the effect of collisions cannot be taken into account in the kinetic equation by introducing a term describing the divergence of a flux in velocity space. This is the case only for near collisions, in which the particle velocity is changed abruptly. On the other hand, we have shown in Part I of this review that in the case of Coulomb particles the change in velocity, which is characterized by the quantities $<\Delta v_i>^{\alpha/\beta}$ and $<\Delta v_i \Delta v_j>^{\alpha/\beta}$ in §6, is due primarily to remote interactions, and that these do not change the velocities greatly.

For example, let $\lambda = \ln(\rho_{max}/\rho_{\perp}) = 15$ (a typical value in a controlled fusion problem). The relative change in particle velocity in a single interaction event is then of the order

$$\frac{|\Delta \mathbf{v}|}{v} \sim \theta_{scat} \approx \frac{\varrho_{\perp}}{\varrho} \approx e^{-\lambda} \frac{\varrho_{max}}{\varrho} \sim 10^{-6} \left(\frac{\varrho_{max}}{\varrho}\right), \tag{8.7}$$

that is to say, the change is microscopically small.

In these interactions particles are transferred to nearby points in velocity space and the overall process can be regarded as a form of diffusion. The motion of the particles can then be regarded as continuous or, more precisely, as almost continuous, consisting as it does, of successive microscopic jumps in velocity space. This pattern of "quasi-continuous" motion can then be described by the picture given above in which the number of particles within a selected volume $\Omega^{(6)}$ changes only as a consequence of the flux of particles through the bounding surface $\Sigma^{(5)}$; thus, the equation of continuity (8.3) applies for the remote interactions.

§ 9. Expression for the Flux

If it is assumed that only the remote interactions are important in a plasma (a situation that obtains when $\lambda \gg 1$ as we have seen in Part I) the kinetic equation can be written in the form of an equation of continuity (8.3):

$$\frac{\partial f_\alpha}{\partial t} + \operatorname{div}_r (\mathbf{v} f_\alpha) + \operatorname{div}_v \mathbf{j} = 0. \tag{9.1}$$

However, the expression for the flux in velocity space $\mathbf{j}$ will now differ from that in Eq. (8.4) since we are taking account of collisions.

Let us now formulate an expression for the flux $\mathbf{j}$. The quasi-continuous motion of particles in velocity space can be regarded as the flow of a gas through an inhomogeneous porous medium.

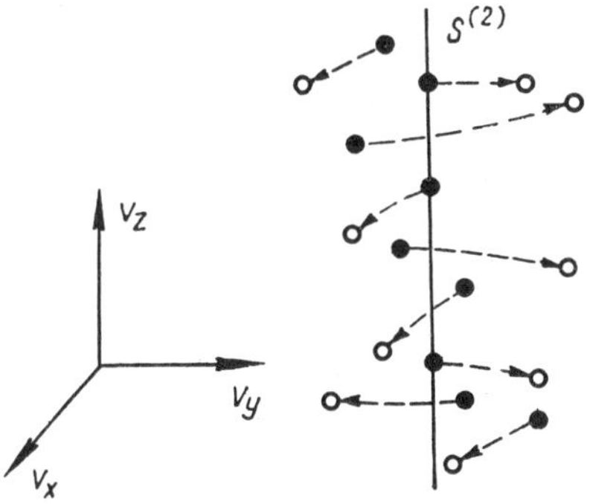

Fig. 6

Gas flow of this kind (in coordinate space) can, in principle, consist of two parts: a kinematic streaming of the form $\mathbf{j} = \rho\mathbf{v}$, and a diffusion flux of the form $\mathbf{j} = -D\nabla_r\rho$. These are the most familiar forms of continuous flow.

On the basis of this analogy we propose that the flux $\mathbf{j}$ in velocity space in Eq. (9.1) should be of the form

$$\mathbf{j} = \dot{\mathbf{v}} f_\alpha - D\nabla_v f_\alpha, \tag{9.2}$$

where the diffusion coefficient D is a tensor quantity because the velocity space is anisotropic in the general case.

In addition to using the analogies given above, we could justify our writing of the flux in the form given in (9.2) on the basis of the following considerations. We have seen that collisions are equivalent to particle jumps in velocity space; in particular, remote collisions are equivalent to microscopically small ($|\Delta v|/v \sim 10^{-6}$) discontinuous displacements. Thus, the total particle flux through some surface in velocity space $S^{(2)}$ (Fig. 6) is determined not only by the particle density at this surface f (as would be the case in strictly continuous flow) but by the particle density in the neighborhood of this surface as well.

In general this situation can be described mathematically by writing the flux as a series expansion

$$j_i = a_i f + b_{ij}\frac{\partial f}{\partial v_j} + c_{ijk}\frac{\partial^2 f}{\partial v_j \partial v_k} + d_{ijkl}\frac{\partial^3 f}{\partial v_j \partial v_k \partial v_l} + \cdots \tag{9.3}$$

(where indices that appear twice indicate summation from 1 to 3) where a_i, b_{ij}, c_{ijk}, etc., are coefficients having the appropriate tensor dimensionality. The smaller the particle jumps the more closely the motion approximates a rigorously continuous flow in which the flux is given completely by the average density at points lying on the surface itself $S^{(2)}$, i.e., by the first term in the expansion in Eq. (9.3) $a_i f_\alpha$. Thus, the small size of the jumps is manifest in the fact that the terms in the series in (9.3) fall off rapidly. To a first approximation the finite size of the jumps, i.e., the fact that the jumps are not infinitesimally small, can be taken into account by retaining two terms in Eq. (9.3):

$$j_i = a_i f_\alpha + b_{ij} \frac{\partial f_\alpha}{\partial v_j}, \tag{9.4}$$

which gives the expression written in Eq. (9.2).

The first "kinematic" term in Eq. (9.2) $\dot{\mathbf{v}} f_\alpha$, which is analogous to the flux $\mathbf{v}\rho$ in hydrodynamics, can be expressed in terms of the force acting on a particle α. This force must be made up of the external force $\mathbf{F}^{(e)}$ and the force due to collisions $\mathbf{F}_{\mathrm{col}}$:

$$\dot{\mathbf{v}} = \frac{\mathbf{F}}{m_\alpha} = \frac{1}{m_\alpha}\left(\mathbf{F}_\alpha^{(e)} + \mathbf{F}_{\mathrm{col}}\right). \tag{9.5}$$

Substituting Eq. (9.2) for the flux [taking account of Eq. (9.5)] in the equation of continuity (9.1) and transferring all terms due to collision effects to the right side we can write the kinetic equation in the form

$$\frac{\partial f_\alpha}{\partial t} + \mathrm{div}_r\,(\mathbf{v} f_\alpha) + \frac{1}{m_\alpha} \nabla_v \left(\mathbf{F}_\alpha^{(e)} f_\alpha\right) = -\nabla_v \mathbf{j}^\alpha, \tag{9.6}$$

where $\mathbf{j}^\alpha$ is the flux of α particles in velocity space produced by collisions:

$$j_i^\alpha = \frac{F_i^\alpha}{m_\alpha} f_\alpha - D_{ik}^\alpha \frac{\partial f_\alpha}{\partial v_k} \tag{9.7}$$

(k denotes summation from 1 to 3).

Following Chandrasekhar [1] we may say that the force $\mathbf{F}^\alpha$, due to collisions and arising from the "kinematic" term $\dot{\mathbf{v}} f$, is the force of dynamical friction (since kinematics in velocity space implies dynamics!). The tensor D_{ik}^α can be called the diffusion tensor in velocity space.

If the plasma contains particles of different species the interaction of particles of a given species α with the others will be additive since all calculations are carried out under the "binary-collision" assumption. Consequently

$$\left.\begin{aligned} \mathbf{j}^{\alpha} &= \sum_{\beta} \mathbf{j}^{\alpha/\beta}, \\ \mathbf{F}^{\alpha} &= \sum_{\beta} \mathbf{F}^{\alpha/\beta}, \\ D_{ik}^{\alpha} &= \sum_{\beta} D_{ik}^{\alpha/\beta}, \end{aligned}\right\} \tag{9.8}$$

where $\mathbf{F}^{\alpha/\beta}$ is the force of dynamical friction experienced by particles α in a medium of (β) particles and $D_{ik}^{\alpha/\beta}$ is the diffusion tensor for (α) particles in a medium of (β) particles.

Since the interaction of a given particle α with other (α) particles is not distinguished from the interaction with particles of another species, it follows that the summation over all $\beta \left(\sum_{\beta}\right)$ in Eq. (9.8) also includes $\beta = \alpha$, i. e., collisions between like particles.

§ 10. Force of Dynamical Friction and the Diffusion Tensor

We now wish to find explicit expressions for $F_i^{\alpha/\beta}$ and $D_{ij}^{\alpha/\beta}$ and to examine the physical meaning of these quantities. For this purpose we again consider the problem treated in Part I, i. e., that of a test particle α moving in a medium of field particles β. Let us assume that at t = 0 the velocity of the (α) particle is $\mathbf{v}_0$. The problem is to find its subsequent motion.

As before, for the purposes of our statistical analysis we introduce an ensemble of test particles α which all have the same velocity $\mathbf{v}_0$ at time t = 0 and consider in detail the motion of the continuous cloud of test particles in velocity space; the cloud will of course expand as the time increases (cf. Fig. 4). Now, however, the description of the process is facilitated by the more convenient apparatus at our disposal.

Whereas, before, the distribution of particles in the cloud required a knowledge of the infinite sequence of moments

$$\overline{v_i},\ \overline{\Delta v_i \Delta v_j},\ \overline{\Delta v_i \Delta v_j \Delta v_k},\ \ldots, \tag{10.1}$$

where $\Delta\overline{v}_i = v_i - \overline{v}_i$ (or a knowledge of the equivalent quantities $\overline{v}_i$, $\overline{v_i v_j}$, $\overline{v_i v_j v_k}$, analogous to the sequence of multipoles—dipole, quadrupole, etc., in electrostatics), the distribution can now be described by assigning directly the density of particles in various portions of the cloud, that is to say, we now make use of the distribution function for test particles in phase space $f_\alpha(t, \mathbf{r}, \mathbf{v})$.

Before we regarded the cloud as an ensemble consisting of a large number of point particles ($N \to \infty$) and averaged the function $W(\mathbf{v})$ over the particle velocity distribution using the formula

$$\overline{W}(t) = \frac{1}{N} \sum_{\nu=1}^{N} W\left(\mathbf{v}^{(\nu)}(t)\right). \tag{10.2}$$

Now, however, knowing $f_\alpha(t, \mathbf{v})$ we regard the cloud as a continuous medium with a density $f_\alpha(t, \mathbf{v})$ and the averaging operation is written in the form

$$\overline{W(t)} = \frac{1}{n_\alpha} \int W(\mathbf{v}) f_\alpha(t, \mathbf{v})\, d\mathbf{v}, \tag{10.3}$$

where $n_\alpha = \int f_\alpha(t, \mathbf{v})\, d\mathbf{v}$.

Physically there is no difference between these two approaches: as N, the number of particles in the cloud, approaches infinity we obtain the representation of a continuous medium.*

In particular, if the distribution is known the moments of the distribution [cf. Eq. (10.1)] can be found from the relations

$$\overline{v}_i = \frac{1}{n_\alpha} \int v_i f_\alpha(\mathbf{v})\, d\mathbf{v}; \quad \overline{\Delta v_i \Delta v_j} = \frac{1}{n_\alpha} \int (v - \overline{v})_i (v - \overline{v})_j f_\alpha(\mathbf{v})\, dv;$$

$$\overline{\Delta v_i \Delta v_j \Delta v_k} = \frac{1}{n_\alpha} \int (v - \overline{v})_i (v - \overline{v})_j (v - \overline{v})_k f_\alpha(\mathbf{v})\, d\mathbf{v}; \tag{10.4}$$

*There is actually a formal difference; this is the fact that in Eq. (10.2), which deals with an ensemble of particles, the velocity $\mathbf{v}(t)$ appears specifically as the velocity of some particle and depends on time. In the distribution function $f(t, \mathbf{r}, \mathbf{v})$, however, which describes a continuous medium, the velocity $\mathbf{v}$ simply denotes a point in velocity space and is obviously independent of time. Similarly, the argument $\mathbf{r}$ in the function $f(t, \mathbf{r}, \mathbf{v})$ is an independent variable, denoting a point in coordinate space.

etc. Similarly, a knowledge of all of the moments (including those of infinitely high order) can be used to determine the distribution function.

Now let us describe the spreading of the cloud by means of the distribution function f_α. At the initial time all the particles in the cloud have the same velocity $\mathbf{v}_0$. Hence at t = 0 the ensemble of particles can be regarded as a uniform plane flux moving in an infinite uniform medium of field particles β.

Then

$$f_\alpha(t, \mathbf{r}, \mathbf{v})\big|_{t=0} = n_\alpha \delta(\mathbf{v} - \mathbf{v}_0), \tag{10.5}$$

where n_α is the spatial density of (α) particles in the flux.

Assuming that there is no external force $\mathbf{F}_\alpha^{(e)}$, so that the distribution of test particles changes only by virtue of collisions with the field particles β, we obtain the kinetic equation for the function f_α [cf. Eqs. (9.6) and (9.7)]

$$\frac{\partial f_\alpha(t, \mathbf{v})}{\partial t} = -\nabla_v \mathbf{j}^{\alpha/\beta}, \tag{10.6}$$

where

$$j_i^{\alpha/\beta} = \frac{F_i^{\alpha/\beta}}{m_\alpha} f_\alpha - D_{ik}^{\alpha/\beta} \frac{\partial f_\alpha}{\partial v_k}.$$

The $\text{div}_r(\mathbf{v}f_\alpha)$ term does not appear because the function $f_\alpha(t, \mathbf{r}, \mathbf{v})$ does not depend on the spatial coordinates x, y, and z.

Our problem then is to obtain explicit expressions for the force of dynamical friction $F_i^{\alpha/\beta}$ and for the diffusion tensor $D_{ik}^{\alpha/\beta}$. With this end in mind we calculate the rate-of-change of the moments (10.4) for the cloud of test particles α using the kinetic expression (10.6); the results are then to be compared with those obtained in Part I. Carrying out this program we find

$$\frac{d}{dt}\overline{\mathbf{v}}_i = \frac{1}{n_\alpha}\int v_i \frac{\partial f_\alpha}{\partial t} d\mathbf{v} = -\frac{1}{n_\alpha}\int v_i \text{div}_v \mathbf{j} d\mathbf{v} = \frac{1}{n_\alpha}\int j_i d\mathbf{v} =$$

$$= \frac{1}{n_\alpha}\int \left(f_\alpha \frac{F_i}{m_\alpha} - D_{ik}\frac{\partial f_\alpha}{\partial v_k}\right) d\mathbf{v} = \frac{1}{n_\alpha}\int f_\alpha \left(\frac{F_i}{m_\alpha} + \frac{\partial D_{ik}}{\partial v_k}\right) d\mathbf{v}. \tag{10.7}$$

Now, substituting the initial value of the function $f_\alpha|_{t=0} = n_\alpha \delta(\mathbf{v} - \mathbf{v}_0)$ in the right side we have

$$\left.\frac{d\bar{v}_i}{dt}\right|_{t=0} = \left(\frac{F_i^{\alpha/\beta}}{m_\alpha} + \frac{\partial}{\partial v_k} D_{ik}^{\alpha/\beta}\right)_{\mathbf{v}=\mathbf{v}_0}. \tag{10.8}$$

The quantity $d\bar{v}_i/dt$ is then the initial rate of displacement of the cloud of test particles in velocity space, which has been computed in Part I and denoted by $<\Delta v_i>^{\alpha/\beta}$. Omitting the zero subscript on $\mathbf{v}_0$ in Eq. (10.8) we find

$$\left.\frac{d\bar{v}_i}{dt}\right|_{t=0} = <\Delta v_i>^{\alpha/\beta} = \frac{F_i^{\alpha/\beta}}{m_\alpha} + \frac{\partial}{\partial v_k} D_{ik}^{\alpha/\beta}. \tag{10.9}$$

Similarly, computing the derivative of the second moment from Eq. (10.4) at $t = 0$ we find

$$\frac{d}{dt}\,\overline{(v-\bar{v})_i\,(v-\bar{v})_k}\,\Big|_{t=0} = <\Delta v_i \Delta v_k>^{\alpha/\beta} = 2D_{ik}^{\alpha/\beta}. \tag{10.10}$$

Thus, the force of dynamical friction $\mathbf{F}^{\alpha/\beta}$ and the diffusion tensor $D_{ik}^{\alpha/\beta}$ that have been introduced formally in §9 are related to $<\Delta v_i>$ and $<\Delta v_i \Delta v_j>$ by Eqs. (10.9) and (10.10); the physical meaning and explicit expressions for $<\Delta v_i>$ and $<\Delta v_i \Delta v_j>$ have been given in Part I.

Finally, using Eq. (6.7) we have

$$\left.\begin{aligned} D_{ik}^{\alpha/\beta} &= \frac{1}{2} <\Delta v_i \Delta v_k>^{\alpha/\beta} = -L^{\alpha/\beta}\frac{\partial^2 \psi_\beta}{\partial v_i \partial v_k};\\ \frac{1}{m_\alpha} F_i^{\alpha/\beta} &= <\Delta v_i>^{\alpha/\beta} - \frac{1}{2}\frac{\partial}{\partial v_k} <\Delta v_i \Delta v_k>^{\alpha/\beta} =\\ &= -\frac{m_\alpha}{m_\beta} L^{\alpha/\beta} \frac{\partial \varphi_\beta}{\partial v_i}. \end{aligned}\right\} \tag{10.11}$$

Substituting these expressions in Eq. (10.6) we obtain the following expression for the collisional flux $\mathbf{j}^{\alpha/\beta}$:

$$\begin{aligned} j_i^{\alpha/\beta} &= \frac{F_i^{\alpha/\beta}}{m_\alpha} f_\alpha - D_{ik}^{\alpha/\beta} \frac{\partial f_\alpha}{\partial v_k} =\\ &= <\Delta v_i>^{\alpha/\beta} f_\alpha - \frac{1}{2}\frac{\partial}{\partial v_k}\left(<\Delta v_i \Delta v_k>^{\alpha/\beta} f_\alpha\right). \end{aligned} \tag{10.12}$$

This form is called the Fokker-Planck form. However, the expression can be made more meaningful by writing it in the form

$$j_i^{\alpha/\beta} = \frac{1}{m_\alpha} F_i^{\alpha/\beta} f_\alpha - D_{ik}^{\alpha/\beta} \frac{\partial f_\alpha}{\partial v_k}, \tag{10.13}$$

where the first and second terms are analogous, in appearance, to the "kinematic" ($\mathbf{j} = \mathbf{v}\rho$) and "diffusion" ($\mathbf{j} = -D\nabla\rho$) flux in ordinary coordinate space. For this reason we shall always write the collisional flux in the form given in (10.13).

In conclusion we wish to determine the accuracy that is obtained with the two-term expression for the flux $\mathbf{j}^{\alpha/\beta}$ (10.13). If this expression is used in conjunction with (10.4) we find that the derivative of the third moment vanishes at t = 0 as do the derivatives of all the higher order terms:

$$\frac{d}{dt} \overline{(v - \bar{v})_i (v - \bar{v})_j (v - \bar{v})_k} \Big|_{t=0} = 0 \tag{10.14}$$

(because of the presence of the factor $(\mathbf{v} - \mathbf{v}_0)\,\delta(\mathbf{v} - \mathbf{v}_0)$ under the integral sign). Now, by definition this derivative must coincide with the quantity $<\Delta v_i \Delta v_j \Delta v_k>$ introduced in Part I, which does not vanish. But, as we have seen, the latter does not contain logarithmically divergent integrals and consequently is due to close trajectories, in contrast with the first two moments $<\Delta v_i>$ and $<\Delta v_i \Delta v_j>$.

Writing the flux with two terms, f and $\partial f/\partial v_k$ [cf. Eq. (10.13)] automatically ensures that the derivatives of all higher moments (starting with the third) can be neglected; as we have seen in Part I, this statement holds with "logarithmic" accuracy ($\sim 1/\lambda$) for the Coulomb case.

To take account of the higher moments, for example the third, it would be necessary to write the flux in a form containing three terms, f, $\partial f/\partial v_i$ and $\partial^2 f/\partial v_i \partial v_k$ [cf. the series in Eq. (9.3)]:

$$j_i = a_i f + b_{ik} \frac{\partial f}{\partial v_k} + c_{ikl} \frac{\partial^2 f}{\partial v_k \partial v_l} \tag{10.15}$$

We would then find

$$\left.\begin{aligned} \frac{d}{dt} \overline{\Delta v_i \Delta v_j \Delta v_k}\Big|_{t=0} = 6c_{ijk} = \,<\Delta v_i \Delta v_j \Delta v_k>^{\alpha/\beta}; \\ \left(\sim \frac{1}{\lambda} \neq 0\right). \end{aligned}\right\} \tag{10.16}$$

However, taking account of terms of order $1/\lambda$ goes beyond the accuracy of the present analysis.

§ 11. Kinetic Equation for the Coulomb Interaction

Combining the results of the preceding sections, we find that for the case of the Coulomb interaction the kinetic equation is of the form

$$\frac{\partial f_\alpha}{\partial t} + \operatorname{div}_r (\mathbf{v} f_\alpha) + \frac{1}{m_\alpha} \operatorname{div}_v (\mathbf{F}^{(e)} f_\alpha) = C^\alpha = \sum_\beta C^{\alpha/\beta}, \quad (11.1)$$

where C^α is the so-called collision term, which consists of a sum of terms $C^{\alpha/\beta}$ each of which describes collisions of particles of a given kind α with particles of type β (including $\beta = \alpha$):

$$C^{\alpha/\beta} = -\operatorname{div}_v j^{\alpha/\beta}, \quad (11.2)$$

where

$$j_i^{\alpha/\beta} = \frac{1}{m_\alpha} F_i^{\alpha/\beta} f_\alpha - D_{ik}^{\alpha/\beta} \nabla_k f_\alpha.$$

In Eqs. (11.1) and (11.2) the subscript $\mathbf{r}$ or v on the operators (div, ∇, Δ,etc.) denotes the space in which the given operator operates. An operator with no subscript refers to velocity space.

The diffusion tensor $D_{ik}^{\alpha/\beta}$ and the force of dynamical friction $F_i^{\alpha/\beta}$ in Eq. (11.2) are given by Eq. (10.11)

$$\left.\begin{aligned} D_{ik}^{\alpha/\beta} &= -L^{\alpha/\beta} \frac{\partial^2 \psi_\beta}{\partial v_i \partial v_k}, \\ F_i^{\alpha/\beta} &= -\frac{m_\alpha^2}{m_\beta} L^{\alpha/\beta} \frac{\partial \varphi_\beta}{\partial v_i}, \end{aligned}\right\} \quad (11.3)$$

from which it follows that

$$F_i^{\alpha/\beta} = \frac{m_\alpha^2}{m_\beta} \frac{\partial}{\partial v_k} D_{ik}^{\alpha/\beta}. \quad (11.4)$$

Here $L^{\alpha/\beta} = \lambda(4\pi e_\alpha e_\beta/m_\alpha)^2$ while ψ_β and φ_β are the potential functions for the distribution of β particles given by the relations:

$$\left.\begin{aligned} f_\beta &= \Delta\varphi_\beta, \ \varphi_\beta = \Delta\psi_\beta; \\ \psi_\beta &= -\frac{1}{8\pi}\int |\mathbf{v}-\mathbf{v}'|\, f'_\beta d\mathbf{v}'; \\ \varphi_\beta &= -\frac{1}{4\pi}\int \frac{f'_\beta d\mathbf{v}'}{|\mathbf{v}-\mathbf{v}'|}. \end{aligned}\right\} \tag{11.5}$$

The physical interpretations of $D_{ik}^{\alpha/\beta}$ and $F_i^{\alpha/\beta}$ have been discussed in the preceding section. The diffusion tensor $D_{ik}^{\alpha/\beta}$ is the initial rate-of-change of the tensor that describes the quadratic deviations of velocity from the mean in the cloud of test particles α:

$$D_{ik}^{\alpha/\beta} = \frac{1}{2}\frac{d}{dt}\overline{(v-\overline{v})_i\,(v-\overline{v})_k}\,\Big|_{t=0}. \tag{11.6}$$

The only difference between the dynamical friction force $F_i^{\alpha/\beta}$ and the mean force $\mathbf{F}_\alpha$ acting on a test particle α in a medium of β particles is the factor $m_\alpha/(m_\alpha + m_\beta)$:

$$\mathbf{F}^{\alpha/\beta} = \frac{m_\alpha}{m_\alpha + m_\beta}\mathbf{F}_\alpha. \tag{11.7}$$

Nevertheless, it should be emphasized that the "real" physical quantities is the average force $\mathbf{F}_\alpha$; the dynamical friction force is a formal concept that is introduced purely as a matter of convenience.

Similarly, the potential functions ψ_β and φ_β in Eq. (11.5) have no simple physical meaning in themselves; however, an interpretation of these quantities can be given without difficulty. As we have indicated, the function φ_β is analogous to the potential that specifies an electric field in electrostatics. To within an accuracy given by an unimportant factor $(-n_\beta/8\pi)$ the function $\psi_\beta(\mathbf{v})$ is geometrically nothing more than the mean distance between the observation point $\mathbf{v}$ and $\mathbf{v}_\beta$, the source points in velocity space at which the field particles are located; thus $\psi_\beta(\mathbf{v})$ is the mean value of the relative velocity

$$\psi_\beta(\mathbf{v}) = \left(-\frac{n_\beta}{8\pi}\right)\overline{|\mathbf{v}-\mathbf{v}_\beta|}^{(\beta)}. \tag{11.8}$$

Here the bar denotes an average over the distribution of β particles in velocity space.

Returning to Eq. (11.1) we note that Hamilton's equations can be used in this case, i.e., the motion of a particle in a field of external forces

$\mathbf{F}^{(e)}$ (this can not be done, for example, when friction is present)

$$\dot{\mathbf{r}} = \frac{\partial H}{\partial \mathbf{p}} = \mathbf{v}, \quad \dot{\mathbf{p}} = -\frac{\partial H}{\partial \mathbf{r}} = \mathbf{F}^{(e)}; \tag{11.9}$$

the second and third terms on the left side of Eq. (11.1) can be written in the form

$$\mathrm{div}_r(\mathbf{v}f_\alpha) + \frac{1}{m_\alpha}\mathrm{div}_v(\mathbf{F}^{(e)}f_\alpha) = (\mathbf{v}\nabla_r) f_\alpha +$$

$$+\frac{1}{m_\alpha}(\mathbf{F}^{(e)}\nabla_v) f_\alpha + f_\alpha\left\{\frac{\partial v_i}{\partial x_i} + \frac{1}{m_\alpha}\frac{\partial}{\partial v_i}F_i^{(e)}\right\}. \tag{11.10}$$

The expression in the curly brackets vanishes:

$$\frac{\partial v_i}{\partial x_i} + \frac{1}{m_\alpha}\frac{\partial}{\partial v_i}F_i^{(e)} = \frac{\partial^2 H}{\partial x_i \partial p_i} - \frac{\partial^2 H}{\partial p_i \partial x_i} = 0. \tag{11.11}$$

Hence, the kinetic equation (11.1) assumes the more familiar form

$$\frac{\partial f_\alpha}{\partial t} + (\mathbf{v}\nabla_r) f_\alpha + \frac{1}{m_\alpha}(\mathbf{F}^{(e)}\nabla_v) f_\alpha = C^\alpha, \tag{11.12}$$

where

$$C^\alpha = -\mathrm{div}_v\left(\sum_\beta \mathbf{j}^{\alpha/\beta}\right). \tag{11.13}$$

If Eq. (11.3) is substituted in Eq. (11.2) (the collision flux), we find

$$\mathbf{j}^{\alpha/\beta} = -L^{\alpha/\beta}\left[\frac{m_\alpha}{m_\beta} f_\alpha \nabla\varphi_\beta - (\nabla f_\alpha \nabla)\nabla\psi_\beta\right]. \tag{11.14}$$

The "self-collision" term $C^{\alpha/\alpha}$ then assumes the form

$$C^{\alpha/\alpha} = L^{\alpha/\alpha}\nabla\left[f_\alpha\nabla\varphi_\alpha - (\nabla f_\alpha\nabla)\nabla\psi_\alpha\right] =$$

$$= L^{\alpha/\alpha}\left(f_\alpha^2 - \frac{\partial^2 f_\alpha}{\partial v_i \partial v_k}\frac{\partial^2 \psi_\alpha}{\partial v_i \partial v_k}\right). \tag{11.15}$$

It is evident that a Maxwellian distribution yields a vanishing self-collisional flux $\mathbf{j}^{\alpha/\alpha}$ as well as a vanishing $C^{\alpha/\alpha}$ term. In conclusion we shall indicate the way Eq. (11.14) (the flux $\mathbf{j}^{\alpha/\beta}$) can be transformed to the form given by Landau in 1936 [6]. For this purpose we use the notation

$$U_{ik} = \frac{\partial^2 |\mathbf{v} - \mathbf{v}'|}{\partial v_i \partial v_k} = \frac{\delta_{ik}}{u} - \frac{u_i u_k}{u^3}, \tag{11.16}$$

where $\mathbf{u} = \mathbf{v} - \mathbf{v}'$.

Since $\varphi_\beta = \partial^2 \psi_\beta / \partial v_k \partial v_k$ we have

$$\left.\begin{aligned} \nabla_i \varphi_\beta &= -\frac{1}{8\pi} \int U_{ik} \frac{\partial f'_\beta}{\partial v'_k}\, d\mathbf{v}', \\ \nabla_i \nabla_k \psi_\beta &= -\frac{1}{8\pi} \int U_{ik} f'_\beta \, d\mathbf{v}, \end{aligned}\right\} \tag{11.17}$$

where $f'_\beta \equiv f_\beta(\mathbf{v}')$.

Substituting Eq. (11.17) in Eq. (11.14) we can write the expression for the flux $\mathbf{j}^{\alpha/\beta}$ in the symmetric form

$$j_i^{\alpha/\beta} = 2\pi\lambda \frac{e_\alpha^2 e_\beta^2}{m_\alpha} \int U_{ik} \left(\frac{f_\alpha}{m_\beta} \frac{\partial f'_\beta}{\partial v'_k} - \frac{f'_\beta}{m_\alpha} \frac{\partial f_\alpha}{\partial v_k} \right) d\mathbf{v}', \tag{11.18}$$

in which it was first given by Landau. It is interesting to note that until recently the erroneous idea was propagated in the foreign literature that the Landau expression is incorrect. This idea is evidently based on a well-known paper by Cohen, Spitzer, and Routly [7] who asserted that Landau did not take account of the force of dynamical friction, a statement that is itself incorrect.

After the work of Landau many important results in this field were obtained by Chandrasekhar [1] in an investigation of stellar dynamics; by regarding the stars as particles interacting via a Coulomb force, Chandrasekhar was able to derive expressions for the force of dynamical friction and the diffusion tensor in the case of a Maxwellian distribution of field particles.

Recent work in this field includes an elegant derivation of the Landau expression by Rosenbluth, MacDonald, and Judd [3]; as we have already noted, this last paper introduces potential functions similar to the ones used here.

§ 12. Kinetic Equation Taking Account of Polarization of the Medium

In earlier sections we have obtained a plasma kinetic equation on the basis of binary particle collisions. The notion of binary collisions is certainly justified for short-range interparticle forces in a rarefied gas. If the interaction range of the particle d (effective diameter of the molecule) is much smaller than the mean distance between particles, which is of order $n^{-1/3}$ where n is the gas density, an interaction sphere of volume $\sim d^3$ will contain a small number of particles on the average:

$$\overline{N}_d = nd^3 \ll 1. \qquad (12.1)$$

Under these conditions one is justified in neglecting the probability of multiple collisions, i. e., those in which the sphere of interaction simultaneously contains three or more molecules; in this case a description in terms of binary collisions is adequate.

However, the Coulomb forces which act between plasma particles are in not short-range forces. While the potential energy U_{12} associated with the interaction between two plasma particles of charge e_1 and e_2 is distorted by the Debye shielding in the presence of the other charges,

$$U_{12}^{(\text{eff})} = \frac{e_1 e_2}{r_{12}} \exp\left(-\frac{r_{12}}{D}\right), \qquad r_{12} = |\mathbf{r}_1 - \mathbf{r}_2|, \qquad (12.2)$$

we see that the interaction between particles effectively extends at least out to a distance of the order of the Debye radius D. For the conditions in which we are interested (quasi-neutral plasma) $D \gg n^{-1/3}$ and the sphere of interaction contains many particles:

$$N_D = nD^3 \gg 1. \qquad (12.3)$$

Thus, it is evident that in a plasma a given particle will simultaneously interact with many particles. Under these conditions the applicability of the formulas derived in the earlier sections on the basis of binary collisions is open to some question.

A rigorous analysis shows that these formulas which, as we have indicated, yield logarithmic accuracy (i. e., they are valid to an accuracy of a factor of order unity under the sign of the Coulomb logarithm) are in fact applicable; taking explicit account of many-body collisions under ordinary conditions (cf. below) leads to the same results. The detailed justification of this extremely interesting conclusion is rather complicated and requires an analysis of the system of equations that describe the correlation functions. The reader interested in this problem should consult the original literature [8-10]. Here we shall treat the problem on the basis of some nonrigorous but hopefully more meaningful considerations.

Let us consider a test particle α moving through a plasma. For simplicity we assume that this particle is infinitely heavy ($m_\alpha \to \infty$). Its motion can then be regarded as specified; the particle will move in a straight line with constant velocity $\mathbf{v}_\alpha$. It follows from Eq. (11.7), which was derived on the basis of binary collisions, that the mean retarding force experienced by the test particle due to the field particles β is the same as the force of dynamical friction:

$$\mathbf{F}^\alpha = \lim_{m_\alpha \to \infty} \frac{m_\alpha + m_\beta}{m_\alpha} \mathbf{F}^{\alpha/\beta} = \\ = \mathbf{F}^{\alpha/\beta} = \lambda \frac{4\pi e_\alpha^2 e_\beta^2}{m_\beta} \nabla_\alpha \int \frac{f_\beta \, d\mathbf{v}_\beta}{|\mathbf{v}_\alpha - \mathbf{v}_\beta|}. \tag{12.4}$$

In other words, the force of dynamical friction is the force that a test particle would experience if it were infinitely heavy (or if it were to move in the specified way, i. e., with constant velocity along a straight line).

Now let us circumscribe a cylinder of radius ρ around the trajectory of this particle (Fig. 7).

Collisions of the test particle with field particles characterized by impact parameters $\rho \gg n^{-1/3}$ will be called many-body collisions. We treat these below separately. The collisions characterized by impact parameters much smaller than the mean distance between particles, i. e., $\rho \ll n^{-1/3}$, are binary collisions. Because of the long-range nature of the Coulomb force in a fully ionized plasma it is difficult to separate the effect of collisions that might be called triple, quadruple, etc., that is to say, lower-order many-body collisions.

We now wish to show that the method used to treat binary collisions need not be restricted to collisions with impact parameters satisfying the condition $\rho \ll n^{-1/3}$, but that it also applies when $\rho \sim n^{-1/3}$, and for even larger impact parameters. It has been pointed out in §2 that the electrostatic potential of the test particle in the plasma is distorted by the Debye

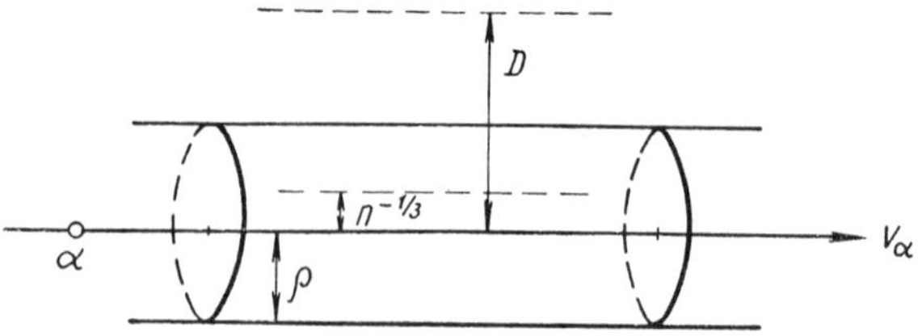

Fig. 7

shielding (2.5); hence the effective potential energy due to the interaction* of a field particle β with a test particle α is of the form in (12.2):

$$U_{\alpha\beta}^{(\mathrm{eff})} = \frac{e_\alpha e_\beta}{r_{\alpha\beta}} \exp\left(-\frac{r_{\alpha\beta}}{D}\right). \tag{12.5}$$

In this formula $r_{\alpha\beta} = |\mathbf{r}_\alpha - \mathbf{r}_\beta|$ and when $\bar{r}_{\alpha\beta} \ll D$ we have simply

$$U_{\alpha\beta}^{(\mathrm{eff})}\Big|_{r_{\alpha\beta} \ll D} = \frac{e_\alpha e_\beta}{r_{\alpha\beta}}. \tag{12.6}$$

In other words the presence of the other particles has no effect on the interaction between two particles separated by a distance smaller than the Debye length. Under these conditions the changes in momentum and energy of both particles are the same as though both particles were isolated from all the other particles. Thus, the binary-collision expression applies for all impact parameters smaller than the Debye radius, i. e., those for which $\rho \ll D$. Because $D \gg n^{-1/3}$, in the present case the collisions can be regarded as binary interactions even when $\rho \gg n^{-1/3}$ so long as $\rho \ll D$. Actually, even when $\rho = D$ the difference between the rigorous interaction relation (12.5), which takes account of the other particles, and a pure Coulomb interaction (12.6), is small (a factor of order unity). If logarithmic accuracy is adequate all collisions up to those for which $\rho = D$ can be treated as binary collisions (as we have done in the preceding sections); the contribution of collisions characterized by $\rho > D$ can then, in general, be neglected.

Cutting off the Coulomb logarithm at the maximum impact parameter $\rho_{max} = D$ provides an approximate way of taking account of the many-body

*The possibility of regarding this quantity as the effective energy of the interaction of two particles is also treated in the review of plasma thermodynamics by A. A. Vedenov in the present volume.

nature of the collisions for which $\rho \gg n^{-1/3}$. However, this many-body effect can be taken into account in a more rational way. A many-body collision means, essentially, that a selected particle (test particle) interacts (collides) with a large number of particles at any given time rather than with a single particle. It is then appropriate to analyze many-body interactions in macroscopic terms, that is to say, as though the selected particle were interacting with a medium. The electromagnetic properties of this medium, plasma, can be fully described by the dielectric tensor $\varepsilon_{ij}(\mathbf{k}, \omega)$ which takes account of the temporal and spatial dispersion. It will be evident that this macroscopic approach, which takes explicit account of the many-body collisions for which $\rho \gg n^{-1/3}$, then provides a natural way of matching to the binary-collision formulas that hold when $\rho \ll D$. Since $D \gg n^{-1/3}$, both sets of formulas must apply in the region of impact parameters $n^{-1/3} \ll \rho \ll D$.

To carry out this program we analyze the motion of an infinitely heavy test particle α in a medium characterized by the dielectric tensor ε_{ij} and determine the mean retarding force exerted on the particle. Using the macroscopic approach, in which the plasma is regarded as a continuous medium, we must solve the Maxwell equations

$$\left.\begin{aligned} \operatorname{rot} \mathbf{E} &= -\frac{1}{c}\frac{\partial \mathbf{B}}{\partial t}, \\ \operatorname{rot} \mathbf{B} &= \frac{4\pi}{c}\mathbf{j}_{\text{true}} + \frac{1}{c}\frac{\partial(\hat{\varepsilon}\cdot\mathbf{E})}{\partial t}, \end{aligned}\right\} \tag{12.7}$$

where the quantity $\hat{\varepsilon}\cdot\mathbf{E}$ is a vector with components $(\hat{\varepsilon}\cdot\mathbf{E})_i = \varepsilon_{ij}E_j$. Here, $\mathbf{j}_{\text{true}} = e_\alpha \mathbf{v}_\alpha \delta(\mathbf{r} - \mathbf{v}_\alpha t)$ is the density of "true" current associated with the test particle α. To solve these equations it is convenient to expand all quantities in Fourier integrals:

$$\left.\begin{aligned} \mathbf{E}(\mathbf{r}, t) &= \int \mathbf{E}(\mathbf{k})\, e^{i\mathbf{k}\mathbf{r}}\, d\mathbf{k}, \\ \mathbf{j}(\mathbf{r}, t) &= \int \mathbf{j}(\mathbf{k})\, e^{i\mathbf{k}\mathbf{r}}\, d\mathbf{k}. \end{aligned}\right\} \tag{12.8}$$

Then, using the well-known relation

$$\delta(\mathbf{r} - \mathbf{v}_\alpha t) = (2\pi)^{-3} \int e^{i\mathbf{k}(\mathbf{r}-\mathbf{v}_\alpha t)}\, d\mathbf{k}, \tag{12.9}$$

we Fourier-analyze the current density

$$\mathbf{j}(\mathbf{k}) = e_\alpha \mathbf{v}_\alpha (2\pi)^{-3} e^{-i\omega t}, \tag{12.10}$$

where $\omega = \mathbf{kv}_\alpha$. The Fourier components of the other quantities have the same time dependence. Eliminating the magnetic field from Eq. (12.7) we find

$$(\varepsilon_{ik} + N_i N_k - \delta_{ik} N^2) E_k = \frac{4\pi}{i\omega} j_i, \tag{12.11}$$

where $\mathbf{N} = \mathbf{k}c/\omega$.

For simplicity we will regard the plasma as a uniform isotropic medium with no magnetic field. The tensor $\varepsilon_{ij}(\mathbf{k}, \omega)$ must then be formed from the tensors δ_{ij} and $k_i k_j$ and can be written

$$\varepsilon_{ij} = \frac{k_i k_j}{k^2} \varepsilon^l + \left(\delta_{ij} - \frac{k_i k_j}{k^2}\right) \varepsilon^{tr}, \tag{12.12}$$

where ε^l and ε^{tr} are scalar functions of $\mathbf{k}$ and ω. Multiplying Eq. (12.11) from the left by the vector $\mathbf{k}$ we find

$$\varepsilon^l \mathbf{kE} = \frac{4\pi}{i\omega} \mathbf{kj}. \tag{12.13}$$

Now, substituting $\mathbf{kE}$ in Eq. (12.11) we find the Fourier components of the field

$$\mathbf{E} = \frac{4\pi}{i\omega} \left\{ \frac{\mathbf{n}(\mathbf{nj})}{\varepsilon^l} - \frac{[\mathbf{n}[\mathbf{nj}]]}{\varepsilon^{tr} - N^2} \right\}, \tag{12.14}$$

where $\mathbf{n} = \mathbf{k}/k$; then Eq. (12.8) is used to find the field itself. At $\mathbf{r} = \mathbf{v}_\alpha t$, the location of the test particle, the field is

$$\mathbf{E} = -i \frac{e_\alpha}{2\pi^2} \int \frac{d\mathbf{k}}{k^2} \left\{ \frac{\mathbf{k}}{\varepsilon^l} + \frac{(\mathbf{kv}_\alpha)[\mathbf{n}[\mathbf{nv}_\alpha]]}{c^2 [1 - (\mathbf{nv}_\alpha/c)^2 \varepsilon^{tr}]} \right\}_{\omega = \mathbf{kv}_\alpha}. \tag{12.15}$$

We shall limit ourselves to nonrelativistic velocities $v \ll c$. In this case the second term in the curly brackets, which is proportional to v^2/c^2 (and which is shown to be the Cerenkov radiation by a simple analysis), can be omitted. The field that is obtained determines the force acting on the test particle

$$\mathbf{F}_{\text{macr}} = e_\alpha \mathbf{E} = -i \frac{e_\alpha^2}{2\pi^2} \int \frac{\mathbf{k}\, d\mathbf{k}}{k^2 \varepsilon^l (\mathbf{k}, \omega)_{\omega = \mathbf{kv}_\alpha}}. \tag{12.16}$$

As it stands this formula is still too general since it gives the retardation of the test particle in an arbitrary medium characterized by a dielectric tensor $\varepsilon_{ij}(\mathbf{k}, \omega)$. To apply the expressions to a plasma we must know the actual form of ε_{ij}.

We shall not be concerned with the detailed derivation of the tensor ε_{ij} for a plasma since this would take us beyond the scope of the present analysis, but shall simply make use of well-known results. The complex dielectric constant $\varepsilon^{l}(\mathbf{k}, \omega)$ (the so-called longitudinal dielectric constant) for a nonrelativistic plasma is

$$\varepsilon^{l}(\mathbf{k}, \omega) = 1 + \sum_{\beta} \frac{4\pi e_{\beta}^{2}}{m_{\beta}\omega k^{2}} \int_{\smile} \frac{\mathbf{k}\mathbf{v}_{\beta}}{\omega - \mathbf{k}\mathbf{v}_{\beta}} \left(\mathbf{k}\frac{\partial f_{\beta}}{\partial \mathbf{v}_{\beta}}\right) d\mathbf{v}_{\beta}. \quad (12.17)$$

The symbol $\smile$ under the integral sign means that in integrating over v_{β} the pole $\omega - \mathbf{k}\mathbf{v}_{\beta} = 0$ in the complex v_{β} plane is to be traversed from below.*

The real and imaginary parts of the dielectric constant $\varepsilon^{l}(\mathbf{k}, \omega)$ can be separated by means of the familiar relation

$$\frac{1}{\omega - \mathbf{k}\mathbf{v}} = P\frac{1}{\omega - \mathbf{k}\mathbf{v}} + i\pi\delta(\omega - \mathbf{k}\mathbf{v}). \quad (12.18)$$

Here, P denotes the principal value of the integral. Also, since the real part of ε^{l} (i.e., Re ε^{l}) is an even function of $\mathbf{k}$ and ω (cf. [11]) the expression for $1/\varepsilon^{l}$ in Eq. (12.16) can be replaced by

$$\frac{1}{\varepsilon^{l}} \to -i\frac{Jm\varepsilon}{|\varepsilon|^{2}} = \frac{i\pi}{|\varepsilon|^{2}} \sum_{\beta} \frac{4\pi e_{\beta}^{2}}{m_{\beta}\omega k^{2}} \int (\mathbf{k}\mathbf{v}_{\beta}) \times$$

$$\times \left(\mathbf{k}\cdot\frac{\partial f_{\beta}}{\partial \mathbf{v}_{\beta}}\right) \delta(\omega - \mathbf{k}\mathbf{v}_{\beta})\, d\mathbf{v}_{\beta}. \quad (12.19)$$

The term with Re ε^{l} in the numerator drops out of Eq. (12.16) in the integration over k because of the even parity feature. The presence of the δ function in Eq. (12.19) also makes it possible to contract the factor $\mathbf{k}\mathbf{v}_{\beta}$ with ω in the denominator.

*The reader who is interested can find the derivation of Eq. (12.17) in Silin and Rukhadze [11], who also derive Eq. (12.15).

Thus, in the plasma case Eq. (12.16) is written in the form

$$\mathbf{F}_{\text{macr}} = \sum_{\beta} \mathbf{F}^{\alpha/\beta}_{\text{macr}},$$

where

$$\mathbf{F}^{\alpha/\beta}_{\text{macr}} = 2\frac{e_\alpha^2 e_\beta^2}{m_\beta}\int \hat{\mathbf{U}} \cdot \frac{\partial f_\beta}{\partial \mathbf{v}_\beta}\, d\mathbf{v}_\beta. \tag{12.20}$$

Here, the dot between the tensor $\hat{\mathbf{U}}$ and the vector $\partial f_\beta/\partial \mathbf{v}_\beta$ denotes contraction over the nearest indices.

The tensor $\hat{\mathbf{U}}$ has the components

$$U_{ij} = \int \frac{k_i k_j \delta(\mathbf{k}\mathbf{v}_\alpha - \mathbf{k}\mathbf{v}_\beta)}{k^4 \cdot |\varepsilon^l(\mathbf{k}, \omega)|^2_{\omega = \mathbf{k}\mathbf{v}_\alpha}}\, d\mathbf{k}. \tag{12.21}$$

We may now ask how this retarding force is related to the friction force obtained earlier in our analysis based on binary collisions.

We note first that in solving Eq. (12.7) it has been assumed that the test particle produces the following current in the medium:

$$\mathbf{j}_{\text{true}} = e_\alpha \mathbf{v}_\alpha \delta(\mathbf{r} - \mathbf{v}_\alpha t). \tag{12.22}$$

This means that the test particle moves in a straight line with a specified velocity $\mathbf{v}_\alpha$ without being deflected and without being scattered. The retarding force defined for these conditions is actually not a true average force but, as was noted in the derivation of Eq. (12.4), is actually the force of dynamical friction (cf. also [12]). Hence, Eq. (12.20) is to be compared with Eq. (12.4)

$$\mathbf{F}^{\alpha/\beta}_{\text{micr}} = \lambda \frac{4\pi e_\alpha^2 e_\beta^2}{m_\beta} \nabla_\alpha \int \frac{f_\beta\, d\mathbf{v}_\beta}{|\mathbf{v}_\alpha - \mathbf{v}_\beta|}, \tag{12.23}$$

which represents the dynamical friction force obtained on the basis of binary collisions. Here, $\lambda = \ln(\rho_{\max}/\rho_{\min})$ where $\rho_{\max} = D$ while $\rho_{\min} = e^2/T$. As we have shown in §§1 and 2, this Coulomb logarithm arises in the integration over impact parameters that extends from $\rho = 0$ to $\rho_{\max} = D$, in which the upper limit is introduced artifically. Arguments to support this cutoff can be reduced to the statement that the polarization of the medium is responsible for the Debye shielding of the Coulomb field of the charges. Hence, collisions characterized by impact parameters $\rho > D$ do not lead to deflection or retardation of the particles. The macroscopic formula (12.20) automatically takes account of polarization of the medium; hence the cutoff at the upper limit should appear automatically. By introducing the unit vector $\mathbf{n} = \mathbf{k}/k$ we can write Eq. (12.17) for ε^l in the form

$$\varepsilon^l(\mathbf{k}, \omega)_{\omega=\mathbf{k}\mathbf{v}_\alpha} =$$
$$= 1 + \frac{1}{k^2}\sum_\beta \frac{4\pi e_\beta^2}{m_\beta(\mathbf{n}\mathbf{v}_\alpha)}\int \frac{\mathbf{n}\mathbf{v}_\beta}{\mathbf{n}\mathbf{v}_\alpha - \mathbf{n}\mathbf{v}_\beta}\left(\mathbf{n}\frac{\partial f_\beta}{\partial \mathbf{v}_\beta}\right) d\mathbf{v}_\beta. \qquad (12.24)$$

For example, if f_β is a Maxwellian distribution with equal temperatures

$$\varepsilon^l(\mathbf{k}, \mathbf{k}\mathbf{v}_\alpha) = 1 + \frac{1}{k^2D^2}\left\{\sum_\beta \left\langle \frac{\mathbf{n}\mathbf{v}_\beta}{\mathbf{n}\mathbf{v}_\beta - \mathbf{n}\mathbf{v}_\alpha}\right\rangle_\beta\right\}. \qquad (12.25)$$

Here, $D = \sqrt{T/4\pi ne^2}$ is the Debye radius while the angle brackets $\langle\ \rangle_\beta$ denote an average over the distribution of (β) particles. The expression in the curly brackets can be regarded as a dimensionless function of order unity if the velocity of the test particle α is of the order of the thermal velocities of the plasma particles. Obviously, for arbitrary nonequilibrium distributions the function $\varepsilon^l(\mathbf{k}, \mathbf{k}\mathbf{v}_\alpha)$ will be of the form

$$\varepsilon^l(\mathbf{k}, \mathbf{k}\mathbf{v}_\alpha) = 1 + \frac{1}{k^2D^2}\xi(\mathbf{v}_\alpha), \qquad (12.26)$$

where $\xi(\mathbf{v}_\alpha)$ is a function of order unity. It thus follows that the tensor U_{ij}, given by Eq. (12.21), is

$$U_{ij} = \int \frac{k_i k_j \delta(\mathbf{k}\mathbf{v}_\alpha - \mathbf{k}\mathbf{v}_\beta)\, d\mathbf{k}}{k^4[1 + (\xi_1/k^2D^2) + (\xi_2/k^4D^4)]}, \qquad (12.27)$$

where ξ_1 and ξ_2 are functions of $\mathbf{v}_\alpha$ of order unity. The wave vector k is of the order of magnitude of the impact parameter $\rho \sim k^{-1}$ and the integration over k in Eq. (12.27) corresponds to integration over impact parameters. As $\rho \to \infty$ this corresponds to $k \to 0$ and the integral in (12.27) converges in a natural way so that it is not necessary to introduce any artificial cutoff. At small k, such that $kD \ll 1$, the quantity ε^l will be large and the integrand will be small. For logarithmic accuracy the integral (12.27) can be computed assuming that the integration does not start at $k = 0$ but at

$k_{min} \sim D^{-1}$, taking $\varepsilon = 1$. Then

$$U_{ij} = \int_{k_{min}}^{\infty} \frac{k_i k_j}{k^4} \delta(\mathbf{k}\mathbf{v}_\alpha - \mathbf{k}\mathbf{v}_\beta)\, d\mathbf{k}. \tag{12.28}$$

This integral diverges logarithmically at large k, i. e., at small values of the impact parameter. However, at small distances, (the order of the interparticle distance $n^{-1/3}$ and smaller) our macroscopic approach is no longer valid and the plasma cannot be regarded as a continuous medium. Thus, the integration in Eq. (12.28) does not start at $k = \infty$; instead it starts at a value k^*_{max} that satisfies the condition $k^*_{max} \ll n^{1/3}$, which, in impact-parameter language, corresponds to the condition $\rho^*_{min} \gg n^{-1/3}$.

The last condition then represents the criterion for the application of a macroscopic analysis. Thus, writing $\mathbf{u} = \mathbf{v}_\alpha - \mathbf{v}_\beta$ and assuming that

$$\left.\begin{aligned} & u_i U_{ij} = 0, \\ & U_{ii} = \int_{k_{min}}^{k^*_{max}} k^{-2}\delta(\mathbf{k}\mathbf{u})\, d\mathbf{k} = \frac{2\pi}{u} \ln\left(\frac{k^*_{max}}{k_{min}}\right), \end{aligned}\right\} \tag{12.29}$$

it is easy to show that

$$U_{ij}(\mathbf{u}) = \pi\lambda^* \left(\frac{\delta_{ij}}{u} - \frac{u_i u_j}{u^3}\right), \tag{12.30}$$

where

$$\lambda^* = \ln \frac{k^*_{max}}{k_{min}} = \ln \frac{D}{\varrho^*_{min}}.$$

It is evident that the quantity λ^* represents part of the Coulomb logarithm. Substituting the value of U_{ij} in Eq. (12.20) we have

$$F_{i\,macr}^{\alpha/\beta} = 2\pi\lambda^* \frac{e_\alpha^2 e_\beta^2}{m_\beta} \int \left(\frac{\delta_{ij}}{u} - \frac{u_i u_j}{u_3}\right) \frac{\partial f_\beta}{\partial v_{j\beta}}\, d\mathbf{v}_\beta. \tag{12.31}$$

The tensor that appears in the brackets can be written in the form

$$\left(\frac{\delta_{ij}}{u}-\frac{u_i u_j}{u^3}\right)_{u=v_\alpha - v_\beta} = \nabla_{i\alpha}\nabla_{j\alpha}|\mathbf{v}_\alpha - \mathbf{v}_\beta| = -\nabla_{i\alpha}\nabla_{j\beta}|v_\alpha - v_\beta|, \tag{12.32}$$

where $\Delta_{i\alpha} \equiv \partial/\partial v_{i\alpha}$.

The integral can then be transformed by parts

$$\int d\mathbf{v}_\beta (\nabla_{j\beta} f_\beta)\nabla_{j\alpha}\nabla_{i\alpha}|\mathbf{v}_\alpha - \mathbf{v}_\beta| = \int d\mathbf{v}_\beta f_\beta \nabla_{i\alpha}\Delta_\beta |\mathbf{v}_\alpha - \mathbf{v}_\beta| =$$

$$= 2\nabla_{i\alpha}\int \frac{f_\beta d\mathbf{v}_\beta}{|\mathbf{v}_\alpha - \mathbf{v}_\beta|}. \tag{12.33}$$

Finally we have

$$\mathbf{F}^{\alpha/\beta}_{\mathrm{macr}} = \lambda^* \frac{4\pi e_\alpha^2 e_\beta^2}{m_\beta}\nabla_\alpha \int \frac{f_\beta d\mathbf{v}_\beta}{|\mathbf{v}_\alpha - \mathbf{v}_\beta|}. \tag{12.34}$$

We recall that $\lambda^* = \ln(D/\rho^*_{\mathrm{min}})$ where $\rho^*_{\mathrm{min}} \gg n^{-1/3}$. Impact parameters of the order of the interparticle distance and smaller have been eliminated. These impact parameters can be treated using the binary-collision formulas which, as we indicated above, apply from $\rho = 0$ to $\rho \ll D$. If we choose ρ^*_{min} to be $\rho^*_{\mathrm{min}} \ll D$ the contribution of binary collisions with impact parameters ranging from $\rho = 0$ to ρ^*_{min} is [cf. Eq. (12.4)]:

$$F^{\alpha/\beta}_{\mathrm{micr}} = \ln\left(\frac{\varrho^*_{\mathrm{min}}}{e^2/T}\right)\frac{4\pi e_\alpha^2 e_\beta^2}{m_\beta}\nabla_\alpha \int \frac{f_\beta\, d\mathbf{v}_\beta}{|\mathbf{v}_\alpha - \mathbf{v}_\beta|}. \tag{12.35}$$

Adding Eqs. (12.34) and (12.35) we obtain Eq. (12.4):

$$\mathbf{F}^{\alpha/\beta} = \mathbf{F}^{\alpha/\beta}_{\mathrm{micr}} + \mathbf{F}^{\alpha/\beta}_{\mathrm{macr}} = \lambda \frac{4\pi e_\alpha^2 e_\beta^2}{m_\beta}\nabla_\alpha \int \frac{f_\beta\, d\mathbf{v}_\beta}{|\mathbf{v}_\alpha - \mathbf{v}_\beta|}, \tag{12.36}$$

where now, however,

$$\lambda = \ln\left(\frac{\varrho^*_{\mathrm{min}}}{e^2/T}\right) + \ln\left(\frac{D}{\varrho^*_{\mathrm{min}}}\right) = \ln\left(\frac{D}{e^2/T}\right), \tag{12.37}$$

that is to say, we now have the complete Coulomb logarithm. These two forces combine in such a natural way because the regions of applicability of the microscopic and macroscopic treatments (binary and many-body collisions) overlap: the first applies from $\rho = 0$ to $\rho \ll D$ and the second from $\rho \gg n^{-1/3}$ to $\rho = \infty$. Hence, when the correct analysis is used there is no need for introducing an artificial cutoff in the impact parameters; taking account of the polarization of the medium automatically introduces this cutoff. Furthermore, to logarithmic accuracy we have shown that all collisions up to $\rho = D$ can be regarded as binary.

Another approach is possible. The structure of Eq. (12.20) for $\mathbf{F}^{\alpha/\beta}_{macr}$ is such that many-body collisions can be regarded essentially as binary collisions complicated by the effect of the medium, that is to say, by the presence of the other particles. Examination of Eqs. (12.27) and (12.28) shows that this complicating effect appears at wave numbers $k \gg D^{-1}$, i.e., impact parameters $\rho \ll D$. Thus, Eq. (12.29) can be extrapolated to the region of wave numbers $k > k^*_{max}$ corresponding to binary collisions which are treated properly. The role of the minimum impact parameter in the Coulomb logarithm is played by $\rho_{min} = e^2/T$, which appears automatically in the binary-collision equations, rather than artificially, as is the case for $\rho_{max} = D$. The integral over wave number $\mathbf{k}$ in Eq. (12.28) diverges logarithmically when $\mathbf{k} \to \infty$. Thus, in order to extrapolate the formulas for many-body collisions to the binary region $k > k^*_{max}$ the integrals over k must be cut off artificially at

$$k_{max} = \varrho_{min}^{-1} = T/e^2. \tag{12.38}$$

When this approach is used the force of dynamical friction is given by Eq. (10.20)

$$F_i^{\alpha/\beta} = 2\frac{e_\alpha^2 e_\beta^2}{m_\beta}\int U_{ij}\frac{\partial f_\beta}{\partial v_{j\beta}}\,d\mathbf{v}_\beta, \tag{12.39}$$

where now, however,

$$U_{ij} = \int_0^{k_{max} = T/e^2} \frac{k_i k_j \delta(\mathbf{k}\mathbf{v}_\alpha - \mathbf{k}\mathbf{v}_\beta)}{k^4 \left|\varepsilon^l(\mathbf{k}, \omega)\right|^2_{\omega = \mathbf{k}\mathbf{v}_\alpha}}\,d\mathbf{k}. \tag{12.40}$$

The term "many-body collisions" could be replaced by the term "wave interactions." It can be shown that Eqs. (12.39) and (12.40) provide a proper description both for binary collisions ("real" collisions) as well as the interaction of a test particle with waves in the plasma. Thus Eqs. (12.39) and (12.40) are not only improved formulas for binary collisions (12.36), but actually possess new physical content. Under ordinary conditions, in which the ion and electron temperatures in the plasma are the same, various plasma oscillations are excited only to the level of equilibrium noise and the formulas for many-body collisions [(12.39) and (12.40)] coincide with Eq. (12.30) (binary collisions) to within logarithmic accuracy.

However, conditions can arise in which the binary-collision formula (12.30) is incorrect; it is then necessary to use Eqs. (12.39) and (12.40). Silin and Gorbunov [13] have shown that these conditions occur, for example, in a highly nonisothermal plasma in which the electron temperature is greater than the ion temperature (by approximately a factor of 1000, $T_e/T_i \sim M/m$). It is easy to understand why the wave interaction is important in this case. The wave, characterized by a frequency ω and wave vector **k**, propagates with a phase velocity ω/k and interacts primarily with those particles whose velocities are close to ω/k. Particles moving in the same direction as the wave will remain in phase with it for a long time interval so that the interaction of these particles with the wave is important. We note that the resonance nature of the wave-particle interaction is responsible for the appearance of a resonance denominator $\omega - \mathbf{kv}$ in the plasma dielectric constant ε^l (12.17). Thus, it is important to take account of the wave-particle interactions if there is a strong excitation of waves whose phase velocity ω/k is of the same order as or smaller than the thermal velocity (i.e., the mean particle velocity). In the example given by Silin and Gorbunov [13] the ion-acoustic waves are strongly excited (these are ion sound waves whose phase velocity is determined by the electron temperature); when $T_e \gg T_i$ the phase velocity of these waves is approximately $v_{\text{phase}} = \sqrt{T_e/M}$. The condition

$$v_{\text{phase}} = \sqrt{T_e/M} \gg \sqrt{T_i/M} = v_{Ti} \tag{12.41}$$

implies weak interaction of these waves with the ions so that the waves are relatively weakly damped (this would not be true if $T_e \sim T_i$). On the other hand,

$$v_{\text{phase}} = \sqrt{T_e/M} \ll \sqrt{T_e/m} = v_{Te}, \tag{12.42}$$

and since there are many slow electrons in the plasma (Maxwellian distribution) it is necessary to take account of the interaction between the electrons and the waves. Finding the force of dynamical friction with Eq. (12.36), which takes account only of the binary collisions, would give incorrect results. Under these conditions the kinetic equation with the usual (binary) collision term in the Landau form is also incorrect.

In order to establish the form of the required collision term that takes account of the particle-wave interaction, in addition to knowing the force of dynamical friction given by Eqs. (12.39) and (12.40) we must know the diffusion tensor for test particles in velocity space. In the macroscopic treatment of many-body collisions the mechanism responsible for this diffusion is the scattering of the test particle on fluctuations of the electric field in the medium; the analysis of this problem is highly complicated.* For this reason we shall treat the subject with a less rigorous but more instructive approach.

The simplest form of the diffusion tensor $\hat{\mathbf{D}}^{\alpha/\beta}$ can be computed for thermodynamic equilibrium, in which case the test particle distribution is Maxwellian:

$$f_\alpha = \mathrm{const}\exp\left(-\frac{m_\alpha v_\alpha^2}{2T_\alpha}\right). \tag{12.43}$$

The particle flux in velocity space [cf. Eq. (10.2)] must vanish:

$$j_i^{\alpha/\beta} = \frac{1}{m_\alpha} F_i^{\alpha/\beta} f_\alpha - D_{ij}^{\alpha/\beta}\frac{\partial f_\alpha}{\partial v_{j\alpha}} = 0\,. \tag{12.44}$$

Substituting $\partial f_\alpha/\partial \mathbf{v}_\alpha$ from Eq. (12.43), after contraction of f_α we obtain the relation between the diffusion tensor and the force of dynamical friction:

$$\frac{1}{m_\alpha} F_i^{\alpha/\beta} = -\, v_{j\alpha} D_{ij}^{\alpha/\beta}\frac{m_\alpha}{T_\alpha}. \tag{12.45}$$

This relation is the analog (in velocity space) of the well-known Einstein relation, which relates ordinary particle diffusion to mobility. Having substituted $\mathbf{F}^{\alpha/\beta}$ from Eq. (12.39) we have

$$F_i^{\alpha/\beta} = -\frac{m_\alpha^2}{T_\alpha} v_{j\alpha} D_{ij}^{\alpha/\beta} = 2\frac{e_\alpha^2 e_\beta^2}{m_\beta}\int d\mathbf{v}_\beta \frac{\partial f_\beta}{\partial v_{j\beta}} \int_0^{T/e^2} \frac{k_i k_j \delta(\mathbf{k}\mathbf{v}_\alpha - \mathbf{k}\mathbf{v}_\beta)}{k^4 |\varepsilon^l|^2}\, d\mathbf{k}. \tag{12.46}$$

---

*The analysis of these fluctuations and the form of the diffusion tensor are given in the review by V. D. Shafranov in Volume III of this series.

This relation holds only under conditions of complete thermodynamic equilibrium; in particular, the field particles β must also be described by a Maxwellian distribution

$$f_\beta = \text{const} \exp\left(-\frac{m_\beta v_\beta^2}{2T_\beta}\right), \quad (12.47)$$

and the temperatures T_α and T_β must be the same ($T_\alpha = T_\beta = T$). The derivative $\partial f_\beta/\partial \mathbf{v}_\beta$ in Eq. (12.46) can then be written

$$\frac{\partial f_\beta}{\partial \mathbf{v}_\beta} = -\frac{m_\beta}{T}\mathbf{v}_\beta f_\beta. \quad (12.48)$$

The scalar product $\mathbf{kv}_\beta$ obtained in the integral over k can be replaced by $\mathbf{kv}_\alpha$ because of the delta-function $\delta(\mathbf{kv}_\alpha - \mathbf{kv}_\beta)$. Equation (12.46) then yields

$$v_{i\alpha} D_{ij}^{\alpha/\beta} = v_{i\alpha}\left\{2\frac{e_\alpha^2 e_\beta^2}{m_\alpha^2}\int U_{ij} f_\beta \, d\mathbf{v}_\beta\right\} \quad (12.49)$$

(where i indicates summation from 1 to 3). It is reasonable to take the expression in the curly brackets as the diffusion tensor

$$D_{ij}^{\alpha/\beta} = 2\frac{e_\alpha^2 e_\beta^2}{m_\alpha^2}\int U_{ij} f_\beta \, d\mathbf{v}_\beta, \quad (12.50)$$

where

$$U_{ij} = \int_0^{T/e^2} \frac{k_i k_j \delta(\mathbf{kv}_\alpha - \mathbf{kv}_\beta)}{k^4 |\varepsilon^l|^2_{\omega = \mathbf{kv}_\alpha}} d\mathbf{k}.$$

In view of the procedure that has been used here it would be assumed that this expression applies only in the case of thermodynamic equilibrium. However, if the wave interaction is not important the tensor $\hat{U}$ can be given by the following approximate expression, which is analogous to Eq. (12.30):

$$U_{ij} = \int_{k_{\min} = D^{-1}}^{k_{\max} = T/e^2} \delta(\mathbf{kv}_\alpha - \mathbf{kv}_\beta)\frac{k_i k_j}{k^4} d\mathbf{k} = \pi\lambda\left(\frac{\delta_{ij}}{u} - \frac{u_i u_j}{u^3}\right)_{\mathbf{u} = \mathbf{v}_\alpha - \mathbf{v}_\beta}, \quad (12.51)$$

where $\lambda = \ln(k_{max}/k_{min}) = \ln(DT/e^2)$ is now the complete Coulomb logarithm. It is easily shown that the diffusion tensor then coincides with the binary diffusion tensor (11.3), which applies in the general case as well as the case of thermodynamic equilibrium. It is reasonable to assume that Eq. (12.50) also applies in the general case. A rigorous analysis based on the solution of the equations for the correlation functions verifies this assumption.

Knowing the force of dynamical friction (12.46) and the diffusion tensor (12.50) we can now write the collision term C^{α} in the kinetic equation for the distribution function for α particles. In accordance with Eqs. (11.1) and (11.2) this term is

$$\left.\begin{aligned} C^{\alpha} &= \sum_{\beta} C^{\alpha/\beta}, \\ C^{\alpha/\beta} &= -\operatorname{div}_v \mathbf{j}^{\alpha/\beta}. \end{aligned}\right\} \quad (12.52)$$

The flux $\mathbf{j}^{\alpha/\beta}$ of (α) particles is

$$j_i^{\alpha/\beta} = \frac{1}{m_\alpha} F_i^{\alpha/\beta} f_\alpha - D_{ij}^{\alpha/\beta} \frac{\partial f_\alpha}{\partial v_{j\alpha}} = 2\frac{e_\alpha^2 e_\beta^2}{m_\alpha} \int U_{ij} \left(\frac{f_\alpha}{m_\beta} \frac{\partial f_\beta}{\partial v_{j\beta}} - \right.$$

$$\left. - \frac{f_\beta}{m_\alpha} \frac{\partial f_\alpha}{\partial v_{j\alpha}} \right) d\mathbf{v}_\beta, \quad (12.53)$$

where

$$U_{ij} = \int_0^{T/e^2} \frac{k_i k_j \delta(\mathbf{k}\mathbf{v}_\alpha - \mathbf{k}\mathbf{v}_\beta)}{k^4 \left| \varepsilon^l(\mathbf{k}, \omega) \right|^2_{\omega = \mathbf{k}\mathbf{v}_\alpha}} d\mathbf{k}.$$

A kinetic equation with this collision term was first obtained through the use of a rather complicated diagram technique by Balescu [14], and later by Lenard [15]. Klimontovich and Temko [16], and Silin [17] have generalized this collision term to the quantum case. In the work of Silin and Gorbunov cited above [13] the collision term (12.53) was used to develop a hydrodynamics for a highly nonisothermal plasma characterized by $T_e \gg T_i$ and it was shown that taking account of the interaction between the electrons and waves leads to transport coefficients which, under certain conditions, are considerably different from the usual ones obtained with the binary collision term. In conclusion we note that in going from Eq. (12.15) to Eq. (12.16) we have limited ourselves to nonrelativistic velocities.

If the second term in the dynamical friction force (12.15) (which corresponds to Cerenkov radiation of transverse waves) is retained it is possible to obtain a relativistic wave-interaction term (cf. [17]).

Finally, we may note that Vedenov, Velikhov, and Sagdeev [18, 19] have considered the case in which the level of excitation of the oscillations in the plasma is appreciably greater than the thermal noise level. Under these conditions binary collisions can be neglected since the particle-wave interactions predominate.

III. KINETIC EFFECTS IN HIGH TEMPERATURE PLASMAS

§ 13. Test Particle in a Medium of Infinitely Heavy Field Particles at Rest

In Part I we have derived formulas describing the behavior of a test particle α in a medium of field particles β; in particular, we found the mean rate-of-change of momentum and energy of the test particle [Eq. (6.10) and Eq. (6.13)]:

$$\frac{\overline{d\mathbf{p}_\alpha}}{dt} = -m_\alpha\left(1+\frac{m_\alpha}{m_\beta}\right)L^{\alpha/\beta}\nabla\varphi_\beta,$$
$$\frac{d\bar{\varepsilon}_\alpha}{dt} = -m_\alpha L^{\alpha/\beta}\left[\varphi_\beta+\left(1+\frac{m_\alpha}{m_\beta}\right)(\mathbf{v}\nabla\varphi_\beta)\right], \tag{13.1}$$

where

$$\varphi_\beta(\mathbf{v}) = -\frac{1}{4\pi}\int\frac{f_\beta(\mathbf{v}')}{|\mathbf{v}-\mathbf{v}'|}d\mathbf{v}'. \tag{13.2}$$

These relations can be made more meaningful if we exploit the analogy with electrostatics by introducing a "potential" φ_{an} and "field" $\mathbf{E}_{an}$ defined by the relations:

$$\left.\begin{aligned}\varphi_{an} &= -4\pi\varphi_\beta = \int\frac{f_\beta(\mathbf{v}')}{|\mathbf{v}-\mathbf{v}'|}d\mathbf{v}',\\ \mathbf{E}_{an} &= -\nabla\varphi_{an},\end{aligned}\right\} \tag{13.3}$$

by means of which Eq. (13.1) can be written in the form

$$\left.\begin{aligned} \frac{\overline{d\mathbf{p}_\alpha}}{dt} &= -q_\alpha\left(1+\frac{m_\alpha}{m_\beta}\right)\mathbf{E}_{an}, \\ \frac{\overline{d\varepsilon_\alpha}}{dt} &= -q_\alpha\left[\left(1+\frac{m_\alpha}{m_\beta}\right)\mathbf{v}\mathbf{E}_{an}-\varphi_{an}\right], \end{aligned}\right\} \tag{13.4}$$

where $q_\alpha = 4\pi\lambda(e_\alpha^2 e_\beta^2/m_\alpha)$ plays the role of the effective "charge" of the test particle α.

Let us now consider some simple examples using these expressions.

The simplest case is the one in which it is assumed that all of the field particles are at rest and have infinite mass ($m_\beta \to \infty$). In a plasma consisting of ions and electrons this will frequently be approximately true of the slowly moving heavy ions if we are concerned with the electron motion only. When $m_\beta \to \infty$ Eq. (3.4) becomes:

$$\left.\begin{aligned} \frac{\overline{d\mathbf{p}_\alpha}}{dt} &= -q_\alpha\mathbf{E}_{an}, \\ \frac{\overline{d\varepsilon_\alpha}}{dt} &= -q_\alpha[(\mathbf{v}\mathbf{E}_{an})-\varphi_{an}]. \end{aligned}\right\} \tag{13.5}$$

We note in passing that the force of dynamical friction $\mathbf{F}^{\alpha/\beta}$ vanishes when $m_\beta \to \infty$. The fixed field particles are analogous to a point charge $Q_{an} = \int f_\beta d\mathbf{v} = n_\beta$ located at the origin of coordinates in velocity space. Hence, by analogy with electrostatics

$$\varphi_{an} = \frac{n_\beta}{v}, \quad E_{an} = \frac{n_\beta}{v^2}\,\frac{\mathbf{v}}{v}. \tag{13.6}$$

Substituting these values in Eq. (13.5) we have

$$\left.\begin{aligned} \frac{\overline{d\mathbf{p}_\alpha}}{dt} &= m_\alpha\frac{\overline{d\mathbf{v}_\alpha}}{dt} = -q_\alpha\frac{n_\beta}{v^3}\mathbf{v}, \\ \frac{\overline{d\varepsilon_\alpha}}{dt} &= 0. \end{aligned}\right\} \tag{13.7}$$

The second result corresponds to the obvious fact that the energy of the test particle α cannot change in elastic collisions with infinitely heavy field particles which are at rest. The first formula is more interesting and shows that as the velocity of the test particle $\mathbf{v}$ gets larger the retarding force that acts upon it $\mathbf{F}_\alpha$ ($F_\alpha \sim 1/v^2$) gets smaller. This unusual "diminishing friction" feature is a specific property of the Coulomb interaction. The first equation in (13.7) can also be written in the form

$$\frac{d\overline{\mathbf{v}}}{dt} = -\frac{\mathbf{v}}{\tau_s^{\alpha/\beta}}, \qquad (13.8)$$

by introducing

$$\tau_s^{\alpha/\beta} = \frac{m_\alpha v^3}{n_\beta q_\alpha} = \frac{4\pi v^3}{n_\beta L^{\alpha/\beta}}.$$

The quantity $\tau_s^{\alpha/\beta}$ has the dimensions of time; physically, as is evident from the form in which the relation is written, this quantity represents the "longitudinal slowing-down time" of the test particle. In the case at hand, collisions will generally not change the absolute magnitude of the velocity $|\mathbf{v}|$ of the test particle so that Eq. (13.8) can be written

$$\frac{d\overline{\mathbf{v}}}{dt} = -\text{const}\cdot\mathbf{v}, \qquad (13.9)$$

whence

$$\overline{\mathbf{v}} = \mathbf{v}_0 e^{-\frac{t}{\tau_s}}.$$

Thus, in a time τ_s the mean velocity is reduced by the factor e = 2.7. In other cases τ_s will not have this simple meaning, but it will always characterize the order of magnitude of the time required for an appreciable change in mean velocity ($\Delta v \sim v$). In general the times τ introduced by means of Eq. (13.2) are called relaxation times [2].

The equations obtained above (13.7) do not, however, give a complete picture of the motion of a test particle. As we have seen earlier, it is necessary to introduce the picture of a continuous cloud of test particles distributed in velocity space. In the present case the velocities of the particles in the cloud do not change in absolute magnitude but the cloud spreads out over the surface of the sphere $|\mathbf{v}| = v_0$ as shown schematically in Fig. 8.

At $t_0 = 0$ the cloud is concentrated at the point $\mathbf{v}_0$; at $t = \infty$ the cloud is obviously spread out uniformly over the entire spherical surface $|\mathbf{v}| = v_0$.

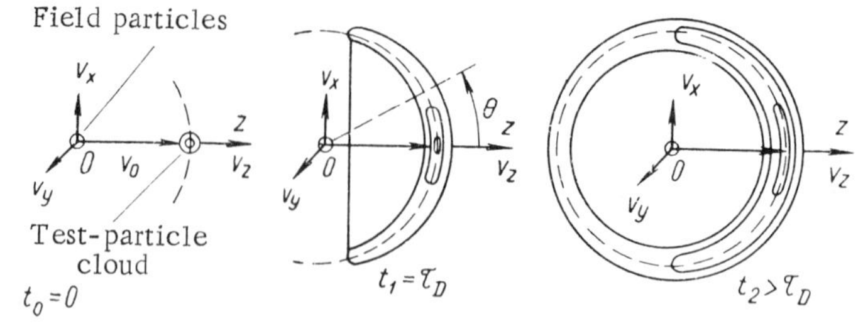

Fig. 8

We already know that the spreading of the cloud can be described completely if the following two quantities are known:

$$\left.\begin{aligned} <\Delta \mathbf{v}>^{\alpha/\beta} &= \frac{1}{m_\alpha}\frac{\overline{d\mathbf{p}_\alpha}}{dt}, \\ <\Delta v_i\,\Delta v_k>^{\alpha/\beta} &= -2L^{\alpha/\beta}\frac{\partial^2\psi_\beta}{\partial v_i\,\partial v_k}. \end{aligned}\right\} \tag{13.10}$$

The first quantity, which characterizes the momentum change, has already been analyzed. The change of energy found in Eq. (13.7) is due only to the sum of diagonal elements of the tensor $<\Delta v_i \Delta v_k>^{\alpha/\beta}$ [cf. Eq. (6.11)]. The introduction of the other components of this tensor will obviously modify the way in which the cloud expands. In order to specify this tensor completely we first compute the potential function for the field particles ψ_β. Since these particles are at rest ($\mathbf{v}_\beta = 0$) we find easily [cf. Eq. (11.8)]:

$$\psi_\beta(\mathbf{v}) = -\frac{n_\beta}{8\pi}\overline{|\mathbf{v}-\mathbf{v}_\beta|}^{(\beta)} = -\frac{n_\beta|\mathbf{v}|}{8\pi}, \tag{13.11}$$

and it then follows from Eq. (13.10) that

$$<\Delta v_i\,\Delta v_k>^{\alpha/\beta} = 2D_{ik}^{\alpha/\beta} = \frac{n_\beta L^{\alpha/\beta}}{4\pi}\left(\frac{\delta_{ik}}{v} - \frac{v_i v_k}{v^3}\right), \tag{13.12}$$

where $D_{ik}^{\alpha/\beta}$ is the diffusion tensor [cf. Eq. (10.11)].

In the coordinate system in which the z axis is along the initial velocity of the test particle $\mathbf{v} = \mathbf{v}_0$ (Fig. 8) this tensor becomes

$$\frac{d}{dt}\overline{(v-\overline{v})_i\,(v-\overline{v})_k}\,\Big|_{t=0} = 2\begin{pmatrix} D_{xx} & 0 & 0 \\ 0 & D_{yy} & 0 \\ 0 & 0 & 0 \end{pmatrix}, \tag{13.13}$$

where $D_{xx} = D_{yy} = n_\beta L^{\alpha/\beta}/8\pi v$. We use the symbols $\parallel$ and $\perp$ to denote the directions parallel and perpendicular to $\mathbf{v}_0$ (cf. Fig. 8); thus,

$$\frac{d}{dt}\overline{(\mathbf{v}-\overline{\mathbf{v}})^2_\parallel} = <(\Delta v_\parallel)^2> = 2D_{zz} = 0. \tag{13.14}$$

Evidently the thickness of the cloud in the longitudinal direction does not change; this result is obviously due to the fact that collisions do not, in general, affect $|\mathbf{v}|$ of the test particles.

In the transverse direction the dimensions of the cloud increase at a rate

$$\frac{d}{dt}\overline{(\mathbf{v}-\overline{\mathbf{v}})^2_\perp} = <(\Delta v_x)^2> + <(\Delta v_y)^2> = 2\,(D_{xx}+D_{yy}) = \frac{n_\beta L^{\alpha/\beta}}{2\pi v}.$$

This relation is conveniently written in the form

$$<(\Delta\mathbf{v})^2_\perp>^{\alpha/\beta} = \frac{v^2}{\tau_d^{\alpha/\beta}}, \tag{13.15}$$

where $\tau_d^{\alpha/\beta} = 2\pi v^3/n_\beta L^{\alpha/\beta}$.

The "deflection time" τ_d defined in this way characterizes the rate of deflection of the original motion of a particle α from its original direction (cf. Fig. 8). In the present case ($v_\beta = 0$, $m_\beta = \infty$) it is evident that this time τ_d is one-half the "longitudinal slowing-down time" τ_s introduced above [cf. Eq. (13.8)].

In addition to the two relaxation times τ_s and τ_d given above, there is an "energy-exchange time" τ_ε, which has been introduced by Spitzer [2]; this time is defined as the rate of increase of the energy spread, i.e., the expansion rate of the cloud in the longitudinal direction $<(\Delta\varepsilon)^2> = m^2v^2<(\Delta v_\parallel)^2>$:

$$\tau_\varepsilon^{\alpha/\beta} = \frac{\varepsilon^2}{<(\Delta\varepsilon)^2>} = \frac{v^2}{4<(\Delta v_\parallel)^2>} = \frac{v^2}{8D_\parallel}. \tag{13.16}$$

The quantity τ_ε is infinite in our case because particle energy does not change ($D_{||} = 0$). It is not convenient to introduce an energy relaxation time on the basis of the expression $<\Delta_\varepsilon> = -\varepsilon/\tau$ as in Eq. (13.8) because $d\bar{\varepsilon}/dt$ usually diminishes exponentially. In particular, the particle would not change its energy at $d\bar{\varepsilon}/dt = 0$, whereas an increase in energy dispersion as a whole would still occur.

§ 14. Solution of the Kinetic Equation for the Preceding Case: "Basic" Relaxation Time

We now use the kinetic equation to analyze the spreading of a cloud of test particles α as a consequence of collisions with field particles β as shown in Fig. 8. It is evident from the relation $F_i^{\alpha/\beta} = (m_\alpha^2/m_\beta)\nabla_k D_{ik}^{\alpha/\beta}$ that the force of dynamical friction $F^{\alpha/\beta}$ vanishes when $m_\beta \to \infty$; hence the kinetic equation becomes

$$\frac{\partial f_a}{\partial t} = -\operatorname{div}_v \mathbf{j}^{\alpha/\beta} = \nabla_i \left(D_{ik}^{\alpha/\beta} \nabla_k f_a\right) = \frac{n_\beta L^{\alpha/\beta}}{8\pi} \frac{\partial}{\partial v_i} \times$$

$$\times \left(\frac{v^2 \delta_{ik} - v_i v_k}{v^3} \frac{\partial f_a}{\partial v_k} \right). \qquad (14.1)$$

Here we have used the expression for the diffusion tensor $D_{ik}^{\alpha/\beta}$ for fixed β particles as given in Eq. (13.12). Introducing a spherical coordinate system v, θ, and φ with **z** axis along $\mathbf{v}_0$, we can write the operator in Eq. (14.1) in the form

$$\frac{\partial}{\partial v_i} \left(\frac{v^2 \delta_{ik} - v_i v_k}{v^3} \cdot \frac{\partial f}{\partial v_k} \right) = \nabla \left[\frac{v^2 \nabla f - \mathbf{v} (\mathbf{v} \nabla f)}{v^3} \right] =$$

$$= \frac{[\mathbf{v} \nabla]^2 f}{v^3} = \frac{\Delta_{\theta,\varphi} f}{v^3}, \qquad (14.2)$$

where

$$\Delta_{\theta,\varphi} = \frac{1}{\sin\theta} \cdot \frac{\partial}{\partial \theta} \left(\sin\theta \frac{\partial}{\partial \theta} \right) + \frac{1}{\sin^2\theta} \cdot \frac{\partial^2}{\partial \varphi^2} \qquad (14.3)$$

is the so-called angular Laplacian, whose eigenfunctions are the well-known Legendre polynomials: $\Delta_{\theta,\varphi} P_l \cos\theta = -l(l+1) P_l(\cos\theta)$ [compare Eq. (14.2) with the operator for the square of the angular momentum $\hat{\mathbf{M}} = [\hat{\mathbf{r}}\hat{\mathbf{p}}] = -i\hbar[\mathbf{r}\nabla_r]$ in quantum mechanics]. The equation that has been obtained

$$\frac{\partial f_\alpha}{\partial t} = \frac{1}{2\tau_s} \Delta_{\theta,\varphi} f_\alpha, \tag{14.4}$$

where $\tau_s = (4\pi v^3)/(n_\beta L^{\alpha/\beta})$ is the longitudinal slowing-down time introduced in Eq. (13.8), can be easily solved by separation of variables. Taking account of the initial condition

$$f_\alpha(t, \mathbf{v})|_{t=0} = n_\alpha \delta(\mathbf{v} - \mathbf{v}_0) = \delta(|\mathbf{v}| - v_0)\,\delta(1 - \cos\theta)\frac{n_\alpha}{2\pi v_0^2}, \tag{14.5}$$

and using the familiar expansion

$$\delta(1 - \cos\theta) = \sum_{l=0}^{\infty}\left(l + \frac{1}{2}\right) P_l(\cos\theta), \tag{14.6}$$

we obtain finally

$$f_\alpha(t, v, \theta) = \frac{n_\alpha}{2\pi v_0^2}\,\delta(|\mathbf{v}| - v_0)\sum_{l=0}^{\infty}\left(l + \frac{1}{2}\right) e^{-\frac{l(l+1)}{2\tau_s}t} P_l(\cos\theta). \tag{14.7}$$

When $t \to \infty$ all $l \neq 0$ terms vanish and

$$f_\alpha(t, v, \theta)|_{t=\infty} = \frac{n_\alpha}{2\pi v_0^2 \cdot 2}\,\delta(|\mathbf{v}| - v_0), \tag{14.8}$$

which corresponds to a uniform distribution over the surface of the sphere $|\mathbf{v}| = v_0$.

Using the solution in (14.7) we have

$$\left.\begin{aligned} \langle v_\parallel\rangle &= \frac{1}{n}\int v\cos\theta\, f d\mathbf{v} = v_0 e^{-t/\tau_s};\\ \langle v_\perp^2\rangle &= \frac{1}{n}\int v^2\sin^2\theta f d\mathbf{v} = \frac{2}{3}v_0^2\left(1 - e^{-3t/\tau_s}\right). \end{aligned}\right\} \tag{14.9}$$

From the last equation, when $t \ll \tau_s$ we have:

$$\langle v_\perp^2\rangle = v_0^2\frac{t}{\tau_d}, \tag{14.10}$$

where $\tau_d = \tau_s/2$.

In the general case the relaxation times τ_s, τ_d, and τ_ε defined by Eqs. (13.8), (13.5), and (13.16),

$$\tau_s = -\frac{v}{<\Delta v_\parallel>}, \quad \tau_d = \frac{v^2}{<(\Delta v)_\perp^2>}, \quad \tau_\varepsilon = \frac{v^2}{4<(\Delta v)_\parallel^2>}, \tag{14.11}$$

are not altogether clear physically. Nonetheless, they serve as convenient qualitative parameters for characterizing collisional processes in a fully ionized plasma. We will denote the longitudinal slowing-down time $\tau_s^{\alpha/\beta}$ for a test particle α computed for the simple case in which the field particles β have infinite mass and are at rest by the symbol $\tau_1^{\alpha/\beta}$ [cf. Eq.(13.8)]:

$$\tau_1^{\alpha/\beta}(\varepsilon_\alpha) = \frac{4\pi v^3}{n_\beta L^{\alpha/\beta}} = \frac{\sqrt{m_\alpha}}{\pi\sqrt{2}(e_\alpha e_\beta)^2} \cdot \frac{\varepsilon_\alpha^{3/2}}{\lambda n_\beta}, \tag{14.12}$$

where $\varepsilon_\alpha = m_\alpha v^2/2$; this quantity will be called the "basic" relaxation time. For example, the basic relaxation time for an electron moving through singly charged ions with $\varepsilon_e = 1$ keV, $n_i = 10^{15}$ cm^{-3}, and $\lambda = 15$ is

$$\tau_1^{e/i} = \frac{\sqrt{m_e}}{\pi\sqrt{2e^4}} \cdot \frac{\varepsilon_e^{3/2}}{\lambda n_i} = 0.5 \cdot 10^{-6} \text{ sec}. \tag{14.13}$$

The deflection time τ_d is one-half of this quantity: $\tau_d = \tau_1/2 = 0.25 \cdot 10^{-6}$sec.

The time τ required for a single collision of the electron with a selected ion can be estimated in rough terms as the transit time of an electron over the Debye radius D [cf. Eq. (2.4)]; under the present conditions, $D = 0.5 \cdot 10^{-3}$ cm, $v_{1\text{keV}} = 2 \cdot 10^9$ cm/sec, so that $\tau \approx D/v \approx 0.25 \cdot 10^{-12}$ sec.

Thus, an electron is deflected through an angle of about 90° in approximately $\tau_d/\tau = \tau_1/2\tau \approx 10^6$ collisions.

§ 15. Spherically Symmetric Distribution of Field Particles

Let us now assume that all of the field particles have finite mass ($m_\beta \neq \infty$) and move with the same absolute velocity $|\mathbf{v}_\beta| = V$, but that the velocity directions are distributed in spherically symmetric fashion (Fig. 9). In electrostatics this distribution would correspond to a uniformly charged spherical surface of radius V and total charge $Q = n_\beta$. Hence:

$$\mathbf{E}_{an}=\begin{cases}0 \text{ for } & v<V\\ \frac{n_\beta}{v^2}\left(\frac{\mathbf{v}}{v}\right), & v>V\end{cases}\qquad \varphi_{an}=\begin{cases}\frac{n_\beta}{V} \text{ for } & v<V,\\ \frac{n_\beta}{v}, & v>V.\end{cases}\tag{15.1}$$

Substituting these expressions in Eq. (13.4) we have:

$$\frac{d\mathbf{p}_\alpha}{dt}=-q_\alpha\left(1+\frac{m_\alpha}{m_\beta}\right)\mathbf{E}_{an}=\begin{cases}0 & \text{for } |\mathbf{v}|<V,\\ -q_\alpha\left(1+\frac{m_\alpha}{m_\beta}\right)\frac{n_\beta}{v^2}\frac{\mathbf{v}}{v} & \text{for } |\mathbf{v}|>V,\end{cases}\tag{15.2}$$

where $q_\alpha = (m_\alpha L^{\alpha/\beta})/4\pi$. Thus, the transfer of momentum exhibits a discontinuity. A test particle moving slower than the field particles ($v < V$) does not exchange momentum with the field particles since the electric field $\mathbf{E}_{an}$ inside a uniformly charged spherical surface is zero. In relaxation-time language this would mean that $\tau_s^{\alpha/\beta} = \infty$ inside the sphere. This peculiar spherical-cavity effect was first noted by Belyaev and Budker [20] and is a characteristic feature of the Coulomb interaction.

We can find the mean rate of energy loss using the second equation in (13.4), and Eq. (15.1):

$$\frac{d\bar{\varepsilon}_\alpha}{dt}=-q_\alpha\left[\left(1+\frac{m_\alpha}{m_\beta}\right)(\mathbf{v}\mathbf{E}_{an})-\varphi_{an}\right]=\begin{cases}q_\alpha\frac{n_\beta}{V} & \text{for } v<V,\\ -\frac{m_\alpha}{m_\beta}q_\alpha\frac{n_\beta}{V}, & v>V,\end{cases}\tag{15.3}$$

this parameter also exhibits a discontinuity, changing sign when $v = V$.

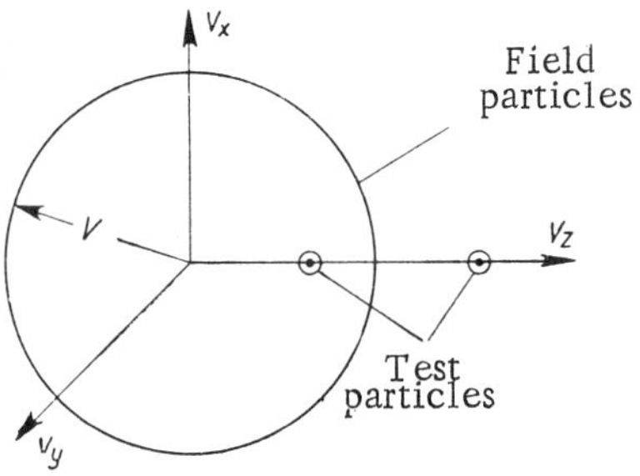

Fig. 9

By analogy with electrostatics it will be evident that in the case of an arbitrary spherically symmetric distribution of field particles $f_\beta = f_\beta(|\mathbf{v}|)$ the test particle α will not exchange momentum with any field particle for which $|\mathbf{v}_\beta| > |\mathbf{v}_\alpha|$.

The equivalent electric field $\mathbf{E}_{an}$ at the location of the field particle in velocity space $\mathbf{v}$ is easily determined from Gauss' theorem:

$$\mathbf{E}_{an} = \frac{4\pi n_\beta(\mathbf{v})}{S_v} = \frac{n_\beta(\mathbf{v})}{v^2}, \tag{15.4}$$

where $S_v = 4\pi v^2$ is the surface of the sphere of radius v and $n_\beta(\mathbf{v}) = \int_0^{v} f'_\beta d\mathbf{v}'$ is the total charge on this sphere.

Hence, for an arbitrary spherically symmetric distribution we have from Eq. (13.4)

$$\frac{\overline{d\mathbf{p}_\alpha}}{dt} = -\left(\frac{\mathbf{v}}{v}\right) q_\alpha \left(1 + \frac{m_\alpha}{m_\beta}\right) \frac{n_\beta(\mathbf{v})}{v^2}. \tag{15.5}$$

In particular, let us consider a Maxwellian distribution of field particles:

$$f_\beta(\mathbf{v}) = n_\beta \left(\frac{m_\beta}{2\pi T_\beta}\right)^{3/2} \exp\left(-\frac{m_\beta v^2}{2T_\beta}\right). \tag{15.6}$$

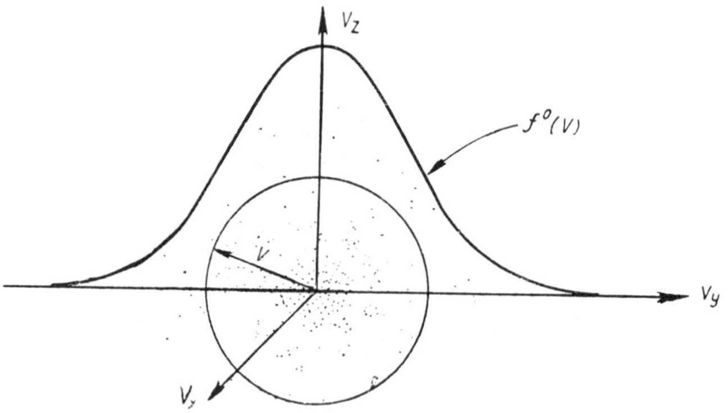

Fig. 10

In this case

$$n_\beta(\mathbf{v}) = \int_0^v f_\beta(\mathbf{v}')\,d\mathbf{v}' = n_\beta \frac{\int_0^{(v)} \exp\left(-\frac{mv^2}{2T}\right) v^2\,dv}{\int_0^\infty \exp\left(-\frac{mv^2}{2T}\right) v^2\,dv} = n_\beta \mu(\mathbf{v}_\beta^2), \tag{15.7}$$

where $\boldsymbol{v}_\beta = \mathbf{v}\sqrt{m_\beta/2T_\beta}$ is the dimensionless velocity, and we have used the notation

$$\mu(\mathbf{v}^2) = \frac{4}{\sqrt{\pi}} \int_0^{|\mathbf{v}|} e^{-t^2} t^2\,dt = \frac{2}{\sqrt{\pi}} \int_0^{\mathbf{v}^2} e^{-y}\sqrt{y}\,dy. \tag{15.8}$$

Thus

$$\mu(x) = \frac{2}{\sqrt{\pi}} \int_0^x e^{-\xi}\sqrt{\xi}\,d\xi. \tag{15.9}$$

The dimensionless function $\mu(\boldsymbol{v}^2)$ has a simple physical meaning: it is the integral over a sphere of finite radius of the Maxwellian distribution normalized to unity as shown in Fig. 10. For this reason the function $\mu(x)$ defined by the integral in (15.9) will be called the Maxwell integral. Numerical values of this integral are given in Table 1. This function approaches unity as the radius of the sphere of integration is increased, i.e., as $x \to \infty$.

Approximate expressions for $\mu(x)$ for two limiting cases are:

$$\mu(x) = \begin{cases} \frac{4x^{3/2}}{3\sqrt{\pi}}\left(1 - \frac{3}{5}x + \frac{3}{14}x^2 - \cdots\right) & (x \ll 1), \\ 1 - \frac{2}{\sqrt{\pi}} e^{-x}\sqrt{x}\left(1 + \frac{1}{2x} - \frac{1}{4x^2} + \cdots\right) & (x \gg 1). \end{cases} \tag{15.10}$$

The function $\mu(x^2)$ can be expressed in terms of the error function $\Phi(x)$:

$$\mu(x^2) = \Phi(x) - x\,\Phi'(x), \tag{15.11}$$

where

$$\Phi(x) = \frac{2}{\sqrt{\pi}} \int_0^x e^{-y^2}\,dy.$$

TABLE 1

Values of the Maxwell Integral

$$\mu(x) = \int_0^{\sqrt{x}} e^{-v^2} v^2\, dv \Bigg/ \int_0^{\infty} e^{-v^2} v^2\, dv = \frac{2}{\sqrt{\pi}} \int_0^{x} e^{-t} \sqrt{t}\, dt,$$

and Related Functions

x	$\sqrt{x}$	$\mu(x)$	$\mu'(x)$	$\frac{\mu(x)}{2x}$	$\mu + \mu' - \frac{\mu}{2x}$	$\frac{\mu}{\mu'}$	$\mu - \mu'$
0	0	0	0	0	0	0	0
0.001	0.0316	0	0.0356	0	0.0356	0	—0.0356
0.01	0.1	0.0008	0.1117	0.04	0.0725	0.0072	—0.1109
0.05	0.2236	0.0082	0.2399	0.082	0.1661	0.0342	—0.2317
0.1	0.3162	0.0222	0.3228	0.111	0.234	0.06877	—0.3006
0.2	0.4472	0.0597	0.4131	0.1493	0.3235	0.1445	—0.3534
0.4	0.6325	0.1505	0.4784	0.1881	0.4408	0.3146	—0.3279
0.6	0.7746	0.2470	0.4808	0.2058	0.5220	0.5137	—0.2338
0.8	0.8944	0.3405	0.4535	0.2128	0.5812	0.7508	—0.1130
1.0	1.0	0.4276	0.4151	0.2138	0.6289	1.0301	0.0125
1.25	1.1180	0.5247	0.3615	0.2099	0.6763	1.4515	0.1632
1.5	1.2247	0.6083	0.3083	0.2027	0.7139	1.9731	0.3000
1.75	1.3229	0.6792	0.2594	0.1941	0.7445	2.6184	0.4198
2.0	1.4142	0.7329	0.2166	0.1832	0.7663	3.3837	0.5163
2.5	1.5811	0.8280	0.1465	0.1656	0.8089	5.6519	0.6815
3.0	1.7321	0.8884	0.0974	0.1481	0.8377	9.1211	0.7910
4.0	2.0	0.9539	0.0413	0.1192	0.8760	23.0969	0.9126
5.0	2.2361	0.9814	0.0170	0.09814	0.9003	57.729	0.9644
10.0	3.1623	1.0	0.0	0.05	0.95	6180.0	1.0
20.0	4.4721	1.0	0.0	0.025	0.975		1.0
40.0	6.3246	1.0	0.0	0.0125	0.9875		1.0
60.0	7.7460	1.0	0.0	0.00833	0.992		1.0
80.0	8.9443	1.0	0.0	0.00625	0.994		1.0
100.0	10.0	1.0	0.0	0.005	0.995		1.0

Because of its simple physical meaning, it is more convenient to use the function $\mu(x)$ rather than $\Phi(x)$ as the basic function in kinetic formulas related to the Maxwellian distribution.

Chandrasekhar [1] has also introduced the function

$$G(x) = \frac{\Phi(x) - x\Phi'(x)}{2x^2} = \frac{\mu(x^2)}{2x^2}, \qquad (15.12)$$

which is tabulated in Spitzer [2].

Substituting Eqs. (15.7) and (15.12) in Eq. (15.4) we have

$$E_{an} = \frac{n_\beta(\mathrm{v})}{v^2} = \frac{n_\beta m_\beta}{T_\beta}\frac{\mu\left(\mathrm{v}_\beta^2\right)}{2\mathrm{v}_\beta^2} = \frac{n_\beta m_\beta}{T_\beta} G\left(\mathrm{v}_\beta\right). \qquad (15.13)$$

Thus the Chandrasekhar function G(x) is analogous (to within a constant) to the electric field of a system of charges distributed continuously in space in accordance with a Maxwellian distribution. Substituting Eq. (15.3) in Eq. (15.5) and writing the latter in the form similar to Eq. (13.8) we find the longitudinal slowing-down time: $\overline{d\mathbf{v}}/dt = -\mathbf{v}/\tau_s$, where

$$\tau_s^{\alpha/\beta} = -\frac{v}{<\Delta v_{\parallel}>} = \frac{v}{\left(1+\frac{m_\alpha}{m_\beta}\right) A_D \frac{m_\beta}{2T_\beta} G\left(\mathrm{v}_\beta\right)}, \qquad (15.14)$$

which is given in this form ($A_D = n_\beta L^{\alpha/\beta}/2\pi$) in Spitzer [2].

This formula can be made more meaningful through the use of the basic relaxation time introduced in the preceding section [cf. Eq. (14.12)]

$$\tau_1^{\alpha/\beta}\left(\varepsilon_\alpha\right) = \frac{4\pi v^3}{n_\beta L^{\alpha/\beta}} = \frac{\sqrt{m_\alpha}}{\pi\sqrt{2}\left(e_\alpha e_\beta\right)^2}\frac{\varepsilon_\alpha^{3/2}}{\lambda n_\beta}, \qquad (15.15)$$

which is equal to the longitudinal slowing-down time τ_s for the case of infinitely heavy field particles; we will also use the Maxwell integral $\mu(x)$ rather than the Chandrasekhar function $G(\mathbf{v}_\beta)$ [cf. Eq. (15.9)]. Thus, using the notation

$$x_\beta = \mathbf{v}_\beta^2 = \frac{m_\beta v^2}{2T_\beta} = \frac{\varepsilon_\beta(v)}{T_\beta} = \frac{m_\beta}{m_\alpha}\cdot\frac{\varepsilon_\alpha}{T_\beta}, \qquad (15.16)$$

where

$$\varepsilon_\alpha = \frac{m_\alpha v^2}{2},$$

we have finally

$$\tau_s^{\alpha/\beta}\left(\varepsilon_\alpha\right) = \frac{\tau_1^{\alpha/\beta}\left(\varepsilon_\alpha\right)}{\left(1+\frac{m_\alpha}{m_\beta}\right)\mu\left(x_\beta\right)}. \qquad (15.17)$$

This form appears to be more convenient than the form used by Spitzer, which is our Eq. (15.14).

§ 16. Runaway Electrons

As an example of the application of the formulas obtained above we consider the so-called runaway-electron effect. Runaway electrons arise because there is a critical electric field (in a plasma consisting of ions and electrons) at which the electrons are accelerated without limit.

Runaway electrons are a consequence of the "diminishing friction" feature of the Coulomb force which was noted above in §13; the phenomenon results from the fact that the frictional force exerted on the electron by the ions diminishes as the velocity increases at high velocities; asymptotically the friction goes according to the Coulomb relation $F_\alpha \sim E_{an} \sim v^{-2}$ [cf. Eq. (13.7)]. Hence, in an actual plasma in which the electron distribution is very close to Maxwellian there will necessarily be a certain number of fast electrons that will escape to the tail even in a weak electric field; these will be accelerated without limit.

However, there is a minimum electric field that is required if the entire electron gas is to be accelerated. To determine this critical field we assume, as a first approximation, that the electron velocity distribution remains Maxwellian throughout. We assume that only the mean velocity changes in the course of time, that is to say, that the position of the center of gravity of the Maxwellian distribution changes in velocity space in the manner shown schematically in Fig. 11.

Mathematically this situation is described by the statement that the electron distribution function is a "moving" Maxwellian distribution:

$$f_e(t, \mathrm{v}) = n\left(\frac{m}{2\pi T_e}\right)^{3/2} \exp\left\{-\frac{m}{2T_e}(\mathrm{v}-\mathrm{v}_0)^2\right\}. \tag{16.1}$$

In practice the ions can be assumed to be at rest and infinitely heavy. The equation of motion for the electrons then becomes [cf. Eq. (13.7)]:

$$m\frac{d\mathbf{v}}{dt} = e\mathbf{E} - q_e\frac{n_i}{v^3}\mathbf{v},$$

where

$$q_e = \frac{m_e L^{e/i}}{4\pi}. \tag{16.2}$$

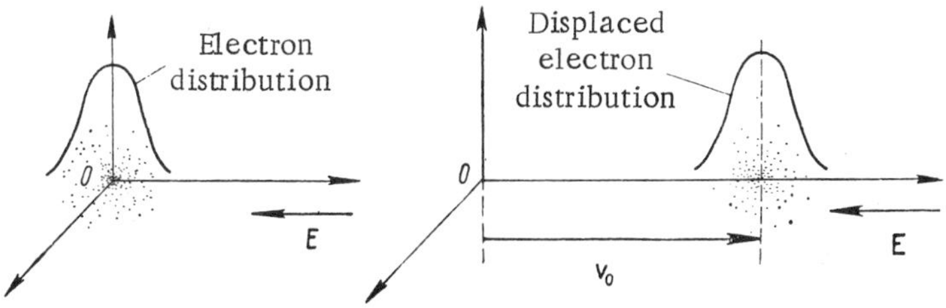

Fig. 11

Multiplying Eq. (16.2) by the function (16.1) and integrating over velocity we obtain an equation describing the motion of the electron gas as a whole:

$$n_e m \frac{d\mathbf{v}_0}{dt} = e n_e \mathbf{E} + n_e \mathbf{F}^{e/i}_{\text{ef. fr.}}, \tag{16.3}$$

where

$$n_e \mathbf{F}^{e/i}_{\text{ef. fr.}} = -q_e n_i \int \frac{\mathbf{v}}{v^3} f_e(t, v)\, d\mathbf{v}. \tag{16.4}$$

Here, by definition the quantity $n_e \mathbf{F}^{e/i}_{\text{ef. fr.}}$ represents the total force of friction acting on all n_e electrons enclosed in 1 cm^3 while the quantity $\mathbf{F}^{e/i}_{\text{ef. fr.}}$ represents the effective force of friction per electron. For reasons of simplicity we assume that the ions are singly charged. Then $n_e = n_i$ for a neutral plasma.

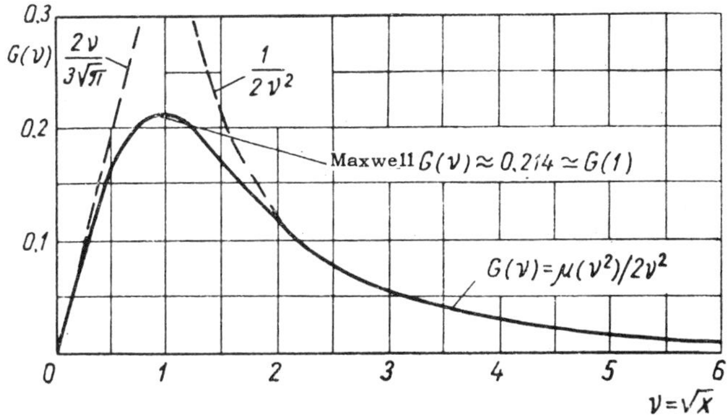

Fig. 12

The integral in Eq. (16.4) is computed easily. However, for our purposes instead of computing this integral directly it will be found more useful to exploit the obvious fact that the force $\mathbf{F}^{e/i}_{ef.fr}$ must equal the average force exerted on an ion by the electrons (since action must equal reaction). Transforming to the coordinate system in which the electron gas as a whole is at rest we can regard the ion as a test particle moving with a velocity $\mathbf{v}_0$ through a medium consisting of electrons distributed with a Maxwellian distribution; the formulas obtained in §15 can then be applied. Starting from this consideration and using Eqs. (13.4) and (15.13) we find

$$\mathbf{F}^{e/i}_{\text{ef. fr.}} = -\mathbf{F}_i = q_i\left(1 + \frac{m_i}{m_e}\right)\mathbf{E}_{\text{an}}(-\mathbf{v}_0)\,|_{m_i\to\infty} =$$

$$= -\frac{e^2\lambda}{D^2}G(\mathbf{v}_e). \tag{16.5}$$

Here $D = (T_e/4\pi ne^2)^{1/2}$ is the Debye radius and $G(\nu) = \mu(\nu^2)/2\nu^2$ is the Chandrasekhar function [cf. Eq. (15.12)].

A curve of this function is shown in Fig. 12 and numerical values are given in Table 1.

The peak of the Chandrasekhar function is located at the point $\nu \approx 1$ and is equal to 0.214. Hence, when the electrons as a whole are described by a moving Maxwellian distribution [cf. Eq. (16.1)] the effective force of friction acting on a single electron due to collisions with ions cannot, in general, be greater than

$$\max F^{e/i}_{\text{ef. fr.}} = -\frac{e^2\lambda}{D^2}\,0.214. \tag{16.6}$$

Substituting Eq. (16.5) in Eq. (16.3) we can write

$$nm\frac{dv_0}{dt} = enE + nF^{e/i}_{\text{ef. fr.}} = en\left[E - \frac{e\lambda}{D^2}G\left(\mathbf{v}_e^0\right)\right], \tag{16.7}$$

where $\nu_e^0 = v_0\sqrt{m_e/2T_e}$. Thus, in view of Eq. (16.6) we see that the electron gas as a whole will be accelerated if the electric field in the plasma exceeds the critical value

$$E_{\text{cr}} = \frac{e\lambda}{D^2}\,0.214 \approx \frac{e}{D^2}; \tag{16.8}$$

in practice (since $\lambda \approx 10$) this is equal to the field of an elementary charge at a distance equal to the Debye radius D. For example, when $T_e = 1$ keV, $n = 10^{15}$ cm^{-3}, and $\lambda = 15$

$$D \approx 10^{-3}\,\text{cm}, \qquad E_{cr} \approx 1\ \text{V/cm}. \tag{16.9}$$

Although this field is relatively small in absolute value it should be noted that it is difficult to produce a field of even this small a magnitude inside a fully ionized plasma, which has a very high electrical conductivity and therefore tends to cancel out all internal electric fields.

We have noted that an exponentially small fraction of the electrons will escape to the tail even in weak fields. An exhaustive investigation of runaway electrons has been made by Dreicer [21], who carried out a numerical integration of the kinetic equation describing $f_e(t, \mathbf{v})$.

§ 17. Maxwellian Distribution of Field Particles. Relaxation Time

Now let us assume that the field particles β are distributed according to a Maxwellian distribution; we wish to compute all quantities characterizing the behavior of a test particle α in this "medium." It will be found convenient to express all functions in terms of the Maxwell integral and its derivative which have been introduced above:

$$\mu(x) = \frac{2}{\sqrt{\pi}} \int_0^x e^{-t} \sqrt{t}\, dt, \quad \mu'(x) = \frac{d\mu(x)}{dx} = \frac{2}{\sqrt{\pi}} e^{-x} \sqrt{x}. \tag{17.1}$$

In particular, introducing the following convenient notation for the dimensionless velocity and its square:

$$\mathbf{v}_\beta = \mathbf{v}\sqrt{m_\beta/2T_\beta}, \quad x_\beta = \mathbf{v}_\beta^2 = \frac{m_\beta v^2}{2T_\beta}, \tag{17.2}$$

we write the Maxwellian distribution in the form

$$f_\beta(\mathbf{v}) = n_\beta \left(\frac{m_\beta}{2\pi T_\beta}\right)^{3/2} e^{-\mathbf{v}_\beta^2} = n_\beta \left(\frac{m_\beta}{2T_\beta}\right)^{3/2} f^0(\mathbf{v}_\beta), \tag{17.3}$$

where $f^0(\mathbf{v}_\beta)$ is a dimensionless function normalized to unity:

$$f^0(\mathbf{v}) = \frac{e^{-v^2}}{\pi^{3/2}} = \frac{\Phi'(v)}{2\pi} = \frac{\mu'(v^2)}{2\pi v}, \qquad \int f^0(\mathbf{v})\,d\mathbf{v} = 1. \quad (17.4)$$

Here $v = |\mathbf{v}|$, while $\Phi(v)$ is the error function [cf. Eq. (15.11)]: we must first find the potential function $\psi_\beta(\mathbf{v})$ and then use it to express all the other quantities. Using Eqs. (17.2) and (17.3) we have

$$\psi_\beta(\mathbf{v}) = \frac{-1}{8\pi}\int |\mathbf{v} - \mathbf{v}'|\,f_\beta(\mathbf{v}')\,d\mathbf{v}' = n_\beta\sqrt{\frac{2T_\beta}{m_\beta}}\,\psi^0(\mathbf{v}_\beta). \quad (17.5)$$

Here $\psi^0(\mathbf{v})$ is a dimensionless function

$$\psi^0(\mathbf{v}) = -\frac{1}{8\pi}\int |\mathbf{v} - \mathbf{v}'|\,f^0(\mathbf{v}')\,d\mathbf{v}', \quad (17.6)$$

which is defined by the relation

$$\Delta_v^2\psi^0(\mathbf{v}) = f^0(\mathbf{v}) = \frac{e^{-v^2}}{\pi^{3/2}}, \quad (17.7)$$

which is analogous to the relation $\Delta_v^2\psi_\beta(\mathbf{v}) = f_\beta(\mathbf{v})$ for the original functions [cf. Eq. (6.5)].

The integral on the right side of Eq. (17.6) can be computed easily by making the substitution $\mathbf{v}' = \mathbf{v} + \mathbf{r}$ and transforming to the spherical coordinate system r, θ, φ with z axis along $\mathbf{v}$:

$$\psi^0(\mathbf{v}) = -\frac{1}{8\pi}\int |\mathbf{v} - \mathbf{v}'|\,\frac{e^{-v'^2}}{\pi^{3/2}}\,d\mathbf{v}' = -\frac{1}{8\pi^{5/2}}\int |\mathbf{r}|\,e^{-(\mathbf{v}+\mathbf{r})^2}\,d\mathbf{r} =$$

$$= -\frac{1}{4\pi^{3/2}}\int_0^\infty r^3\,dr\int_0^\pi e^{-(v^2+r^2+2vr\cos\theta)}\sin\theta\,d\theta. \quad (17.8)$$

Integrating with respect to θ and transforming the remaining terms we obtain finally

$$\psi^0(\mathbf{v}) = -\frac{1}{16\pi}\left[\Phi'(v) + \left(2v + \frac{1}{v}\right)\Phi(v)\right] =$$

$$= -\frac{1}{8\pi v}\left[(x+1)\,\mu'(x) + \left(x + \frac{1}{2}\right)\mu(x)\right]_{x=v^2}. \quad (17.9)$$

The primes denote derivatives with respect to the argument so that

$$\Phi'(v) = \frac{d}{dv}\,\Phi(v), \quad \mu'(v^2) = \frac{d}{d(v^2)}\,\mu(v^2) = \frac{d\mu(v^2)}{2v\,dv}. \quad (17.10)$$

For reference purposes we also give the values of the derivatives of the function $\psi^0(\mathbf{v})$:

$$\frac{d\psi^0(v)}{dv} = -\frac{1}{8\pi}\left(\mu + \mu' - \frac{\mu}{2x}\right)_{x=v^2}, \quad \frac{d^2\psi^0(v)}{dv^2} = -\frac{\mu}{8\pi v^3},$$

$$\Delta_v\psi^0(v) = -\frac{\mu+\mu'}{4\pi v}, \quad \Delta_v\Delta_v\psi^0(v) = \frac{\mu'}{2\pi v} = f^0(v). \quad (17.11)$$

Here we are to understand $\mu \equiv \mu(v^2)$.

We have now computed the potential function $\psi_\beta(\mathbf{v})$ [cf. Eqs. (17.5) and (17.9)]. It is spherically symmetric, like the original Maxwellian distribution. The diffusion tensor and the spreading of the cloud of test particles α can now be found from Eqs. (6.7) and (11.3) by computing the second derivatives of the function $\psi_\beta(\mathbf{v})$:

$$\langle \Delta v_i \Delta v_\kappa \rangle^{\alpha/\beta} = 2D_{i\kappa}^{\alpha/\beta} = -2L^{\alpha/\beta}\frac{\partial^2\psi_\beta(\mathbf{v})}{\partial v_i \partial v_\kappa} =$$

$$= -\left[2L^{\alpha/\beta}n_\beta\left(\frac{m_\beta}{2T_\beta}\right)^{1/2}\right]\frac{\partial^2\psi^0(\mathbf{v})}{\partial v_i \partial v_\kappa}\bigg|_{\mathbf{v}=\mathbf{v}_\beta}, \quad (17.12)$$

where

$$\frac{\partial^2\psi^0(|\mathbf{v}|)}{\partial v_i \partial v_\kappa} = \frac{\partial}{\partial v_i}\left(\frac{v_\kappa}{v}\frac{d\psi^0(v)}{dv}\right) =$$

$$= \delta_{i\kappa}\frac{d\psi^0}{v\,dv} + \frac{v_i v_\kappa}{v^2}\left(\frac{d^2\psi^0}{dv^2} - \frac{\partial\psi^0}{v\,dv}\right). \quad (17.13)$$

The tensor that has been obtained will be diagonal in the coordinate system in which the z axis is in the direction of the test particle velocity $\mathbf{v}$

$$\langle \Delta v_i \Delta v_\kappa \rangle^{\alpha/\beta} =$$

$$= 2\begin{pmatrix} D_{xx} & 0 & 0 \\ 0 & D_{yy} & 0 \\ 0 & 0 & D_{zz} \end{pmatrix} = \begin{pmatrix} \langle(\Delta v_x)^2\rangle & 0 & 0 \\ 0 & \langle(\Delta v_y)^2\rangle & 0 \\ 0 & 0 & \langle(\Delta v_z)^2\rangle \end{pmatrix}, \quad (17.14)$$

where

$$<(\Delta v_x)^2> = <(\Delta v_y)^2> = -K\left(\frac{d\psi^0(\nu)}{\nu d\nu}\right)_{\nu=\nu_\beta}$$

and

$$<(\Delta v_z)^2 = -K\left(\frac{d^2\psi^0(\nu)}{d\nu^2}\right)_{\nu=\nu_\beta}. \tag{17.15}$$

Here we use the letter K to denote the constant factor appearing in the square brackets in Eq. (17.12).

Substituting the values of the derivatives of $\psi^0(\nu)$ from Eq. (17.11) we then have

$$\begin{aligned} <(\Delta v)^2_\perp> &= <(\Delta v_x)^2> + <(\Delta v_y)^2> = \\ &= \frac{K}{4\pi\nu_\beta}\left(\mu + \mu' - \frac{\mu}{2x_\beta}\right), \\ <(\Delta v)^2_\parallel> &= <(\Delta v_z)^2> = \frac{K}{4\pi\nu_\beta}\cdot\frac{\mu}{2x_\beta}, \end{aligned} \tag{17.16}$$

where $x_\beta = \nu_\beta^2$. It is now possible to find the deflection time

$$\tau_d^{\alpha/\beta} = \frac{v^2}{<(\Delta v)^2_\perp>} = \frac{\tau_1^{\alpha/\beta}}{2\left(\mu + \mu' - \frac{\mu}{2x_\beta}\right)} \tag{17.17}$$

and the energy-exchange time

$$\tau_\varepsilon^{\alpha/\beta} = \frac{v^2}{4<(\Delta v_\parallel)^2>} = \frac{\tau_1^{\alpha/\beta}}{4\mu/x_\beta}. \tag{17.18}$$

For completeness we also write down the longitudinal slowing-down time $\tau_s^{\alpha/\beta}$ defined in the preceding section:

$$\tau_s^{\alpha/\beta} = -\frac{v}{<\Delta v_\parallel>} = \frac{\tau_1^{\alpha/\beta}}{\left(1 + \frac{m_\alpha}{m_\beta}\right)\mu(x_\beta)}. \tag{17.19}$$

In these formulas τ_1 is the basic relaxation time defined by Eq. (15.15). We will introduce a number of relaxation times below. To avoid confusion it should be noted that any formula of the kind $df/dt = g$, which contains a time derivative, can be written in the form

$$\frac{df}{dt} = g \rightarrow \frac{df}{dt} = \frac{f}{\tau_f}, \tag{17.20}$$

where

$$\tau_f = \frac{f}{g},$$

defines the "relaxation time" of the quantity "f" as τ_f. Hence the relaxation time can be defined somewhat arbitrarily. In the case of a spherically symmetric distribution, however, a knowledge of the three characteristic times τ_s, τ_d, and τ_ε is equivalent to a knowledge of the quantities $\langle \Delta v_i \rangle$ and $\langle \Delta v_i \Delta v_k \rangle$ and suffices for a full statistical description of the behavior of the test particle α. By virtue of Eq. (6.9) these characteristic times are related by the differential expressions

$$-\frac{1}{\tau_s^{\alpha/\beta}} = \left(1 + \frac{m_\alpha}{m_\beta}\right) \frac{\partial}{\partial (v^2)} \left(\frac{v^2}{\tau_d^{\alpha/\beta}} + \frac{v^2}{4\tau_\varepsilon^{\alpha/\beta}}\right). \tag{17.21}$$

Knowing the function $\psi_\beta(\mathbf{v})$ we can now find the second potential function $\varphi_\beta(\mathbf{v})$:

$$\varphi_\beta(\mathbf{v}) = \Delta_v \psi_\beta(\mathbf{v}) = n_\beta \sqrt{\frac{m_\beta}{2T_\beta}} \Delta_{\mathrm{v}} \psi^0(\mathbf{v})\,|_{\mathrm{v}=\mathrm{v}_\beta} =$$

$$= -\frac{1}{4\pi} n_\beta \sqrt{\frac{m_\beta}{2T_\beta}} \frac{\mu(\mathrm{v}_\beta^2) + \mu'(\mathrm{v}_\beta^2)}{\mathrm{v}_\beta} = -\frac{1}{4\pi} \varphi_{\mathrm{an}}. \tag{17.22}$$

These can now be used to determine the potential and field analogous to the corresponding electrostatic quantities:

$$\varphi_{\mathrm{an}} = \frac{n_\beta}{v} [\mu(x_\beta) + \mu'(x_\beta)], \quad \mathbf{E}_{\mathrm{an}} = -\nabla_v \varphi_{\mathrm{an}} = \frac{n_\beta}{v^2} \mu(x_\beta) \left(\frac{\mathbf{v}}{v}\right). \tag{17.23}$$

At large "distances" where $\mu(x_\beta) \rightarrow 1$ these become "Coulomb" expressions. We have given the field E_{an} in an earlier section [cf. Eq. (15.13)]. Using

Eq. (17.23) we can compute the energy-loss rate of the test particle [cf. Eq. (13.4)]:

$$\frac{d\varepsilon_\alpha}{dt} = -q_\alpha\left[\left(1+\frac{m_\alpha}{m_\beta}\right)(\mathbf{v}\mathbf{E}_{an}) - \varphi_{an}\right] =$$

$$= -\frac{2\varepsilon_\alpha}{\tau_1^{\alpha/\beta}}\left[\frac{m_\alpha}{m_\beta}\mu(x_\beta) - \mu'(x_\beta)\right], \tag{17.24}$$

where $x_\beta = m_\beta v^2/2T_\beta = (m_\beta/m_\alpha)\cdot(\varepsilon_\alpha/T_\beta)$. The derivative $d\varepsilon/dt$ changes sign at the point x_β^* where $(m_\alpha/m_\beta)\mu(x_\beta^*) - \mu'(x_\beta^*) = 0$, i.e., where

$$\frac{m_\beta}{m_\alpha} = \frac{\mu(x_\beta^*)}{\mu'(x_\beta^*)}. \tag{17.25}$$

Equations (17.24) and (17.25) will be investigated in greater detail in §19.

§ 18. Plane Flux in an Equilibrium Plasma

We now consider an example that exhibits the usefulness of the relaxation-time concept as a means of obtaining a clearer description of various plasma phenomena. Assume that a uniform plane flux of particles α moves through a quasi-neutral plasma consisting of electrons and singly charged ions distributed according to a Maxwellian distribution with temperature $T = T_e = T_i$. The masses will be denoted by $m \equiv m_e$ and $M \equiv m_i$, respectively, without subscripts. The particles in the flux can be electrons or ions of the same species as the field particles. The results can be generalized to the case ($T_e \neq T_i$; $e_i \neq e_e$; $m_\alpha \neq m$; M) without difficulty; we will, in fact, generalize the results below.

Since the plane flux is equivalent to an ensemble of test particles α it is sufficient to consider three basic processes experienced by the particles in the flux: momentum transfer, particle deflection, and energy exchange. These processes are described by the following three equations:

$$\frac{dp_\alpha}{dt} = m_\alpha\left(<\Delta\mathbf{v}>^{\alpha/e} + <\Delta\mathbf{v}>^{\alpha/i}\right) =$$

$$= m_\alpha\left(\frac{\mathbf{v}}{\tau_s^{\alpha/e}} + \frac{\mathbf{v}}{\tau_s^{\alpha/i}}\right) = -\frac{m_\alpha\mathbf{v}}{\tau_s^\alpha}; \tag{18.1}$$

$$\frac{d}{dt}\overline{(\Delta v_\perp)^2_\alpha} = <(\Delta v)^2_\perp>^{\alpha/e} + <(\Delta v)^2_\perp>^{\alpha/i} =$$

$$= \frac{v^2}{\tau_d^{\alpha/e}} + \frac{v^2}{\tau_d^{\alpha/i}} = \frac{v^2}{\tau_d^\alpha}; \tag{18.2}$$

$$\frac{d}{dt}\overline{(\Delta\varepsilon)^2_\alpha} = (m_\alpha v)^2 \,(<(\Delta v_\parallel)^2>^{\alpha/e} +$$

$$+ <(\Delta v_\parallel)^2>^{\alpha/i}) = \frac{\varepsilon^2}{\tau_\varepsilon^{\alpha/e}} + \frac{\varepsilon^2}{\tau_\varepsilon^{\alpha/i}} = \frac{\varepsilon^2}{\tau_\varepsilon^\alpha}. \tag{18.3}$$

Here we have introduced "total" relaxation times τ_s^α, τ_d^α, and τ_ε^α related to the "partial" relaxation times $\tau_s^{\alpha/\beta}$, $\tau_d^{\alpha/\beta}$, and $\tau_\varepsilon^{\alpha/\beta}$ by expressions of the form

$$\frac{1}{\tau^\alpha} = \sum_\beta \frac{1}{\tau^{\alpha/\beta}} = \frac{1}{\tau^{\alpha/e}} + \frac{1}{\tau^{\alpha/i}}. \tag{18.4}$$

The "partial" relaxation times, i.e., the slowing-down time, the deflection time, and the energy-exchange time, are expressed by Eqs. (17.17), (17.18), and (17.19),respectively:

$$\tau_s^{\alpha/\beta} = \frac{\tau_1^{\alpha/\beta}}{\left(1 + \frac{m_\alpha}{m_\beta}\right)\mu}, \quad \tau_d^{\alpha/\beta} = \frac{\tau_1^{\alpha/\beta}}{2\left(\mu + \mu' - \frac{\mu}{2x_\beta}\right)}, \tag{18.5}$$

$$\tau_\varepsilon^{\alpha/\beta} = \frac{\tau_1^{\alpha/\beta}}{4\mu/x_\beta},$$

where we have used the notation

$$\mu = \mu(x_\beta), \; x_\beta = \frac{\varepsilon_\beta}{T_\beta} = \frac{m_\beta}{m_\alpha}\cdot\frac{\varepsilon_\alpha}{T_\beta}, \quad \tau_1^{\alpha/\beta} = \frac{\sqrt{m_\alpha}}{\pi\sqrt{2}\,e_\alpha^2 e_\beta^2}\cdot\frac{\varepsilon_\alpha^{3/2}}{\lambda n_\beta}. \tag{18.6}$$

We shall find it sufficient to consider four kinds of collision: e/i, e/e, i/i, and i/e.

In the first example we assume that the energy of the flux particles ε_α is fixed and so large that the inequality $x_\beta \gg 1$ holds for all cases. Under these consitions

$$\tau_1^{\alpha/\beta} \sim \sqrt{m_\alpha}, \; \mu(x_\beta) = 1, \; \mu'(x_\beta) \cong 0. \tag{18.7}$$

TABLE 2. Relaxation Time for $x_\beta \gg 1$

τ	α/β			
	e/i	e/e	i/i	i/e
$\tau_s^{\alpha/\beta}$	«1»	0,5	$0{,}5\sqrt{\frac{M}{m}}$	$\sqrt{\frac{m}{M}}$
$\tau_d^{\alpha/\beta}$	0,5	0,5	$0{,}5\sqrt{\frac{M}{m}}$	$0{,}5\sqrt{\frac{M}{m}}$
$\tau_\varepsilon^{\alpha/\beta}$	$\left(\frac{\varepsilon}{4T}\right)\frac{M}{m}$	$\left(\frac{\varepsilon}{4T}\right)$	$\left(\frac{\varepsilon}{4T}\right)\sqrt{\frac{M}{m}}$	$\left(\frac{\varepsilon}{4T}\right)\sqrt{\frac{m}{M}}$
Condition of applicability	$\varepsilon_e \gg \frac{m}{M}T$	$\varepsilon_e \gg T$	$\varepsilon_i \gg T$	$\varepsilon_i \gg \frac{M}{m}T$

TABLE 3. Relaxation Time for $\varepsilon_\alpha = (^3\!/_2)T$

τ	α/β			
	e/i	e/e	i/i	i/e
$\tau_s^{\alpha/\beta}$	«1»	0.82	$0.82\sqrt{\frac{M}{m}}$	$0.73\frac{M}{m}$
$\tau_d^{\alpha/\beta}$	0.5	0.70	$0.70\sqrt{\frac{M}{m}}$	$0.54\frac{M}{m}$
$\tau_\varepsilon^{\alpha/\beta}$	$0.37\frac{M}{m}$	0.62	$0.62\sqrt{\frac{M}{m}}$	$0.27\frac{M}{m}$

Thus, by referring all quantities to the electron-ion basic relaxation time $\tau_1^{e/i}$ we can obtain the values of τ_s, τ_d, and τ_ε for the various cases (Table 2).

In the last line of Table 2 we indicate the conditions of applicability, which follow from the requirement $x_\beta = (\varepsilon/T)(m_\beta/m_\alpha) \gg 1$.

It is evident that under these conditions an electron flux is retarded only twice as much by the electrons as by the ions ($\tau_s^{e/e} = 0.5\tau_s^{e/i}$) whereas an ion flux is retarded almost exclusively by the electrons [$\tau_s^{i/e} = 2(m/M)\tau_s^{i/i}$]. Furthermore, the electron slowing-down and deflection occur almost simultaneously ($\tau_s^e = 4/3\tau_d^e$) whereas the ions are slowed down with almost no deflection [$\tau_s^i = 4(m/M)\tau_d^i$].

As another example we take the energy of the flux particles to be equal to the mean thermal energy of the plasma particles, i.e., $\varepsilon_\alpha = (3/2)T$. Using the values of the functions $\mu(x)$ and $(u + \mu' - \mu/2x)$ given in Table 1 and the expansion (15.10) needed for the case i/e we obtain τ_s, τ_d, and τ_ε (Table 3).

It is evident that all relaxation times divide into three orders: ~1, $\sim\sqrt{M/m}$, and ~M/m. The corresponding processes will be distinguished by the process rates that we use in §20 in our general analysis of plasma relaxation effects. Comparison of the data in Table 3 with those of Table 2 shows that in the case of an electron flux the relative efficiency of e/i and e/e collisions is almost the same; for ions the situation is completely different. In the first case a "superfast" ion for which $\varepsilon \gg (M/m)T$ is retarded by and exchanges energy with the electrons almost exclusively:

$$\tau_{s,\,\varepsilon}^{i/e} \sim \frac{m}{M}\,\tau_{s,\,\varepsilon}^{i/i} \qquad (18.8)$$

(however, $\tau_d^{i/e} = \tau_d^{i/i}$); on the other hand, in the case of a "thermal" ion with $\varepsilon = (3/2)T$ the interactions are primarily with ions:

$$\tau_{s,\,d,\,\varepsilon}^{i/i} \sim \sqrt{\frac{m}{M}}\,\tau_{s,\,d,\,\varepsilon}^{i/e}\,. \qquad (18.9)$$

We note that the longitudinal slowing-down times $\tau_s^{i/e}$ and $\tau_s^{i/i}$ become comparable at an energy $\varepsilon_i^{(s)}$ such that

$$\varepsilon_i^{(s)} = T\left(\frac{9\pi}{4}\,\frac{M}{m}\right)^{1/3}. \qquad (18.10)$$

The energy-exchange times $\tau_\varepsilon^{i/\beta}$ become comparable at almost the same energy:

$$\varepsilon_i^{(\varepsilon)} = T\left(\frac{9\pi}{16}\frac{M}{m}\right)^{1/3} = 0.63\varepsilon_i^{(s)}, \tag{18.11}$$

$$\left(\tau_\varepsilon^{i/i} = \tau_\varepsilon^{i/e}\right).$$

For hydrogen ions (M/m = 1823) and deuterium ions (M/m = 3646) we have, respectively,

$$\left.\frac{\varepsilon_i^{(s)}}{T}\right|_{\mathrm{H}} = 24, \qquad \left.\frac{\varepsilon_i^{(s)}}{T}\right|_{\mathrm{D}} = 2^{1/3}\left.\frac{\varepsilon_i^{(s)}}{T}\right|_{\mathrm{H}} = 30. \tag{18.12}$$

Thus $\varepsilon_i^{(\varepsilon)} = 0.63\,\varepsilon_i^{(s)}$.

§ 19. Energy Transfer

We continue the analysis of a plane flux of electrons or ions of the same species as the field ions and now investigate the question of energy transfer. In contrast with momentum, which is always transferred from the moving flux to the plasma (dp/dt < 0) (so that the flux must be retarded) the energy change of the flux particles, described by Eq. (17.24),

$$\frac{d\bar{\varepsilon}_\alpha}{dt} = -\frac{2\varepsilon_\alpha}{\tau_1^{\alpha/e}}\left[\frac{m_\alpha}{m}\mu - \mu'\right]_{x_e} - \frac{2\varepsilon_\alpha}{\tau_1^{\alpha/i}}\left[\frac{m_\alpha}{M}\mu - \mu'\right]_{x_i}, \tag{19.1}$$

can have either sign; a flux of fast particles will heat the plasma whereas a flux of slow particles (in the limit, fixed particles) will cool the plasma. For this reason, before discussing the relative energy transfer for various kinds of collisions, we must decide the direction of transfer. It follows from Eq. (17.24) that this direction is determined by the sign of the expression

$$\frac{m_\alpha}{m_\beta}\mu(x_\beta) - \mu'(x_\beta) = \begin{cases} >0, & \text{for} \quad \alpha \to \beta, \\ <0, & \text{for} \quad \beta \to \alpha, \end{cases} \tag{19.2}$$

which vanishes at the point x_β^* given by Eq. (17.25):

$$\frac{m_\beta}{m_\alpha} = \frac{\mu(x_\beta^*)}{\mu'(x_\beta^*)}, \tag{19.3}$$

where

$$\overset{*}{x}_\beta = \frac{m_\beta}{m_\alpha} \cdot \frac{\overset{*}{\varepsilon}_\alpha}{T_\beta}. \qquad (19.4)$$

Using Table 1 and the approximate expressions for $\mu(x)$ [cf. Eq. (15.10)] we find

$$\frac{\mu(x)}{\mu'(x)} = \begin{cases} \frac{2}{3}x & (\text{for } x \ll 1), \\ 1 & (\text{for } x \cong 1, \text{ more precisely, } 0.98), \\ \frac{e^x}{2}\sqrt{\frac{\pi}{x}} & (\text{for } x \gg 1). \end{cases} \qquad (19.5)$$

Then, using Eq. (19.3) we can find the critical energy $\overset{*}{\varepsilon}_\alpha$ at which the direction of energy transfer changes sign (Table 4).

The low value of $\overset{*}{\varepsilon}_\alpha/T$ in Table 4 for the case e/i is due to the specific properties of the Coulomb interaction.

TABLE 4. Critical Energy

α/β	e/i	e/e	i/i	i/e
$\frac{\overset{*}{\varepsilon}_\alpha}{T}$	$\approx \frac{m}{M} \ln\left(\frac{M}{m}\frac{10}{3}\right) \approx \frac{1}{210}$ for H; $\frac{1}{390}$ for D	1	1	3/2

TABLE 5. Energy Transfer Time τ_t for $\varepsilon = 2T$

α/β	e/i	e/e	i/i	i/e
$\tau_\Pi^{\alpha/\beta}$	$0.5\,\frac{M}{m}$	«1»	$\sqrt{\frac{M}{m}}$	$0.94\,\frac{M}{m}$

It should be noted that the indicated critical energy is nothing like the mean thermal energy of the particles in the medium (3/2) T_β, as might be expected at first glance. This is a result of the fact that a plane flux of particles with this energy acts as though it were in "instantaneous" equilibrium, $(d\varepsilon/dt)_{t=0} = 0$, with the medium; this is not complete thermodynamic equilibrium, for which a Maxwellian distribution would be required (cf. § 20). If ε_α exceeds the value ε^*_α shown in Table 4 the energy is transferred from the flux α to the plasma β; if, on the other hand $\varepsilon_\alpha < \varepsilon^*_\alpha$,

$$\left(\frac{d\bar{\varepsilon}_\alpha}{dt}\right)^{\alpha/\beta} = \begin{cases} <0 \ (\text{for} \ \ \varepsilon_\alpha > \varepsilon^*_\alpha), \\ \ \ 0 \ (\text{for} \ \ \varepsilon_\alpha = \varepsilon^*_\alpha), \\ >0 \ (\text{for} \ \ \varepsilon_\alpha < \varepsilon^*_\alpha). \end{cases} \tag{19.6}$$

Returning to Eq. (19.1) we consider a case of practical importance: this is the case of an ion flux for which $\varepsilon_\alpha \gg (3/2)T$. According to Table 4 the incident flux heats the ions and electrons in the plasma; to gain an idea of the heating rates we must compare the relative magnitude of the first (i/i) and second (i/e) terms in the equation:

$$\frac{d\varepsilon_\alpha}{dt} = -\frac{2\varepsilon}{\tau_1^{i/i}}\left[\mu\left(\frac{\varepsilon}{T}\right) - \mu'\left(\frac{\varepsilon}{T}\right)\right] - \\ -\frac{2\varepsilon}{\tau_1^{i/e}}\left[\frac{M}{m}\mu\left(\frac{m\varepsilon}{MT}\right) - \mu'\left(\frac{m\varepsilon}{MT}\right)\right]. \tag{19.7}$$

Since the ions are singly charged we have $\tau_1^{i/i} = \tau_1^{i/e}$. When $\varepsilon \gg (3/2)T$ we can make the approximation $\mu - \mu' \approx 1$ in the first (i/i) term. Two cases are possible. If the energy ε_α is so large that $\varepsilon_\alpha \gg (M/m)\,T$, then

$$\frac{d\varepsilon_\alpha}{dt} = -\frac{2\varepsilon_\alpha}{\tau_1^{i/i}} - \frac{2\varepsilon_\alpha}{\tau_1^{i/e}}\frac{M}{m}. \tag{19.8}$$

In this case the electrons are heated more than the ions (by a factor M/m). In the other case, when

$$\frac{\varepsilon}{T} \gg \frac{3}{2}, \quad \frac{m}{M}\frac{\varepsilon}{T} \ll 1, \tag{19.9}$$

we expand $\mu(x)$ and $\mu'(x)$ in the (i/e) term, thus obtaining

$$\frac{d\varepsilon_\alpha}{dt} = -\frac{2\varepsilon}{\tau_1^{i/i}} - \frac{2\varepsilon}{\tau_1^{i/e}}\left[\left(\frac{\varepsilon}{T} - \frac{3}{2}\right)\left(\frac{m\varepsilon}{MT}\right)^{1/2}\frac{4}{3\sqrt{\pi}}\right], \quad (19.10)$$

and, if $(\varepsilon/T - 3/2) \sim 1$ the flux heats the ions primarily.

The ions and electrons are heated at equal rates when the expression in square brackets in Eq. (19.10) equals unity, that is to say, when the energy ε_α^{**} is approximately

$$\left.\frac{\varepsilon_\alpha^{**}}{T}\right|_{\alpha=i} = \left(\frac{9\pi}{16}\cdot\frac{M}{m}\right)^{1/3}, \quad (19.11)$$

which gives 14.7 for hydrogen ions H(M = 1823 m) and 18.5 for deuterium ions D.

The critical energy ε_i^{**} is evidently the same as the energy $\varepsilon_i^{(\varepsilon)}$ found in the preceding section from the condition $\tau_\varepsilon^{i/i} = \tau_\varepsilon^{i/e}$. This situation results from the judicious choice of the coefficients in the definition of $\tau_\varepsilon^{\alpha/\beta}$, which characterizes the longitudinal spreading of the ensemble cloud. Using the general definition of τ [Eq. (17.20)] we can introduce the specific energy transfer time τ_t on the basis of Eq. (17.24):

$$\frac{d\bar{\varepsilon}_\alpha}{dt} = -\frac{\varepsilon_\alpha}{\tau_t^{\alpha/\beta}}, \quad (19.12)$$

where

$$\tau_t^{\alpha/\beta} = \frac{\tau_1^{\alpha/\beta}(\varepsilon_\alpha)}{2\left[\frac{m_\alpha}{m_\beta}\mu - \mu'\right]_{x_\beta}}; \quad (19.13)$$

at the critical points (19.5) $\varepsilon_\alpha = \varepsilon_\alpha^*$ (cf. Table 4), where $d\bar{\varepsilon}/dt = 0$, this time would become infinite. If these points are eliminated together with the points in their immediate vicinity the energy-transfer time that we have introduced $\tau_t^{\alpha/\beta}$ is of the same order of magnitude as the energy-exchange time $\tau_\varepsilon^{\alpha/\beta}$ at thermal energies. In Table 5 we give values of τ_t for ε = 2T (rather than (3/2) T, which is the critical energy for (i/e) collisions, cf. Table 4).

It is evident from Table 5 that τ_t for ε = 2T is approximately the same as $\tau_\varepsilon^{\alpha/\beta}$ for ε = (3/2)T (cf. Table 3).

Great interest attaches to the question of energy transfer from nuclear-reaction products to the plasma particles that serve as the fuel in projected thermonuclear reactors. For example, consider a deuterium plasma in which the following reactions occur:

$$d + d \to \mathrm{T} + p + 4.0 \text{ Mev},$$
$$d + d \to \mathrm{He}^3 + n + 3.3 \text{ Mev}.$$

The charged particles p, T, and He^3 formed in these reactions have the following energies:

$$\varepsilon_p^0 = 3 \text{ Mev}, \quad \varepsilon_T^0 = 1 \text{ Mev}, \quad \varepsilon_{\mathrm{He}^3}^0 = 0.83 \text{ Mev}. \qquad (19.14)$$

In particular, the most energetic of these, the proton (p), colliding with deuterons (i = d) and electrons (e) in the plasma will lose its energy in accordance with Eq. (19.12):

$$\frac{d\varepsilon_p}{dt} = -\frac{\varepsilon_p}{\tau_t^{p/d}} - \frac{\varepsilon_p}{\tau_t^{p/e}} = -\frac{\varepsilon_p}{\tau_t^{(p)}}, \qquad (19.15)$$

where, correspondingly, we have

$$\left.\begin{aligned} \tau_t^{p/d} &= \frac{\tau_1^{p/d}}{\mu\left(2\frac{\varepsilon}{T}\right) - 2\mu'\left(2\frac{\varepsilon}{T}\right)} \\ &\text{and} \\ \tau_t^{p/e} &= \frac{\tau_1^{p/e}}{2\frac{M}{m}\mu\left(\frac{m\varepsilon}{MT}\right) - 2\mu'\left(\frac{m\varepsilon}{MT}\right)}. \end{aligned}\right\} \qquad (19.16)$$

To be definite let us assume a plasma temperature $T = T_i = T_e = 50$ keV. At the initial time, $\varepsilon_p^0 = 3$ MeV $= 3 \cdot 10^3$ keV so that

$$\frac{\varepsilon}{T} = \frac{3000}{50} = 60 \text{ and } \frac{m\varepsilon}{MT} = \frac{60}{1823} = \frac{1}{30}. \qquad (19.17)$$

Using the asymptotic form for $\mu(x)$ in one case and the series expansion in the other [cf. Eq. (15.10)] we have

$$\tau_t^{p/d} = \tau_1^p(\varepsilon)$$

and

$$\tau_t^{p/e} = \left[\frac{\sqrt{\pi}/4}{\frac{2\varepsilon}{3T} - 1} \left(\frac{MT}{m\varepsilon} \right)^{1/2} \right] \tau_1^p(\varepsilon) = \frac{\tau_1^p(\varepsilon)}{16}, \qquad (19.18)$$

where $\tau_1^p(\varepsilon) = \tau_1^{p/d} = \tau_1^{p/e}$. For example, with $n = 10^{13}$ cm^{-3}, $\varepsilon = 3$ MeV, $\lambda = 20$, this basic time is [cf. Eq. (18.6)]:

$$\tau_1^p = 285 \text{ sec } (!). \qquad (19.19)$$

Thus, at the beginning of the process the energy is transferred to the electrons sixteen times more rapidly than to the deuterons. The electron and deuteron heating rates become approximately equal ($\tau_t^{p/d} = \tau_t^{p/e}$) at a proton energy ε_p^{**} at which [cf. Eq. (19.18)]

$$\frac{\sqrt{\pi}/4}{\frac{2\varepsilon^{**}}{3T} - 1} \left(\frac{MT}{m\varepsilon^{**}} \right)^{1/2} \cong 1, \qquad (19.20)$$

whence

$$\varepsilon_p^{**} \approx \left(\frac{9\pi M}{64m} \right)^{1/3} T = 9.3T = 0.5 \text{ MeV}.$$

Below this energy, $\varepsilon_p < 0.5$ MeV, the proton heat goes primarily to the deuterons. For example, when $\varepsilon_p = 2T = 100$ keV, from Eqs. (19.16) and (19.18) we find:

$$\tau_t^{p/d} = 1.15\tau_1^p$$

and

$$\tau_t^{p/e} = \left(\frac{9\pi M}{32m} \right)^{1/2} \tau_1^p = 40\tau_1^p, \qquad (19.21)$$

where, for the values $n = 10^{13}$ cm^{-3}, $\varepsilon = 0.1$ MeV, $\lambda = 20$ here we find $\tau_1^p = 1.7$ sec in contrast with the results found in Eq. (19.19).

§ 20. Approach to Equilibrium in a Two-Component Plasma

Table 3, giving the relaxation times which we have formulated in §18 for the case $\varepsilon_\alpha = (3/2)T$, yields proper orders of magnitude when $\varepsilon_\alpha \sim T$.

Under these conditions this table can be used for qualitative analysis of the approach to equilibrium in a plasma which is initially in a nonequilibrium state. According to Table 3 all relaxation processes proceed in three stages.

In the first stage ($\tau \sim$ "1") e/i collisions lead to the establishment of an isotropic velocity distribution for the electrons. This process has been considered in §14. Simultaneously, e/e collisions gradually force the electrons to an equilibrium Maxwellian distribution. This randomization process is considered below.

In the second stage ($\tau \sim \sqrt{M/m}$) i/i collisions force the ions to relax to an isotropic equilibrium distribution.

In the third stage ($\tau \sim M/m$), because of i/e and e/i collisions the electrons and ions (which have reached Maxwellian states separately, but may still have different temperatures T_e and T_i) are brought to comparable temperatures.

To treat the last process we use Eq. (19.11)

$$\frac{d\varepsilon_\alpha}{dt} = -\frac{2\varepsilon_\alpha}{\tau_1^{\alpha/\beta}\{\varepsilon_\alpha\}}\left[\frac{m_\alpha}{m_\beta}\mu(x_\beta) - \mu'(x_\beta)\right],$$

where

$$\tau_1\{\varepsilon\} \sim \varepsilon^{3/2} \tag{20.1}$$

describes the change in the energy of a test particle α in a medium of Maxwellian particles β. Assuming that the test particles α are also characterized by a Maxwellian distribution with temperature T_α we can simply average Eq. (20.1) over this last distribution. Then, assuming that the operation of averaging over the Maxwellian distribution of (α) particles is nothing more than integration over dx_α (where $x_\alpha = \varepsilon_\alpha/T_\alpha$) with a weight factor $\mu'(x_\alpha)$, and that $\tau_1\{\varepsilon\} \sim \varepsilon^{3/2}$, we have

$$\frac{3}{2}\cdot\frac{dT_\alpha}{dt} = -\frac{2T_\alpha}{\tau_1^{\alpha/\beta}\{T_\alpha\}}\int_0^\infty \frac{x_\alpha}{x_\alpha^{3/2}}\left[\frac{m_\alpha}{m_\beta}\mu(x_\beta) - \mu'(x_\beta)\right]\mu'(x_\alpha)\,d_\alpha. \tag{20.2}$$

Here $x_\beta = (m_\beta T_\alpha/m_\alpha T_\beta)\,x_\alpha$. Substituting the expression for $\mu'(x)$ and integrating once by parts we have

$$\frac{3}{2}\cdot\frac{dT_\alpha}{dt}=-\frac{2T_\alpha}{\tau_1^{\alpha/\beta}\{T_\alpha\}}\int_0^\infty\left[\frac{m_\alpha}{m_\beta}\mu(x_\beta)-\mu'(x_\beta)\right]\frac{2}{\sqrt{\pi}}e^{-x_\alpha}dx_\alpha=$$

$$=-\frac{2T_\alpha}{\tau_1^{\alpha/\beta}\{T_\alpha\}}\frac{4m_\beta T_\alpha}{\pi m_\alpha T_\beta}\int_0^\infty e^{-(x_\alpha+x_\beta)}\left(\frac{m_\alpha}{m_\beta}-\frac{1}{2x_\beta}+1\right)\sqrt{x_\beta}\,dx_\alpha=$$

$$=-\frac{2T_\alpha}{\tau_1^{\alpha/\beta}\{T_\alpha\}}\frac{2}{\sqrt{\pi}}\frac{m_\alpha}{m_\beta}\frac{1-\dfrac{T_\beta}{T_\alpha}}{\left(\dfrac{m_\alpha}{m_\beta}\dfrac{T_\beta}{T_\alpha}+1\right)^{3/2}}=$$

$$=-\frac{m_\alpha 4}{m_\beta\sqrt{\pi}}\frac{T_\alpha-T_\beta}{\tau_1^{\alpha/\beta}\left\{T_\alpha+\dfrac{m_\alpha}{m_\beta}T_\beta\right\}}. \tag{20.3}$$

The quantity $\tau_1^{\alpha/\beta}\{\varepsilon_\alpha\}$ is the basic relaxation time [cf. Eq. (18.6)] in which the argument ε_α is replaced by $T_\alpha + (m_\alpha/m_\beta)T_\beta$. In particular, it is evident from this formula that

$$n_\alpha\frac{dT_\alpha}{dt}=-n_\beta\frac{dT_\beta}{dt} \tag{20.4}$$

as required by energy conservation.

Equation (20.3) was first obtained by Spitzer [22] and, independently, by Kogan [23]. This equation can also be written in the form given by Spitzer

$$\frac{dT_\alpha}{dt}=\frac{T_\beta-T_\alpha}{\tau_T^{\alpha/\beta}}, \tag{20.5}$$

by introducing the equipartition time for the temperatures

$$\tau_T^{\alpha/\beta}=\frac{3\sqrt{\pi}}{8}\frac{m_\beta}{m_\alpha}\tau_1^{\alpha/\beta}\left\{T_\alpha+\frac{m_\alpha}{m_\beta}T_\beta\right\}. \tag{20.6}$$

Then, assuming that α and β can refer to two Maxwellian groups of like particles it is easily shown that

$$\tau_T^{e/e}:\tau_T^{i/i}:\tau_T^{e/i}:\tau_T^{i/e}=\text{"1"}:\sqrt{\frac{M}{m}}:\frac{M}{m}:\frac{M}{m}. \tag{20.7}$$

when $T_\alpha \sim T_\beta$.

Comparing Eq. (20.7) with the last line of Table 3 we see that when $T_\alpha \sim T_\beta$,

$$\tau_T^{\alpha/\beta} \sim \tau_\varepsilon^{\alpha/\beta}(\varepsilon)\big|_{\varepsilon\sim T}, \tag{20.8}$$

which provides further physical justification for using the terminology energy-exchange time for the quantity τ_ε introduced in Eq. (13.16).

Now let us now consider in somewhat greater detail the thermalization process mentioned above, i. e., the establishment of a Maxwellian distribution for (α) particles as a result of like-particle (α/α) collisions. This process is described by the kinetic equation [Eqs. (11.12) and (11.15)], with the subscript α omitted:

$$\frac{\partial f}{\partial t} = -\operatorname{div}_v \mathbf{j} = L\left(f^2 - \frac{\partial^2 f}{\partial v_i \partial v_K} \cdot \frac{\partial^2 \psi}{\partial v_i \partial v_K}\right), \tag{20.9}$$

where

$$f(t, \mathbf{v}) = \Delta_v^2 \psi \quad \text{and} \quad L = \lambda\left(\frac{4\pi e^2}{m}\right)^2.$$

This equation can not be solved in general form. However, from the requirement that the entropy must increase in Eq. (20.9) it is clear that any specified initial distribution of particles $f(0, \mathbf{v})$ must gradually transform into a Maxwellian distribution $f^0(\mathbf{v})$, for which the entropy is a maximum.

Because of energy conservation the temperature of the final distribution is determined by the mean energy associated with the relative motion of the particles at the initial time

$$\frac{3}{2} T = \bar{\varepsilon}_{\mathrm{rel}} = \frac{1}{n} \int \frac{m}{2} (\mathbf{v} - \langle \mathbf{v} \rangle_0)^2 f(0, \mathbf{v})\, d\mathbf{v}. \tag{20.10}$$

Writing Eq. (20.9) in dimensionless form we conclude that equilibrium is established in a characteristic time of order

$$\tau_1^{\alpha/\alpha}(T) = \frac{\sqrt{m_\alpha}}{\pi \sqrt{2}\, e_\alpha^4} \, \frac{T^{3/2}}{\lambda n_\alpha}, \tag{20.11}$$

where $T = (2/3)\bar{\varepsilon}_{\mathrm{rel}}$, in accordance with Table 3.

As an example, following Kogan [23] we consider the rate of equilibration of longitudinal and transverse temperatures for a gas of charged particles in a magnetic field; the initial distribution is given by

$$f(0,\ \mathbf{v}) = \text{const}\ e^{-\frac{mv_{\|}^2}{2T_{\|}} - \frac{mv_{\perp}^2}{2T_{\perp}}} \tag{20.12}$$

The constant here is determined from normalization conditions: const = $n(m/2\pi)^{3/2}\, T_1(T_{\|})^{1/2}$. Taking the magnetic field along the z axis so that $v_{\|} = v_z$ and $v_{\perp}^2 = v_x^2 + v_y^2$, we have

$$\bar{\varepsilon}_{\|} = \frac{\overline{mv_z^2}}{2} = \frac{T_{\|}}{2},\quad \bar{\varepsilon}_{\perp} = \frac{\overline{mv_{\perp}^2}}{2} = \frac{T_{\perp}}{2} + \frac{T_{\perp}}{2} = T_{\perp}. \tag{20.13}$$

Making use of the kinetic equation (20.9) and energy conservation, it then follows that

$$\frac{dT_{\perp}}{dt} = -\frac{d}{dt}\frac{T_{\|}}{2} = -\frac{1}{n}\int \frac{mv_z^2}{2}\cdot\frac{\partial f}{\partial t}\, d\mathbf{v} = -\frac{m}{n}\int v_z j_z\, d\mathbf{v}. \tag{20.14}$$

To compute $\mathbf{j}_z$ in the present case it is simplest to write the flux in the Landau form [cf. Eq. (11.18)]:

$$j_z^{\alpha/\alpha} = \frac{L^{\alpha/\alpha}}{8\pi}\int U_{zi}\left(f\frac{\partial f'}{\partial v_i'} - f'\frac{\partial f}{\partial v_i}\right) d\mathbf{v}', \tag{20.15}$$

where $U_{zi} = \delta_{zi}/u - u_z u_i/u^3$ and $\mathbf{u} = \mathbf{v} - \mathbf{v}'$. Using Eq. (20.12) for $f(0, \mathbf{v})$ we have

$$\frac{\partial f}{\partial v_x} = -\frac{m}{T_{\perp}} v_x f,\quad \frac{\partial f}{\partial v_y} = -\frac{m}{T_{\perp}} v_y f,\quad \frac{\partial f}{\partial v_z} = -\frac{m}{T_{\|}} v_z f, \tag{20.16}$$

and similarly for the primed quantities. Substituting these expressions in Eq. (20.15) and carrying out the summation over the subscript i we have

$$U_{zi}\left(f\frac{\partial f'}{\partial v_i'} - f'\frac{\partial f}{\partial v_i}\right) = mff'\left(U_{zx}\frac{u_x}{T_{\perp}} + \right.$$

$$\left. + U_{zy}\frac{u_y}{T_{\perp}} + U_{zz}\frac{u_z}{T_{\|}}\right) = m\frac{T_{\perp} - T_{\|}}{T_{\perp}T_{\|}} ff' \frac{u_z u_{\perp}^2}{u^3}. \tag{20.17}$$

Then, from Eqs. (20.14) and (20.15)

$$\frac{dT_\perp}{dt} = -\frac{d}{dt}\frac{T_\parallel}{2} = -2\pi e^4\lambda \frac{1}{n}\frac{T_\perp - T_\parallel}{T_\perp T_\parallel}\int\int ff' \frac{v_z u_z u_\perp^2}{u^3}\, d\mathbf{v}\, d\mathbf{v}'. \tag{20.18}$$

The integral containing the function $f(0, \mathbf{v})$ specified by Eq. (20.12) can be computed exactly (cf. [23]) but we shall limit ourselves to the case of small temperature differences $|T_\perp - T_\parallel| \ll T_\parallel$. Introducing the notation

$$\Delta T = T_\perp - T_\parallel, \qquad T = \frac{2}{3}(\bar{\varepsilon}_\parallel + \bar{\varepsilon}_\perp) = \frac{T_\parallel}{3} + \frac{2T_\perp}{3}, \tag{20.19}$$

and keeping the first-order term in ΔT we see that the integral in Eq.(20.18) need not be computed with the function $f(0, \mathbf{v})$ from Eq. (20.12); instead it can be computed with the Maxwellian distribution

$$f_m^0(\mathbf{v}) = n\left(\frac{m}{2\pi T}\right)^{3/2} e^{-\frac{mv^2}{2T}}. \tag{20.20}$$

Here, for convenience we have used the particle mass m as a subscript on the function. We now introduce as new variables of integration the velocity of the center-of-mass of the two particles, and the relative velocity,

$$\mathbf{V} = \frac{\mathbf{v} + \mathbf{v}}{2} \text{ and } \mathbf{u} = \mathbf{v} - \mathbf{v}'. \tag{20.21}$$

We assume that with this substitution the following relations hold:

$$\mathbf{v} = \mathbf{V} + \frac{1}{2}\mathbf{u}, \qquad \mathbf{v}' = \mathbf{V} - \frac{1}{2}\mathbf{u},$$
$$\mathbf{v}^2 + \mathbf{v}'^2 = 2\mathbf{V}^2 + \frac{1}{2}\mathbf{u}^2, \tag{20.22}$$

and furthermore that

$$f_m^0(\mathbf{v})\, f_m^0(\mathbf{v}')\, d\mathbf{v}\, d\mathbf{v}' = f_{2m}^0(\mathbf{V})\, f_{\frac{m}{2}}^0(\mathbf{u})\, d\mathbf{V}\, d\mathbf{u}, \tag{20.23}$$

where 2m is the total mass and (m/2) is the reduced mass; then we can write

$$\int\int f_m^0(\mathbf{v})\, f_m^0(\mathbf{v}')\, \frac{v_z u_z u_\perp^2}{u^3}\, d\mathbf{v}\, d\mathbf{v}' =$$

$$= \int\int f_{2m}^0(\mathbf{V})\, f_{\frac{m}{2}}^0(\mathbf{u}) \left(\mathbf{V}_z + \frac{u_z}{2} \right) \frac{u_z u_\perp^2}{u^3}\, d\mathbf{V}\, d\mathbf{u} =$$

$$= n \int f_{\frac{m}{2}}^0(\mathbf{u})\, \frac{u_z^2 u_\perp^2}{2u^3}\, d\mathbf{u} = \frac{n}{2} \left(\overline{\cos^2\theta \sin^2\theta}\right) \int f_{\frac{m}{2}}^0(\mathbf{u})\, u\, d\mathbf{u} =$$

$$= \frac{n}{2} \left(\frac{2}{15} \right) n \sqrt{\frac{16T}{\pi m}} \qquad (20.24)$$

Substituting this value in Eq. (20.18) finally we find

$$\frac{dT_\perp}{dt} = -\frac{1}{2} \cdot \frac{dT_\parallel}{dt} = -\frac{T_\perp - T_\parallel}{\frac{15}{8} \sqrt{2\pi}\, \tau_1(T)} . \qquad (20.25)$$

Evidently the temperature difference vanishes exponentially:

$$\frac{d\Delta T}{dt} = 3 \frac{dT_\perp}{dt} = -\frac{\Delta T}{\tau}, \text{ whence } \Delta T(t) = \Delta T(0)\, e^{-\frac{t}{\tau}} \qquad (20.26)$$

The temperature difference is reduced by a factor e = 2.7 in a time

$$\tau = \frac{5}{8} \sqrt{2\pi}\, \tau_1(T) = 1.56 \tau_1(T), \qquad (20.27)$$

where $\tau_1(T)$ is the basic relaxation time, in which the argument has been replaced by T [cf. Eq. (20.11)].

LITERATURE CITED

1. S. Chandrasekhar, Principles of Stellar Dynamics, University of Chicago Press, Chicago, 1942.
2. L. Spitzer, Jr., Physics of Fully Ionized Gases, Interscience, New York, 1962.
3. Rosenbluth, MacDonald, and Judd, Phys. Rev., 107, 1 (1957).
4. B. A. Trubnikov, ZhETF, 34, 1341 (1958), Soviet Phys. JETP, 7, 926 (1958).
5. Chapman and Cowling, Mathematical Theory of Nonuniform Gases, Cambridge University Press, 1953.
6. L. D. Landau, ZhETF (J. Exptl. Theoret. Phys. USSR), 7, 203 (1937).
7. Cohen, Spitzer, and Routley, Phys. Rev., 80, 230 (1937).
8. N. N. Bogolyubov, Dynamical Problems in Statistical Physics (in Russian) Gostekhizdat, Moscow, 1946.
9. B. B. Kadomtsev, ZhETF, 33, 151 (1957), Soviet Phys. JETP, 6, 117 (1958).
10. V. I. Kogan, DAN, 135, 1374 (1960), Soviet Phys. Doklady, 5, 1316 (1960).
11. V. P. Silin and A. A. Rukadze, Electromagnetic Properties of Plasma and Plasma-like Media (in Russian) Gosatomizdat, Moscow, 1961.
12. Gasiorowicz, Neuman, and Riddell, Phys. Rev., 110, 922 (1956).
13. V. P. Silin and L. M. Gorbunov, DAN, 145, 1265 (1962), Soviet Phys. Doklady, 7, 751 (1963).
14. S. Balescu, Phys. Fluids, 3, 52 (1960).
15. A. Lenard, Ann. Phys., 3, 90 (1960).
16. Yu. L. Klimontovich and S. V. Temko, ZhETF, 33, 132 (1957), Soviet Phys. JETP, 6, 102 (1958).
17. V. P. Silin, ZhETF, 40, 1768 (1961), Soviet Phys. JETP, 13, 1244 (1961).
18. Vedenov, Velikhov, and Sagdeev, Nuclear Fusion 1, 82 (1961).
19. A. A. Vedenov, Atomnaya energiya (Atomic Energy) 12, 5 (1962).
20. S. T. Belyaev and G. I. Budker, DAN, 107, 807 (1956), Soviet Phys. Doklady, 1, 218 (1957).
21. H. Dreicer, Proceedings of the 2nd International Conference on the Peaceful Uses of Atomic Energy, Geneva, 1958, Vol. 31, p. 57.
22. L. Spitzer, Jr., Monthly Notices Roy. Astron. Soc., 110, 396 (1940).
23. V. I. Kogan, Plasma Physics and the Problem of Controlled Thermonuclear Reactions (translated from the Russian) Pergamon Press, New York, 1959, Vol. I.

TRANSPORT PROCESSES IN A PLASMA

S. I. Braginskii

§ 1. Transport Equations

The state of an ionized gas (plasma) can be specified by the distribution functions $f_a(t, \mathbf{r}, \mathbf{v})$ that characterize each particle component. These functions describe the density of particles of species a at time t at the point $\mathbf{r}$, $\mathbf{v}$ in phase space; the quantity $f_a(t, \mathbf{r}, \mathbf{v})\, d\mathbf{r} d\mathbf{v}$ then represents the number of particles in the six-dimensional volume element $d\mathbf{r}\, d\mathbf{v}$. In the simplest case the plasma consists of electrons (a = e) and a single ion species (a = i); in more complicated cases the plasma may contain several ion species in addition to neutral particles (a = n) such as atoms, molecules, excited atoms, and so on. The behavior of the ionized gas is described by a system of kinetic equations (Boltzmann equations) which carry the distribution functions forward in time (cf. for example [1, 2, 3, 39]):

$$\frac{\partial f_a}{\partial t} + \frac{\partial}{\partial x_\beta}(v_\beta f_a) + \frac{\partial}{\partial v_\beta}\left(\frac{F_{a\beta}}{m_a} f_a\right) = C_a. \tag{1.1}$$

Here, $\mathbf{F}_a$ is the force exerted at point $\mathbf{r}$ on a particle of species a and velocity $\mathbf{v}$; m_a is the particle mass. For particles that carry a charge e_a and are located in an electric field $\mathbf{E}$ and a magnetic field $\mathbf{B}$

$$\mathbf{F}_a = e_a\mathbf{E} + \frac{e_a}{c}[\mathbf{v}\mathbf{B}]. \tag{1.2}$$

The kinetic equation does not take account of thermal fluctuations. The function $f_a(t, \mathbf{r}, \mathbf{v})$ that appears in Eq. (1.1) represents a smoothed density averaged over a volume containing a large number of particles.

The force $\mathbf{F}_a$ on the left side of the kinetic equation is also a "smoothed" macroscopic force and represents an average over a volume containing many particles and over times long compared with the appropriate time of flight; the same is true of the fields $\mathbf{E}$ and $\mathbf{B}$. The force $\mathbf{F}_a$ does not take account of rapidly fluctuating microfields and microforces that arise when particles come very close to each other. These effects (which we will simply call collisions) are taken into account by the collision term C_a on the right side of the equation. The problem of separating the self-consistent field from the microfields is an extremely complicated one and has been treated by many authors, for example, Kadomtsev [37].

Particles of species a can collide with each other and with other particle species. Thus, one must actually write

$$C_a = \sum_b C_{ab}(f_a, f_b), \tag{1.3}$$

where C_{ab} gives the change per unit time in the distribution function for particles of species a due to collisions with particles of species b. The C_{ab} terms can describe either elastic or inelastic collisions.* The so-called Boltzmann collision term, which describes elastic collisions, is given in the Appendix. In the case of elastic collisions between charged particles we shall use the collision term in the relatively simple form first given by Landau [11]. The collision term for inelastic collisions is extremely complicated and cannot always be written in explicit form. Inelastic collisions will be neglected in this review.

Certain properties of the collision term can be deduced even when its explicit form is not known. If processes that convert particles of one species into another, (ionization, dissociation, etc.) are neglected the collision terms satisfy the conditions

$$\int C_{ab}\, d\mathbf{v} = 0; \tag{1.4}$$

$$\int m_a \mathbf{v} C_{aa}\, d\mathbf{v} = 0; \tag{1.5}$$

$$\int \frac{m_a v^2}{2} C_{aa}\, d\mathbf{v} = 0. \tag{1.6}$$

*For example, excited atoms are treated as a different "species" from the unexcited atoms and are assigned a different subscript. We also note that Eq. (1.1) does not make explicit reference to the rotational degrees of freedom, which can be important, for example, in dealing with molecules. In order to take these rotational effects into account it would be necessary to introduce a distribution function that would depend on the total rotational moment of the particle **M** (in addition to **r** and **v**). Formally it can be assumed that **M** and the internal degrees of freedom are taken into account by the subscript a; actually, however, taking account of rotation is extremely complicated and will not done here. We shall simply assume that appropriate averages have been taken over the rotational variable.

When multiplied by $d\mathbf{r}$ the integral in (1.4) represents the change in the total number of particles of species a in a volume element $d\mathbf{r}$ due to collisions with particles of species b; in elastic collisions, however, no such change occurs and the integral vanishes. The integrals in (1.5) and (1.6) denote the change in momentum and energy, respectively, for particles of species a resulting from collisions between like particles; since momentum and energy are conserved in such collisions these integrals must also vanish. Similarly, the following relations hold for elastic collisions between different particle species, a and b, in which the total momentum and energy are conserved:

$$\int m_a \mathbf{v} C_{ab}\, d\mathbf{v} + \int m_b \mathbf{v} C_{ba}\, d\mathbf{v} = 0; \tag{1.5'}$$

$$\int (m_a v^2/2)\, C_{ab}\, d\mathbf{v} + \int (m_b v^2/2)\, C_{ba}\, d\mathbf{v} = 0. \tag{1.6'}$$

It is a general result of statistical mechanics that the particles of any gas in thermal equilibrium are characterized by a Maxwellian velocity distribution f^0:

$$f^0 = \frac{n}{(2\pi T/m)^{3/2}}\, e^{-\frac{m}{2T}(\mathbf{v}-\mathbf{V})^2}. \tag{1.7}$$

The subscript a has been omitted; n is the density, i. e., the number of particles of a given species per unit volume; T is the temperature of the gas; $\mathbf{V}$ is the velocity of the gas as a whole. The temperature will always be expressed in energy units so that the Boltzmann constant will not appear in the formulas. When the Maxwellian distribution is used the left side of the kinetic equation vanishes. Thus, regardless of the actual form of the collision term, when a Maxwellian distribution is used the collision term must vanish. Furthermore, if the distribution function changes only by virtue of collisions, it can be shown that no matter what the initial conditions are the distribution function must approach a Maxwellian in the course of time; this is a statement of the well-known H-theorem of Boltzmann, a proof of which can be found in [1, 2, 3]. The approach of the distribution function to a Maxwellian by means of collisions is called relaxation. Relaxation generally occurs in a time of the order of the mean time between collisions.

The description of a plasma by means of distribution functions is a rather detailed one and may not always be necessary. It is frequently sufficient to describe a plasma more simply in terms of certain average quantities, for example, the number of particles of a given species per unit volume

$$n_a(t, \mathbf{r}) = \int f_a(t, \mathbf{r}, \mathbf{v})\, d\mathbf{v}, \tag{1.8}$$

the mean velocity of these particles

$$\mathbf{V}_a(t, \mathbf{r}) = \frac{1}{n_a} \int \mathbf{v} f(t, \mathbf{r}, \mathbf{v})\, d\mathbf{v} = \langle \mathbf{v} \rangle_a, \tag{1.9}$$

and the mean energy or temperature. In thermal equilibrium, i. e., when the distribution function is a Maxwellian, the mean kinetic energy per particle $m\langle v^2\rangle/2$ can be related simply to the temperature; furthermore, in the coordinate system in which $V = 0$ the simple relation $m\langle v^2\rangle/2 = (3/2)T$ holds. If the gas is not in thermal equilibrium, it is possible to define a temperature by introducing the quantity $m\langle v^2\rangle/3$ in the coordinate system in which $V = 0$. The temperature defined in this way is a function of t and **r** and other local macroscopic characteristics of the gas

$$T_a(t, \mathbf{r}) = \frac{1}{n_a} \int \frac{m_a}{3} (\mathbf{v} - \mathbf{V}_a)^2 f_a(t, \mathbf{r}, \mathbf{v})\, d\mathbf{v} = \frac{m_a}{3} \langle (\mathbf{v} - \mathbf{V}_a)^2 \rangle. \tag{1.10}$$

In general, the macroscopic parameters n_a, $\mathbf{V}_a$, and T_a in a nonequilibrium state are different for different particle species. In some cases, these parameters, which have simple physical meanings, are supplemented by other more complicated parameters.

The equations that describe the behavior of the macroscopic parameters, which are called the transport equations, can be obtained from the kinetic equation. Equation (1.1) is multiplied by 1, $m_a\mathbf{V}$, and $m_a v^2/2$, respectively, and integrated over velocity. Carrying out this procedure and using Eq. (1.4) we find

$$\frac{\partial n}{\partial t} + \operatorname{div}(n\mathbf{V}) = 0, \tag{1.11}$$

$$\frac{\partial}{\partial t}(mnV_\alpha) + \frac{\partial}{\partial x_\beta}(mn\langle v_\alpha v_\beta\rangle) - en\left(E_\alpha + \frac{1}{c}[\mathbf{VB}]_\alpha\right) = \int mv_\alpha C\, d\mathbf{v}, \tag{1.12}$$

$$\frac{\partial}{\partial t}\left(\frac{mn}{2}\langle v^2\rangle\right) + \operatorname{div}\left(\frac{mn}{2}\langle v^2\mathbf{v}\rangle\right) - en\,\mathbf{E}\cdot\mathbf{V} = \int \frac{mv^2}{2} C\, d\mathbf{v}. \tag{1.13}$$

The subscript a will be omitted for reasons of simplicity hereinafter. The angle brackets denote averages over the velocity distribution function.

The order of integration over velocity and differentiation over time and coordinates are interchanged in the first two terms in Eq. (1.1); the third term is integrated by parts and it as assumed that the distribution function vanishes rapidly as $v \to \infty$. Equation (1.11) expresses the conservation of particles and is called the particle transport equation or the equution of continuity. If particles are produced or annihilated Eq. (1.4) no longer applies and the zero on the right side of Eq. (1.11) must be replaced by an appropriate intensity for the particle source.

It will be found convenient to transform Eqs. (1.12) and (1.13) as follows. The velocity is divided into two components – a mean velocity $\mathbf{V}$ and a random velocity $\mathbf{v}' = \mathbf{v} - \mathbf{V}$; it is evident that $<\mathbf{v}'> = 0$. The second term in Eq. (1.12) is written

$$<v_\alpha v_\beta> = <(V_\alpha + v'_\alpha)(V_\beta + v'_\beta)> =$$
$$= V_\alpha V_\beta + <v'_\alpha v'_\beta>, \text{ because } <v'_\alpha> = <v'_\beta> = 0.$$

Expressing $\partial n/\partial t$ by means of the equation of continuity it is now possible to write Eq. (1.12) in the form

$$mn \frac{dV_\alpha}{dt} = -\frac{\partial p}{\partial x_\alpha} - \frac{\partial \pi_{\alpha\beta}}{\partial x_\beta} + en\left(E_\alpha + \frac{1}{c}[\mathbf{VB}]_\alpha\right) + R_\alpha, \quad (1.14)$$

where

$$\frac{d}{dt} = \frac{\partial}{\partial t} + V_\beta \frac{\partial}{\partial x_\beta} = \frac{\partial}{\partial t} + (\mathbf{V} \cdot \nabla) \quad (1.15)$$

is the so-called substantive derivative, and

$$p = nm<v'^2>/3 = nT, \quad (1.16)$$

$$\pi_{\alpha\beta} = nm<v'_\alpha v'_\beta - (v'^2/3)\,\delta_{\alpha\beta}>, \quad (1.17)$$

$$\mathbf{R} = \int m\mathbf{v}' C\, d\mathbf{v}. \quad (1.18)$$

The quantity p is the scalar pressure for particles of a given species. The complete pressure tensor for a given species is

$$P_{\alpha\beta} = \int m v'_\alpha v'_\beta f(t, \mathbf{r}, \mathbf{v})\, d\mathbf{v} = nm\langle v'_\alpha v'_\beta\rangle = p\delta_{\alpha\beta} + \pi_{\alpha\beta}. \tag{1.19}$$

If the velocity distribution function (for the random velocity) is isotropic, then $\langle v_x'^2\rangle = \langle v_y'^2\rangle = \langle v_z'^2\rangle = (1/3)\langle v'^2\rangle$, $\langle v_x' v_y'\rangle = \langle v_x' v_z'\rangle = \langle v_y' v_z'\rangle = 0$, so that $P_{\alpha\beta} = p\delta_{\alpha\beta}$. The tensor $\pi_{\alpha\beta}$ represents the part of $P_{\alpha\beta}$ that arises as a result of the deviation of the distribution from spherical symmetry. The quantity $\pi_{\alpha\beta}$ will be called the stress tensor. Like $P_{\alpha\beta}$ this tensor is symmetric $\pi_{\alpha\beta} = \pi_{\beta\alpha}$.

The quantity **R** represents the mean change in the momentum of the particles of a given species due to collisions with all other particles.

Equation (1.14) is called the momentum transport equation or simply the equation of motion. It represents a generalization of the corresponding equation in gas dynamics.

Carrying out similar transformations

$$\left\langle \frac{v^2}{2} v_\beta \right\rangle = \frac{1}{2} V^2 V_\beta + V_\alpha \langle v'_\alpha v'_\beta\rangle + \frac{1}{2}\langle v'^2\rangle V_\beta +$$

$$+ \left\langle \frac{1}{2} v'^2 v'_\beta \right\rangle = \left(\frac{1}{2}V^2 + \frac{5}{2}\frac{P}{mn}\right) V_\beta + \frac{1}{mn} V_\alpha \pi_{\alpha\beta} + \left\langle \frac{1}{2} v'^2 v_\beta \right\rangle,$$

we can reduce Eq. (1.13) to the form

$$\frac{\partial}{\partial t}\left(\frac{nm}{2}V^2 + \frac{3}{2}nT\right) + \frac{\partial}{\partial x_\beta}\left\{\left(\frac{nm}{2}V^2 + \frac{5}{2}nT\right)V_\beta + \right.$$

$$\left. + (\pi_{\alpha\beta}\cdot V_\alpha) + q_\beta\right\} = en\,\mathbf{EV} + \mathbf{RV} + Q. \tag{1.20}$$

Here we have introduced the notation

$$\mathbf{q} = \int \frac{m}{2} v'^2 \mathbf{v} f(t, \mathbf{r}, \mathbf{v})\, d\mathbf{v} = nm\left\langle \frac{v'^2}{2}\mathbf{v}\right\rangle, \tag{1.21}$$

$$Q = \int \frac{mv'^2}{2} C\, d\mathbf{v}. \tag{1.22}$$

The vector **q** is the flux density of heat carried by particles of a given species and represents the transport of the energy associated with the random motion in the coordinate system in which the particle gas as a whole is at rest at a given point in space.

The quantity Q is the heat generated in a gas of particles of a given species as a consequence of collisions with particles of other species.

Equation (1.20) is called the energy transport equation. The first term in Eq. (1.20) represents the change in the total energy of particles of a given species: this consists of the kinetic energy $nmV^2/2$ and the internal energy $(3/2)nT$ (per unit volume). The term in the curly brackets represents the total energy flux and consists of the macroscopic transport of the total energy with velocity **V**, the microscopic energy flux, i.e., the heat flux **q**, and the work done by the total pressure forces

$$\frac{\partial V_\alpha P_{\alpha\beta}}{\partial x_\beta} = \frac{\partial (pV_\beta + \pi_{\alpha\beta} V_\alpha)}{\partial x_\beta}.$$

The term on the right side takes account of the work done by any other forces and the heat generation.

In some cases it is convenient to eliminate the kinetic energy from Eq. (1.20) by means of the equation of continuity and the equation of motion. We then obtain an equation for the transport of internal energy, or the heat-balance equation:

$$\frac{3}{2}\frac{\partial nT}{\partial t} + \operatorname{div}\left(\frac{3}{2} nT\mathbf{V}\right) + nT \operatorname{div}\mathbf{V} + \pi_{\alpha\beta}\frac{\partial V_\alpha}{\partial x_\beta} + \operatorname{div}\mathbf{q} = Q. \tag{1.23}$$

The equation of continuity (1.11) can now be used to obtain

$$\frac{3}{2}\frac{\partial nT}{\partial t} + \operatorname{div}\left(\frac{3}{2} nT\mathbf{V}\right) = \frac{3}{2} n \frac{dT}{dt}.$$

Introducing the quantity

$$s = \ln (T^{3/2}/n) = \ln (p^{3/2}/n^{5/2}),$$

and again using (1.11) we can also write Eq. (1.23) in the form

$$Tn\frac{ds}{dt} = T\left\{\frac{\partial ns}{\partial t} + \operatorname{div}(ns\mathbf{V})\right\} = -\operatorname{div}\mathbf{q} - \pi_{\alpha\beta}\frac{\partial V_\alpha}{\partial x_\beta} + Q. \tag{1.23'}$$

To within an unimportant constant the quantity s represents the entropy per particle.

Let $\mathbf{R}_{ab}$ be the change of momentum and Q_{ab} the heat generated in a gas of particles of species a as a consequence of collisions with particles of species b. Then $\mathbf{R}_a = \sum_b \mathbf{R}_{ab}$, and $Q_a = \sum_b Q_{ab}$. Using the fact that particles, momentum, and energy are conserved in collision (1.4)-(1.6) we find

$$R_{ba} = - R_{ab},$$

$$Q_{ab} + Q_{ba} = - \mathbf{R}_{ab} \mathbf{V}_a - \mathbf{R}_{ba} \mathbf{V}_b = - \mathbf{R}_{ab} (\mathbf{V}_a - \mathbf{V}_b). \quad (1.24)$$

If Eqs. (1.11), (1.14), and (1.23) are to be actually used to find the parameters n, **V**, and T it is first necessary to establish the relation between $\pi_{\alpha\beta}$, **q**, **R**, and Q and the parameters n, **V**, and T. This relation can be stated phenomenologically or by kinetic methods. If the second approach is used an approximate solution for the kinetic equations must be obtained in order to express the distribution function at a given point in terms of n, **V**, and T; this relation is then used in Eqs. (1.17), (1.18), (1.21), and (1.22) to obtain an expression for $\pi_{\alpha\beta}$, **q**, **R**, and Q at the same point. In principle this approximate local solution of the kinetic equation is valid in the case of practical importance in which certain requirements pertinent to the macroscopic analysis of a plasma are satisfied. Essentially these requirements state that all quantities must vary slowly in space (small gradients) and time. The possibility of using a local solution derives from the existence of the relaxation process, which causes any arbitrary distribution to become a Maxwellian as a consequence of collisions. The Maxwellian distribution represents the solution of the kinetic equation for the case in which the gradients and time derivatives vanish identically. If these quantities are nonvanishing, but small, the distribution function will still be close to a Maxwellian and the difference (proportional to the small gradient) will also be small. Thus, if one is interested in changes occurring in time intervals much greater than the collision time and if all quantities vary slowly over distances traversed by the particles between collisions, the solution of the kinetic equation will approximate a Maxwellian; specifically, the solution will be of the form

$$f_a(t, \mathbf{r}, \mathbf{v}) = f_a^0 + f_a^1 = \frac{n_a(t, \mathbf{r})}{(2\pi T_a/m_a)^{3/2}} e^{-\frac{m_a}{2T_a(t, \mathbf{r})}[\mathbf{v} - \mathbf{V}_a(t, \mathbf{r})]^2} + f_a^1, \quad (1.25)$$

where $|f_a^1| \ll f_a^0$. The first-order term f_a^1 can be treated as a small correction or perturbation on the zero-order distribution function f_a^0. This correction will be proportional to effects that disturb the Maxwellian distribution, i. e., gradients, electric fields, etc. The Maxwellian function and its derivatives are determined uniquely by the parameters n, **V**, and T and by the derivatives of these parameters; hence, these same quantities can be used to express the correction f^1 and, in the final analysis, $\pi_{\alpha\beta}$, **q**, **R**, and Q. These latter quantities are then proportional to the effects that produce the deviations from equilibrium. The corresponding coefficients of proportionality (for example, the coefficient of friction between particles of different species, the thermal conductivity, viscosity etc.) are called the transport coefficients, and determination of these coefficients is the basic goal of kinetic theory.

The program we have mapped out can only be carried to a successful conclusion in a fully ionized gas with one ion species.

Such a system will be called a simple plasma and will be the primary subject of discussion in the present review.

The transport coefficients for a simple plasma are given in §§2 and 4. These coefficients are given qualitative physical interpretations and evaluated in order-of-magnitude terms in §3, and computed numerically from the kinetic equation in §4. The use of the transport equations to describe a plasma in a strong magnetic field frequently leads to paradoxes which have been the source of various errors and ambiguities in the literature. Some of these paradoxes are considered in §5. The application of the transport equations for particles of different species in analyses which assume a plasma model based on a single complex gas is described in §6 (fully ionized plasma) and 7 (partially ionized plasma). This magnetohydrodynamic model of a plasma is frequently used in practice and can, in some cases, be justified by means of the kinetic equations and the transport equations; in some cases the model is used purely in the interests of simplicity. The individual sections of this review are more or less independent of each other so that §§4 and 5 can be omitted without loss of understanding of the remaining text.

§ 2. Transport Equations for a Simple Plasma (Summary of Results)

For purposes of reference, in this section we list the transport equations for a fully ionized plasma consisting of electrons and a single ion species with charge Ze. The transport coefficients of a fully ionized plasma have been computed by many authors. A method for obtaining the transport equations from the kinetic equations is given in detail in the monograph by Chapman and Cowling [1]. This same work contains expressions for the heat flux and the stress tensor for a single-component ionized gas in a magnetic field; the electrical conductivity in a magnetic field is also derived. The transport coefficients for a fully ionized gas have also been computed in [12-22] and in other places. Although these coefficients have been derived by various methods and in various forms, in all cases they apply only when the local distribution is very close to a Maxwellian. The results listed here are derived in §4 following the method used in [17].

With the exception of the electrical conductivity, at the present time no transport coefficient for a simple plasma has yet been measured experimentally.

The transport equations for a simple plasma comprise the equations of continuity, motion, and heat balance for the electrons and for the ions:

$$\frac{\partial n_e}{\partial t} + \operatorname{div}(n_e \mathbf{V}_e) = 0, \qquad (2.1e)$$

$$\frac{\partial n_i}{\partial t} + \operatorname{div}(n_i \mathbf{V}_i) = 0, \qquad (2.1i)$$

$$m_e n_e \frac{d_e V_{e\alpha}}{dt} = -\frac{\partial p_e}{\partial x_\alpha} - \frac{\partial \pi_{e\alpha\beta}}{\partial x_\beta} - e n_e \left(E_\alpha + \frac{1}{c}[\mathbf{V}_e \mathbf{B}]_\alpha\right) + R_\alpha, \qquad (2.2e)$$

$$m_i n_i \frac{d_i V_{i\alpha}}{dt} = -\frac{\partial p_i}{\partial x_\alpha} - \frac{\partial \pi_{i\alpha\beta}}{\partial x_\beta} + Zen_i \left(E_\alpha + \frac{1}{c}[\mathbf{V}_i \mathbf{B}]_\alpha\right) - R_\alpha, \qquad (2.2i)$$

$$\frac{3}{2} n_e \frac{d_e T_e}{dt} + p_e \operatorname{div} \mathbf{V}_e = -\operatorname{div} \mathbf{q}_e - \pi_{e\alpha\beta} \frac{\partial V_{e\alpha}}{\partial x_\beta} + Q_e, \qquad (2.3e)$$

$$\frac{3}{2} n_i \frac{d_i T_i}{dt} + p_i \operatorname{div} \mathbf{V}_i = -\operatorname{div} \mathbf{q}_i - \pi_{i\alpha\beta} \frac{\partial V_{i\alpha}}{\partial x_\beta} + Q_i, \qquad (2.3i)$$

where

$$p_e = n_e T_e, \; p_i = n_i T_i,$$

$$\frac{d_e}{dt} = \frac{\partial}{\partial t} + (\mathbf{V}_e \nabla), \quad \frac{d_i}{dt} = \frac{\partial}{\partial t} + (\mathbf{V}_i \nabla). \qquad (2.4)$$

In the expressions for the transport coefficients used below we shall make use of the fact that the plasma is neutral, writing $n = n_e = Zn_i$. We also exploit the fact that the ratio m_e/m_i is small.

The electron and ion collision times (in seconds) can be written in the form:*

$$\tau_e = \frac{3\sqrt{m_e}\,T_e^{3/2}}{4\sqrt{2\pi}\,\lambda e^4 Z^2 n_i} = \frac{3.5\cdot 10^4}{(\lambda/10)}\cdot\frac{T_e^{3/2}}{Zn}, \qquad (2.5e)$$

$$\tau_i = \frac{3\sqrt{m_i}\,T_i^{3/2}}{4\sqrt{\pi}\,\lambda e^4 Z^4 n_i} = \frac{3.0\cdot 10^6}{(\lambda/10)}\left(\frac{m_i}{2m_p}\right)^{1/2}\frac{T_i^{3/2}}{Z^3 n}, \qquad (2.5i)$$

where m_p is the mass of the proton and λ is the Coulomb logarithm [6] (for $T_e < 50$eV, $\lambda = 23.4 - 1.15 \log n + 3.45 \log T_e$; for $T_e > 50$eV, $\lambda = 25.3 - 1.15 \log n + 2.3 \log T_e$).

The cyclotron frequencies ($\sec^{-1}$) for the electrons and ions are

$$\omega_e = \frac{eB}{m_e c} = 1.76\cdot 10^7 B, \qquad (2.6e)$$

$$\omega_i = \frac{ZeB}{m_i c} = 0.96\cdot 10^4 \frac{ZB}{m_i/m_p}. \qquad (2.6i)$$

In a magnetic field the transport coefficients depend on the quantity $\omega\tau$. In this section we shall only give the limiting expressions for large values of $\omega_e\tau_e$ and $\omega_i\tau_i$. These can also be used to obtain expressions for the case $B = 0$ by assuming that the transport coefficients in the direction of the magnetic field are equal to the transport coefficients in the absence of the field. Expressions for arbitrary values of $\omega\tau$ are given in §4.

The symbols $\|$ and $\perp$ on the vectors mean that we are to take the component parallel or perpendicular to the magnetic field respectively; for example $\mathbf{u}_{\|} = \mathbf{h}(\mathbf{uh})$, $\mathbf{u}_{\perp} = [\mathbf{h}\,[\mathbf{uh}]]$, where $\mathbf{h} = \mathbf{B}/B$ is a unit vector in the direction of the magnetic field.

The transfer of momentum from ions to electrons by collisions $\mathbf{R} = \mathbf{R}_u + \mathbf{R}_T$ is made up of two parts: the force of friction $\mathbf{R}_u$ due to the existence of a relative velocity $\mathbf{u} = \mathbf{V}_e - \mathbf{V}_i$, and a thermal force $\mathbf{R}_T$,

*In all the practical formulas here and below the temperature is expressed in electron volts, the magnetic field in gauss, and all other quantities in cgs units.

TABLE 1

Z	Formula number					
	(2. 8)	(2. 9) and (2. 10)		(2. 11)	(2. 12)	(2. 13)
1	0.51	0.71	3/2	5/2	3.16	4.66
2	0.44	0.9	3/2	5/2	4.9	4.0
3	0.40	1.0	3/2	5/2	6.1	3.7
4	0.38	1.1	3/2	5/2	6.9	3.6
∞	0.29	1.5	3/2	5/2	12.5	3.2

which arises by virtue of a gradient in the electron temperature. The electron heat flux is made up of two analogous parts; $\mathbf{q}_e = \mathbf{q}_u^e + \mathbf{q}_T^e$. The relative velocity of the electrons and ions is related simply to the current density; specifically, $\mathbf{j} = -en\mathbf{u}$.

At large values of $\omega_e\tau_e$ the relations derived in §4 give the following expressions for the momentum transfer via collisions and for the electron heat flux (Z = 1):

The friction force:

$$\mathbf{R}_u = -\frac{m_e n_e}{\tau_e}(0.51\mathbf{u}_{\parallel} + \mathbf{u}_{\perp}) = en\left(\frac{\mathbf{j}_{\parallel}}{\sigma_{\parallel}} + \frac{\mathbf{j}_{\perp}}{\sigma_{\perp}}\right), \tag{2.6}$$

where the electrical conductivities are

$$\sigma_{\perp} = \frac{e^2 n_e \tau_e}{m_e} = \sigma_1 T_e^{3/2}, \tag{2.7}$$

$$\sigma_{\parallel} = 1.96\sigma_{\perp} = 1.96\sigma_1 T_e^{3/2}, \tag{2.8}$$

where

$$\sigma_1 = \frac{0.9\cdot 10^{13}}{(\lambda/10)\,Z}\ \mathrm{sec}^{-1}\cdot \mathrm{eV}^{-3/2}.$$

The thermal force:

$$\mathbf{R}_T = -0.71 n_e \nabla_{\parallel} T_e - \frac{3}{2}\frac{n_e}{\omega_e\tau_e}[\mathbf{h}\nabla T_e]. \tag{2.9}$$

The electron heat flux:

$$\mathbf{q}_u^e = 0.71 n_e T_e \mathbf{u}_\parallel + \frac{3}{2}\frac{n_e T_e}{\omega_e \tau_e}[\mathbf{h}\mathbf{u}], \tag{2.10}$$

$$\mathbf{q}_T^e = -\varkappa_\parallel^e \nabla_\parallel T_e - \varkappa_\perp^e \nabla_\perp T_e - \frac{5}{2}\frac{c n_e T_e}{eB}[\mathbf{h}\nabla T_e], \tag{2.11}$$

where the thermal conductivities are:

$$\varkappa_\parallel^e = 3.16\frac{n_e T_e \tau_e}{m_e}, \tag{2.12}$$

$$\varkappa_\perp^e = 4.66\frac{n_e T_e}{m_e \omega_e^2 \tau_e}. \tag{2.13}$$

If $Z \neq 1$ the coefficients in these expressions are modified in accordance with Table 1.

When $\omega_i \tau_i \gg 1$ the ion heat flux is

$$\mathbf{q}_i = -\varkappa_\parallel^i \nabla_\parallel T_i - \varkappa_\perp^i \nabla_\perp T_i + \frac{5}{2}\frac{c n_i T_i}{ZeB}[\mathbf{h}\nabla T_i], \tag{2.14}$$

$$\varkappa_\parallel^i = 3.9\frac{n_i T_i \tau_i}{m_i}, \tag{2.15}$$

$$\varkappa_\perp^i = 2\frac{n_i T_i}{m_i \omega_i^2 \tau_i}. \tag{2.16}$$

The heat acquired by the ions in collisions with electrons is

$$Q_i = Q_\Delta = \frac{3m_e}{m_i}\frac{n_e}{\tau_e}(T_e - T_i). \tag{2.17}$$

The heat generated in the electrons as a consequence of collisions with ions is

$$Q_e = -\mathbf{R}\mathbf{u} - Q_\Delta = \frac{j_\parallel^2}{\sigma_\parallel} + \frac{j_\perp^2}{\sigma_\perp} + \frac{1}{c n_e}\mathbf{j}\mathbf{R}_T - \frac{3m_e}{m_i}\frac{n_e}{\tau_e}(T_e - T_i). \tag{2.18}$$

The stress tensor in the absence of a magnetic field is

$$\pi_{\alpha\beta} = -\eta_0 W_{\alpha\beta}, \tag{2.19}$$

where the rate-of-strain tensor

$$W_{\alpha\beta} = \frac{\partial V_\alpha}{\partial x_\beta} + \frac{\partial V_\beta}{\partial x_\alpha} - \frac{2}{3}\,\delta_{\alpha\beta}\,\mathrm{div}\,\mathbf{V}. \tag{2.20}$$

In a strong magnetic field ($\omega\tau \gg 1$) the components of the tensor $\pi_{\alpha\beta}$ have the following form in the coordinate system with z axis parallel to the magnetic field:

$$\left.\begin{aligned}
\pi_{zz} &= -\eta_0 W_{zz},\\
\pi_{xx} &= -\eta_0 \frac{1}{2}(W_{xx} + W_{yy}) - \eta_1 \frac{1}{2}(W_{xx} - W_{yy}) - \eta_3 W_{xy},\\
\pi_{yy} &= -\eta_0 \frac{1}{2}(W_{xx} + W_{yy}) - \eta_1 \frac{1}{2}(W_{yy} - W_{xx}) + \eta_3 W_{xy},\\
\pi_{xy} &= \pi_{yx} = -\eta_1 W_{xy} + \eta_3 \frac{1}{2}(W_{xx} - W_{yy}),\\
\pi_{xz} &= \pi_{zx} = -\eta_2 W_{xz} - \eta_4 W_{yz},\\
\pi_{yz} &= \pi_{zy} = -\eta_2 W_{yz} + \eta_4 W_{xz}.
\end{aligned}\right\} \tag{2.21}$$

The expressions in (2.21) apply for both ions and electrons but the tensors $W_{\alpha\beta}$ and the viscosity coefficients are obviously different for the two species.

The ion viscosity coefficients are

$$\eta_0^i = 0.96 n_i T_i \tau_i, \tag{2.22}$$

$$\eta_1^i = \frac{3}{10}\frac{n_i T_i}{\omega_i^2 \tau_i}, \quad \eta_2^i = 4\eta_1^i, \tag{2.23}$$

$$\eta_3^i = \frac{1}{2}\frac{n_i T_i}{\omega_i}, \quad \eta_4^i = 2\eta_3^i. \tag{2.24}$$

The electron viscosity coefficients are ($Z = 1$)

$$\eta_0^e = 0.73 n_e T_e \tau_e, \tag{2.25}$$

$$\eta_1^e = 0.51 \frac{n_e T_e}{\omega_e^2 \tau_e}, \quad \eta_2^e = 4\eta_1^e, \tag{2.26}$$

$$\eta_3^e = -\frac{1}{2}\frac{n_e T_e}{\omega_e}; \quad \eta_4^e = 2\eta_3^e. \tag{2.27}$$

The heat generated as a result of viscosity is

$$Q_{\text{vis}} = -\pi_{\alpha\beta}\frac{\partial V_\alpha}{\partial x_\beta} = -\frac{1}{2}\pi_{\alpha\beta}W_{\alpha\beta}$$

or, neglecting terms of order $(\omega\tau)^{-2}$,

$$Q_{\text{vis}} = -\pi_{\alpha\beta}\frac{\partial V_\alpha}{\partial x_\beta} = \frac{3}{4}\eta_0 W_{zz}^2 = \frac{\eta_0}{3}\left(\frac{\partial V_x}{\partial x} + \frac{\partial V_y}{\partial y} - 2\frac{\partial V_z}{\partial z}\right)^2. \tag{2.28}$$

An expression for $\pi_{\alpha\beta}$ in an arbitrary coordinate system is given in §4.

§ 3. Kinetics of a Simple Plasma (Qualitative Description)

Particle Motion and Collisions. The transport coefficients in §2 can be derived through the use of some simple ideas based on the motion of individual particles and the properties of Coulomb collisions.

In the absence of a magnetic field a free particle moves in a straight line with constant velocity. Collisions distort the particle trajectory and change the magnitude of the velocity. The resulting motion can be represented roughly as taking place along a broken line consisting of randomly directed segments with lengths of order $l = v\tau$ where $v \sim (2T/m)^{1/2}$ is the characteristic thermal velocity and τ is the characteristic time interval between collisions which change the direction of motion.

In a magnetic field the charged particle moves without collisions along a helix with radius of order $r = mvc/eB$ that winds around the magnetic line of force. Collisions disturb this regular motion; one way of looking at the situation is to say that after a time interval $\sim\tau$ the particle starts to describe a new helix that is not an extension of the earlier one. Two limiting cases must be distinguished. In a weak magnetic field $r \gg l$ or, $\omega\tau \ll 1$ ($\omega = eB/mc$ is the cyclotron frequency). In a strong field $r \ll l$, $\omega\tau \gg 1$. In a weak field the portions of the helix traversed by the particle between collisions are not very different from segments of straight lines. In a strong field the particle can describe many turns between collisions. When $\omega\tau \gg 1$ the magnetic field has a strong effect on transport properties in the transverse direction; on the other hand, particles can still move freely along the field, traveling a distance $\sim l$ between collisions as if $B = 0$. Thus, the magnetic field does not affect the longitudinal flow;

the transport coefficients are the same for longitudinal flows and for flows in an arbitrary direction with B = 0.

It should be noted that Coulomb collisions are not really true collisions (in the sense of instantaneous collisions); because of the long range of the Coulomb force the stochastic interaction between charged particles goes on continuously and causes a continuous randomization of particle velocities. However, this feature only affects the actual form of the collision term and is not important as far as our qualitative description is concerned. A qualitative description requires only that we know the characteristic time intervals between collisions; these times may be conveniently taken to be the time required for the total integrated change in the direction of the velocity to add up to an angle of order unity.

A quantitative analysis of Coulomb collisions requires the use of an appropriate expression for the collision term (cf. §4). Speaking roughly, we may say that the effective scattering cross section for Coulomb collisions is about one order of magnitude greater than $\pi(e_1e_2/\varepsilon)^2$ where e_1 and e_2 are the charges of the colliding particles, ε is the distance of closest approach. Thus, the mean free path for Coulomb collisions is proportional to the square of the energy of the particles or the square of the temperature.

As in §2, we shall make use of two characteristic times: τ_e, the electron-ion scattering time and τ_i, the ion-ion scattering time. The first of these depends only on the electron temperature because the electrons have much higher velocities and the relative velocity is determined by the electrons in electron-ion collisions. The second characteristic time depends on the ion temperature. All of the other characteristic times can be expressed conveniently in terms of τ_e and τ_i.

A characteristic feature of a fully ionized plasma is the very small ratio of the masses of the plasma components, the electrons and ions. Because this ratio is so small, the electron gas and the ion gas reach equilibria separately in a time much shorter than that required for the two gases to come to equilibrium with each other. Say that the electron equilibration time is $\sim\tau_{ee}$ and that the ion equilibration time is $\sim\tau_{ii}$ while the electron-ion equilibration time is $\sim\tau_{ei}^{\varepsilon}$. If the electron and ion temperatures are of the same order we find

$$\tau_{ee} : \tau_{ii} : \tau_{ei}^{\varepsilon} = 1 : (m_i/m_e)^{1/2} : (m_i/m_e).$$

On the other hand, the mean free path is determined by the particle energies and is thus of the same order for the electrons and ions even though the ion velocity is $(m_e/m_i)^{1/2}$ times the electron velocity so that $\tau_{ii} \sim (m_i/m_e)^{1/2}\tau_{ee}$. The relative velocity in electron-ion collisions is of the same order as for electron-electron collisions so that both processes have approximately the same probability. Large fractional energy exchanges occur between like particles in a single collision, hence $\tau_{ee} \sim \tau_e$, $\tau_{ii} \sim \tau_i$. On the other hand, only a small fraction of the energy is transferred (the order of the mass ratio) in collisions of a light particle with a heavy particle so that

$$\tau_{ei}^{\varepsilon} \sim (m_i/m_e)\, \tau_e \sim (m_i/m_e)\, \tau_{ee}.$$

If the ion temperature is smaller than the electron temperature, as is frequently the case, the ion path is smaller and τ_{ii} is reduced. However, both of the other characteristic times remain unchanged so that $\tau_{ee} \ll \tau_{ei}^{\varepsilon}$ and $\tau_{ii} \ll \tau_{ei}^{\varepsilon}$ as before. If the ion temperature is greater than the electron temperature the quantity τ_{ii} increases, but the condition $\tau_{ii} \ll \tau_{ei}^{\varepsilon}$ is still satisfied so long as $T_i/T_e \ll (m_i/m_e)^{1/3}$.

Thus, a local equilibrium (Maxwellian distribution) is established within each of the components in a simple plasma before it is established between the components. It is precisely this circumstance that makes it possible to obtain transport equations when the electron and ion temperatures are different. The transfer of momentum from the ions to the electrons occurs in about the same time $\sim\tau_{ei}^{\varepsilon}$ as the transfer of energy; hence ion-electron momentum transfer is small compared with ion-ion momentum transfer. For this reason collisions of ions with electrons generally have very little effect on the form of the ion distribution function. On the other hand, the transfer of momentum from the electrons to the ions occurs in a time of the same order as the electron-electron momentum transfer time $\tau_e \sim \tau_{ee}$, so that collisions of electrons with ions have an important effect on the form of the electron distribution function.

The Friction Force $\mathbf{R}_u$. In collisions of electrons with ions which have zero mean velocity ($V_i = 0$) the electron velocities remain essentially unchanged in magnitude but do undergo random changes in direction. Thus, the electrons lose their ordered velocity with respect to the ions $\mathbf{u} = \mathbf{V}_e - \mathbf{V}_i$ in a time $\sim\tau_e$ and consequently lose momentum $m_e\mathbf{u}$ per electron (which is given to the ions). This means that a frictional force $(m_e n_e/\tau_e)\mathbf{u}$ is exerted on the electrons; this force is equal and opposite to the force exerted on the ions. We note that the quantity τ_e defined by Eq. (2.5e) is chosen in such a way that the frictional force $\mathbf{R}^0$ that appears in the interaction of an electron Maxwellian distribution shifted with respect to the ion function by an amount $\mathbf{u}$ will have the simple form $\mathbf{R}^0 = -(m_e n_e/\tau_e)\mathbf{u}$ (without numerical coefficients). Actually, if any force, say an electric field, produces an electron velocity $\mathbf{u}$ directed along $\mathbf{B}$ (or if $B = 0$) the electron distribution function is not a Maxwellian simply shifted as a whole by an amount $\mathbf{u}$. This results from the fact that the Coulomb cross section diminishes with increasing electron energy ($\tau \sim v^3$); hence, a Coulomb force shifts the faster electrons more (with respect to the ions) than the slow electrons. The distribution function is then distorted in such a way that the mean velocity $\mathbf{u}$, i.e., transport of electric current, depends more on the fast electrons so that the friction coefficient is smaller than for a true shifted Maxwellian. This effect would vanish if electron-electron collisions, which tend to establish a Maxwellian distribution, were to occur much more frequently than the electron-ion collisions, which distort the distribution. Since $\tau_{ee} \sim \tau_e$, however, an "effect of order unity" is obtained, that is to say, the distortion of the Maxwellian is of the same order as the shift. For example when $Z = 1$ the friction coefficient is reduced by a factor 0.51. The friction coefficient is reduced still more for higher values of Z, where electron-ion collisions are relatively more important than electron-electron collisions.

In the motion of electrons with respect to ions across a strong magnetic field ($\mathbf{u} = \mathbf{u}_\perp$) the correction to the shifted Maxwellian is of order $(\omega_e\tau_e)^{-1}$; thus, when $\omega_e\tau_e \gg 1$ this correction can be neglected so that the transverse frictional force is simply $\mathbf{R}_\perp = -(m_e n_e/\tau_e)\mathbf{u}_\perp$. In a strong magnetic field the coefficient of friction between electrons and ions is then smaller for a longitudinal current than for a transverse current, that is to say, the longitudinal electric conductivity $\sigma_\parallel$ is greater than the transverse conductivity $\sigma_\perp$. When $Z = 1$ we find $\sigma_\parallel \approx 2\sigma_\perp$.*

Thermal Force R_T. Let us assume that the electrons and ions are at rest on the average ($V_e = V_i = 0$); then, the number of electrons moving from left to right and from right to left per unit time will be exactly the same through any cross section, say $x = x_0$. The order of magnitude of these two compensating fluxes is $n_e v_e$. As a result of electron-ion collisions these fluxes experience frictional forces $\mathbf{R}_+$ and $\mathbf{R}_-$ of order $m_e n_e v_e/\tau_e$; in a completely homogeneous situation these frictional forces balance exactly and there is no resultant force. Collisions of electrons with ions can, however, produce a resultant force if the velocity distribution of the electrons coming from the left is different from the distribution characterizing electrons coming from the right, in which case the forces $\mathbf{R}_+$ and

*The presence of runaway electrons increases the ratio $\sigma_\parallel/\sigma_\perp$.

R_- do not cancel. For example, if electrons coming from the right have higher average energies than those coming from the left the force acting on the fast "right" electrons will be less than the force acting on the slower "left" electrons (since $\tau \sim v^3$); as a result a force directed to the left is produced.

Let us assume that there is a temperature gradient along the x axis (Fig. 1) and no magnetic field (or that there is a magnetic field along ΔT). At the point $x = x_0$ collisions will be experienced by electrons that have come from the right and from the left and that have traversed distances of the order of the mean free path $l \sim v\tau$; thus, electrons coming from the right come from regions in which the temperature is approximately $l\,\partial T_e/\partial x$ greater than in the regions from which the electrons from the left originate. The unbalanced part of the forces R_+ and R_- will be of order

$$R_T \sim \frac{l}{T_e}\frac{\partial T_e}{\partial x}\frac{m_e n_e v_e}{\tau_e} \sim \frac{m_e v_e^2}{T_e} n_e \frac{\partial T_e}{\partial x} \sim n_e \frac{\partial T_e}{\partial x}$$

and will be directed to the left, that is to say, in the opposite direction to the temperature gradient [minus sign in Eq. (2.9)]. As in the case of the longitudinal friction force R_u (and for the same reason) the size of this effect increases with increasing Z (cf. Table 1). It should be emphasized that the thermal force arises specifically as a consequence of collisions; hence its magnitude and sign depend on the actual velocity dependence of the collision frequency (in the present case $\tau \sim v^3$) even though the thermal force const $n\partial T_e/\partial x$ does not contain τ explicitly.

Let us now investigate the case in which there is a strong magnetic field along the z axis while the temperature gradient is still along the x axis (Fig. 2). In a strong magnetic field ($\omega_e\tau_e \gg 1$) the electrons gyrate in circles of radius $r_e \sim v_e/\omega_e$; at the point $x = x_0$ there will be electrons

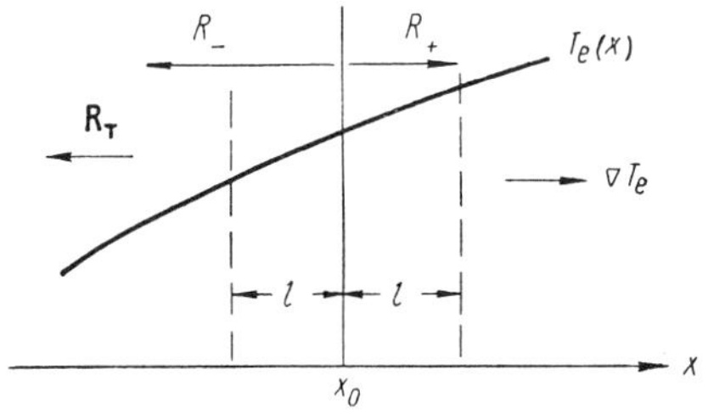

Fig. 1

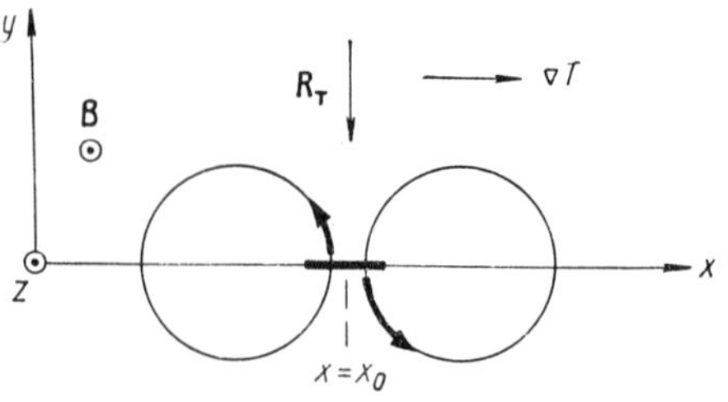

Fig. 2

that come from the right and from the left and that have traversed distances of order r_e. These electrons "carry" a temperature difference of order $r_e \partial T_e / \partial x$ and produce, as is evident from Fig. 2, an unbalance in the friction forces for fluxes directed along the y axis. On the other hand, the fluxes along the x axis at the point $x = x_0$ are due to electrons that come from regions where $x = x_0$, so that the frictional forces are balanced in this case. As a result of collisions with ions there then arises a thermal force directed perpendicularly to both **B** and ΔT_e, i.e., along the y axis; the order of magnitude of this quantity is

$$R_T \sim \frac{r_e}{T_e} \frac{\partial T_e}{\partial x} \frac{m_e n_e v_e}{\tau_e} \sim \frac{n_e}{\omega_e \tau_e} \frac{\partial T_e}{\partial x}.$$

It is easy to verify that the sign of the thermal force (minus) is precisely the same as in Eq. (2.9).

We may note that the effect of a magnetic field on the thermal force is directly analogous to the well-known phenomenon in metals, where it is known as the Nernst effect [19].

Electron Heat Flux $\mathbf{q}_u^e$. The existence of thermal forces is intimately related to the presence of terms proportional to the relative velocity **u** in the expression for the electron heat flux. Starting from the general principles of the thermodynamics of irreversible processes (the so-called principle of symmetry of the kinetic coefficients, or the Onsager principle) it can be shown that a knowledge of the terms in the frictional force which are proportional to ∇T_e can be used to find the terms in the heat flux that are proportional to **u**. This is actually done in detail in §4. For the present purposes, however, the qualitative significance of these terms can be stated as follows. As we have shown above, because $\tau \sim v^3$ the current along the magnetic field (or the current with no magnetic field) is carried predominantly by the faster electrons. Thus, in the coordi-

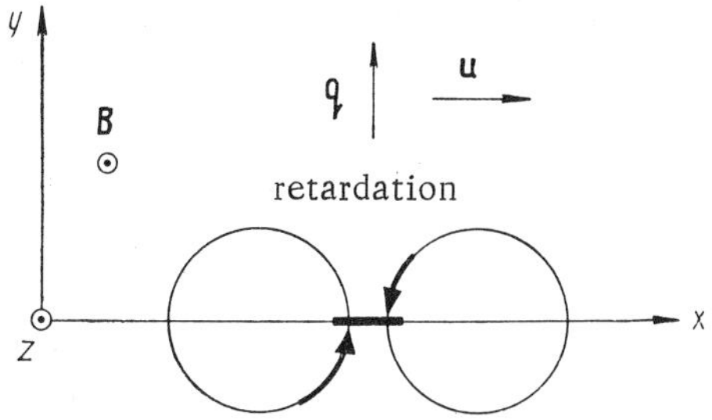

Fig. 3

nate system in which $V_e = 0$, more fast electrons move in the direction of **u** and more slow electrons move in the direction **−u**. Although the electron fluxes are balanced in this system, the energy fluxes are not and heat flows in the **u** direction. It is clear from the considerations used in the analysis of the friction force that this effect is of "order unity" so that the corresponding heat flow will be of order $\sim n_e T_e u$. Like the longitudinal thermal force, this heat flow is due to collisions although it does not contain τ explicitly.

Heat also flows when a current flows across a strong magnetic field $\mathbf{u} = \mathbf{u}_\perp$, but for a different reason. The friction force exerted on the electrons by the ions accelerates the electrons over one half cycle of rotation of the electrons, and retards them over the other (Fig. 3). Hence an area in the plane defined by **u** and **B** is intersected by accelerated electrons and by retarded electrons. The difference in the energies of these two electron groups is of order $(m_e u/\tau_e) r_e$. As a result, when $u = u_x$, $B = B_z$, a heat flux of the following magnitude arises

$$q_y \sim \frac{m_e u_x}{\tau_e} r_e n_e v_e \sim \frac{m_e u_x}{\tau_e} \frac{v_e^2}{\omega_e} n_e \sim \frac{n_e T_e}{\omega_e \tau_e} u_x.$$

Gas Kinetic Approximations (Kinetic Theory). Before analyzing the remaining effects we wish to review some simple approximations that should be familiar from the elementary kinetic theory of gases; these approximations are used to determine the order of magnitude of the diffusion coefficient, the thermal conductivity, and the viscosity of gases. There is a rather general analogy between these processes, in which matter, energy, and momentum are transported.

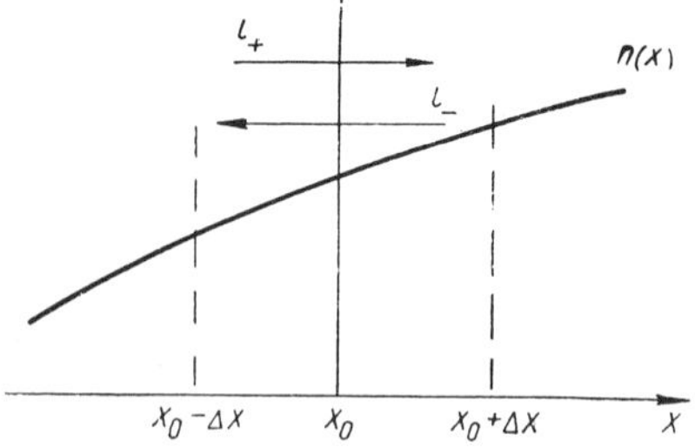

Fig. 4

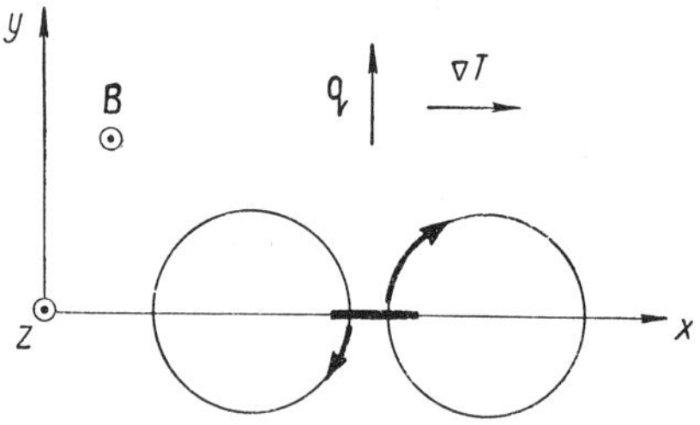

Fig. 5

Let us first consider diffusion. Diffusion occurs in a specified medium which we will assume to be fixed and not affected by the particles that diffuse through it.

Assume that the particle density is n(x) (Fig. 4) and that each particle is displaced through a distance Δx, with equal probability for motion to the right or to the left, in the time τ between two successive collisions. In unit time, the plane $x = x_0$ is traversed in the positive direction (from the left) by half of the particles which experience collisions in the layer between $x_0 - \Delta x$ and x_0; the other half of the particles move to the left as a result of collisions. Assuming that n(x) does not change greatly over a distance Δx so that

$$n(x) = n(x_0) + \left.\frac{\partial n}{\partial x}\right|_{x=x_0} (x - x_0),$$

we find that the unidirectional flux from the left is

$$i_+ = \frac{1}{2} \int\limits_{x_0-\Delta x}^{x_0} \frac{1}{\tau} n(x)\, dx = \frac{1}{2} \left[n(x_0) - \frac{\partial n}{\partial x} \frac{\Delta x}{2} \right] \frac{\Delta x}{\tau}.$$

The diffusion flux is the difference between the flux moving to the left and the flux moving to the right $i = i_+ - i_-$ and is given by

$$i = -\frac{(\Delta x)^2}{2\tau}\frac{\partial n}{\partial x} = -D\frac{\partial n}{\partial x}; \qquad D = \frac{(\Delta x)^2}{2\tau}. \tag{3.1}$$

This relation can still be used to estimate the diffusion coefficient if Δx and τ are not constant but proper values must be used for Δx and τ.*

The heat and momentum fluxes can be estimated in similar fashion.

Suppose that there is no particle flux. The unidirectional heat flux, for example from the left to the right, will be of order $q_+ \sim (\Delta x/\tau)\, nT$. Because of the presence of a temperature gradient a relative fraction of order $(\Delta x/T)(\partial T/\partial x)$ of the unidirectional fluxes is not balanced and there arises a heat flux q equal to

$$q = -\varkappa\frac{\partial T}{\partial x}; \qquad \varkappa \sim \frac{n(\Delta x)^2}{\tau} \sim nD. \tag{3.2}$$

Now assume that the velocity V_y varies with x; in precisely the same way there will be a flux π_{yx} of y momentum along the x axis because of the

---

*We note that different particles can have different Δx and τ; if Δx and τ depend on velocity, Eq. (3.1) describes particles with a given velocity and the total flux is obtained by summing (or integrating) the particle fluxes for all velocity classes:

$$i = -\frac{\partial}{\partial x}\int\left[\frac{(\Delta x)^2}{2\tau}\right]_v f(\mathrm{v})\, d\mathrm{v} = -\frac{\partial}{\partial x}\left\{\left\langle\frac{(\Delta x)^2}{2\tau}\right\rangle n\right\}, \tag{3.1'}$$

where the angle brackets denote averages over the particles at point x_0. For example if $\Delta x = v_x\tau$ and τ = const,

$$(\Delta x)^2 = v_x^2\tau^2; \quad < v_x^2 > = \frac{T}{m},$$
$$i = -\frac{\partial}{\partial x}\left\{\frac{\tau}{2} < v_x^2 > n\right\} = -\frac{\tau}{2m}\frac{\partial nT}{\partial x} = -\frac{\tau}{2m}\frac{\partial p}{\partial x}. \tag{3.1"}$$

However, if τ depends on v the flux will contain a term proportional to ∇p in addition to the term proportional to ∇T. This effect is called thermal diffusion. In moving through the medium the particles experience a friction force of order mi/τ. It is evident from Eq. (3.1) that diffusion of particles can be regarded as motion with friction under the effect of a force ∇p. The thermal diffusion can be regarded as motion with friction under the effect of a corresponding thermal force.

lack of cancellation between the two unidirectional momentum fluxes, each of which is of order $(\Delta x/\tau)\, nmV_y$:

$$\pi_{yx} = -\eta \frac{\partial V_y}{\partial x}, \quad \eta \sim \frac{mn\,(\Delta x)^2}{\tau} \sim mnD. \tag{3.3}$$

Equations (3.2) and (3.3) give the connection between the thermal conductivity $\varkappa$, the viscosity η, and the diffusion coefficient.

If a particle moves freely between collisions we note that $\Delta x \sim l \sim v\tau$ and Eq. (3.1) gives the usual expression $D \sim lv$ found in texbooks on the kinetic theory of gases. However Eq. (3.1) is more general than $D \sim lv$ since the approximation $D \sim (\Delta x)^2/\tau$ applies in those cases in which the displacement of the particle between collisions is not equal to the mean free path. The same considerations apply to Eqs. (3.2) and (3.3); thus, these expressions can be used to estimate the transport coefficients in the presence of a magnetic field.

Thermal Conductivity. The thermal conductivities appearing in the expressions for the electron and ion heat fluxes parallel and perpendicular to a magnetic field can be easily estimated using the kinetic-theory relation in (3.2). Here we need only take account of the fact that in motion across a strong magnetic field ($\omega\tau \gg 1$) a particle is displaced by a distance of the order of the Larmor radius (between collisions) rather than the usual mean free path $(\Delta x)_\perp \sim r \sim v/\omega$ so that $\varkappa_\perp \sim nr^2/\tau \sim nT/m\omega^2\tau$; on the other hand the particle moves freely along the field $(\Delta x)_\parallel \sim l \sim v\tau$ so that $\varkappa_\parallel \sim nl^2/\tau \sim nT\tau/m$. Thus, $\varkappa_\parallel/\varkappa_\perp \sim (\omega\tau)^2$. These estimates apply for both ions and electrons so that the subscripts i and e can be omitted and we need only use the velocities, temperatures, etc., appropriate to the species at hand. We note that if $T_e \sim T_i$ the electron thermal conductivity in direction of the field is greater than the ion conductivity $\varkappa_\parallel^e/\varkappa_\parallel^i \sim (m_i/m_e)^{1/2}$; on the other hand, the ion thermal conductivity is greater in the transverse direction: $\varkappa_\perp^e/\varkappa_\perp^i \sim (m_e/m_i)^{1/2}$.

The relations in (2.11) and (2.14) also contain the "transverse" heat fluxes that are perpendicular to both **B** and ∇T. These fluxes arise because an area lying in the plane of **B** and ∇T (Fig. 5) will, on the average, be traversed by more fast particles from one side than from the other; if the unidirectional particle fluxes $\sim nv$ are balanced, the unidirectional energy fluxes, of order nTv, will have an unbalanced part of order $(r/T)\,\partial T/\partial x$. As a result there is produced a heat flux

$$q_y \sim nvr\frac{\partial T}{\partial x} \sim \frac{cnT}{eB}\frac{\partial T}{\partial x}.$$

These fluxes are of opposite sign for the ions and electrons. The transverse fluxes carry heat along isotherms and do not cool the plasma or increase its entropy.

Viscosity. The viscosity of a plasma in a magnetic field is complicated because it is a tensor quantity. Expressions for the stress tensor when $\omega\tau \gg 1$ are given in §2; expressions for arbitrary $\omega\tau$ are given in §4. These expressions show that the viscous stress is not a simple function of the velocity derivatives $\partial V_\alpha/\partial x_\beta$ either with or without a magnetic field; rather, it depends on combinations of these derivatives in a way given by the so-called rate-of-strain tensor

$$W_{\alpha\beta} = \frac{\partial V_\alpha}{\partial x_\beta} + \frac{\partial V_\beta}{\partial x_\alpha} - \frac{2}{3}\delta_{\alpha\beta}\,\mathrm{div}\,\mathbf{V}.$$

It is easily shown that this tensor vanishes if the plasma rotates as a rigid body $\mathbf{V} = [\mathbf{\Omega r}]$ or if it undergoes a uniform isotropic compression, $\mathbf{V} = \mathrm{const}\,\mathbf{r}$; that is to say, this tensor vanishes if the volume elements of the plasma are not deformed. The tensors $W_{\alpha\beta}$ and $\pi_{\alpha\beta}$ are symmetric and have zero trace: $W_{\alpha\alpha} = 0$.

In the absence of a magnetic field the relation between $\pi_{\alpha\beta}$ and $W_{\alpha\beta}$ is the simple one, $\pi_{\alpha\beta} = -\eta_0 W_{\alpha\beta}$. The magnitude of the viscosity coefficient can be estimated from the usual kinetic-theory formula (3.3) by substituting $\Delta x \sim l \sim v\tau$; this procedure yields $\eta_0 \sim nT\tau$.

The presence of a magnetic field leads to significant differences between momentum transfer along the magnetic field and across the field; moreover, the direction of the transported momentum itself becomes important. In this case the relation between $\pi_{\alpha\beta}$ and $W_{\alpha\beta}$ is much more complicated and contains five independent viscosity coefficients. Since a symmetric tensor with zero trace has five independent components the most general linear homogeneous dependence requires precisely five independent coefficients of proportionality.

We now consider several simple cases involving plasma viscosity in a strong magnetic field $\omega\tau \gg 1$. In all of these cases it is assumed that the magnetic field is along the z axis.

First assume that the velocity is along the z axis and exhibits a derivative in this same direction; the momentum flux that arises is of the same order as in the absence of the field $\pi_{zz} \sim -\eta_0 \partial V_z/\partial z$ and the viscous stress is $F_z = (\partial/\partial z)\,\eta_0(\partial V_z/\partial z)$ since the longitudinal momentum is freely transported along the magnetic field.

Now suppose that the velocity V_z varies in a direction perpendicular to the field direction, say along the x axis. In this case momentum is transported across the magnetic field and in estimating the viscosity coefficient from Eq. (3.3) we must substitute $\Delta x \sim r$; this relation gives the following momentum flux and viscous stress:

$$\pi_{zx} \sim -\eta_\perp \frac{\partial V_z}{\partial x}, \quad F_z \sim \frac{\partial}{\partial x}\eta_\perp \frac{\partial V_z}{\partial x},$$

where

$$\eta_\perp \sim \frac{\eta_0}{(\omega\tau)^2} \sim \eta_1 \sim \eta_2$$

An analogous reduction of the viscosity by a factor of $(\omega\tau)^2$ obtains in the case in which the transverse velocity V_y varies along the x axis. In this case

$$\pi_{xy} \sim -\eta_\perp \frac{\partial V_y}{\partial x}, \quad F_y \sim \frac{\partial}{\partial x}\eta_\perp \frac{\partial V_y}{\partial x}.$$

The transport of transverse momentum is inhibited by the magnetic field even when this momentum is transported in the field direction. For example, if V_x varies in the z direction, i.e., if $\partial V_x/\partial z \neq 0$, the rate-of-strain tensor $W_{\alpha\beta}$ turns out to be the same as for $\partial V_z/\partial x \neq 0$ so that $\pi_{\alpha\beta}$ will also be the same: $\pi_{xz} \sim -\eta_\perp \partial V_x/\partial z$. It might be said that as a consequence of its gyration the particle loses its "memory" of transverse ordered velocity in a time $\sim \omega^{-1}$, during which it can only be displaced by a distance of the order of the Larmor radius.

As is evident from Eq. (2.21), the stress tensor also contains terms that are only reduced by a factor $\omega\tau$ (rather than $(\omega\tau)^2$) compared with the case $B = 0$. When $\partial V_y/\partial x \neq 0$, for example, there still are viscous fluxes and stresses given by

$$\pi_{xx} = -\pi_{yy} \sim \frac{nT}{\omega}\frac{\partial V_y}{\partial x} \sim \frac{\eta_0}{\omega\tau}\frac{\partial V_y}{\partial x}, \quad F_x \sim \frac{\partial}{\partial x}\frac{nT}{\omega}\frac{\partial V_y}{\partial x}.$$

When $\partial V_x/\partial z \neq 0$, there is a flux and stress

$$\pi_{yz} \sim \frac{nT}{\omega}\frac{\partial V_x}{\partial z} \sim \frac{\eta_0}{\omega\tau}\frac{\partial V_x}{\partial z}, \quad F_y \sim \frac{\partial}{\partial z}\frac{nT}{\omega}\frac{\partial V_x}{\partial z}.$$

These stresses are perpendicular to the velocity and do not result in dissipation of energy. The terms in the momentum flux that are independent of

τ are analogous to the transverse terms in the heat flux $\sim(nT/m\omega)[\mathbf{h}\nabla T]$; we shall not interpret these terms in detail, but refer the reader to a paper by Kaufmann[22] which contains a lucid discussion of this point.

Finally, we consider compression of a plasma in a direction perpendicular to a strong magnetic field, which leads to a correction in the scalar pressure because of a completely different mechanism. For example, assume that $V = V_x$ changes in the x direction so that $\operatorname{div}\mathbf{V} = \partial V_x/\partial x = -\dot{n}/n \neq 0$; the magnetic lines of force are also compressed and the magnetic field increases: $B \sim n$. In the growing field the transverse energy of the particles is increased and the energy is distributed over all three degrees of freedom as a consequence of collisions. However, equipartition of the energy does not occur in zero time; as a result the transverse pressure is found to be greater than the longitudinal pressure by a fractional amount of order $\tau\dot{B}/B = -\tau\dot{n}/n$, giving rise to a stress.

$$\pi_{xx} = \pi_{yy} \sim -p\frac{\tau\dot{n}}{n} \sim -\eta_0\frac{\partial V_x}{\partial x}, \quad \pi_{zz} \sim \eta_0\frac{\partial V_x}{\partial x}.$$

Thus, for motion characterized by $\operatorname{div}\mathbf{V} \neq 0$ the viscosity coefficient in a strong magnetic field is of the same order as with no field. The establishment of equilibrium is an irreversible process which, as is well known, always implies the dissipation of energy in the form of heat. In the present case the heat generated is

$$Q_{\text{vis}} = -\pi_{\alpha\beta}\frac{\partial V_\alpha}{\partial x_\beta} = -\pi_{xx}\frac{\partial V_x}{\partial x} \sim \eta_0\left(\frac{\partial V_x}{\partial x}\right)^2 \sim \eta_0\left(\frac{\dot{B}}{B}\right)^2.$$

Plasma heating based on this process is sometimes called gyrorelaxational heating.

In contrast with the case of thermal conductivity, where the electron conductivity is greater along the field (for $\omega_i\tau_i \gg 1$), when $T_e \sim T_i$ the ion viscosity is always much larger than the electron viscosity:

$$\eta_0^i \sim \left(\frac{m_i}{m_e}\right)^{1/2}\eta_0^e, \quad \frac{\eta_0^i}{\omega_i\tau_i} \sim \frac{m_i}{m_e}\frac{\eta_0^e}{\omega_e\tau_e}, \quad \frac{\eta_0^i}{\omega_i^2\tau_i^2} \sim \left(\frac{m_i}{m_e}\right)^{3/2}\frac{\eta_0^e}{\omega_e^2\tau_e^2}.$$

For this reason the viscosity of a plasma is determined essentially by the ions.

We may also note that the existence of thermal fluxes can also lead to the transfer of momentum and the production of viscous stresses even when V = 0. These stresses are always small but, in a strong magnetic field, can in principle be of the same order as the terms in Eq. (2.21) that contain the viscosity coefficient reduced by the factor $(\omega\tau)^2$. These stress terms can be estimated roughly by adding to the tensor $W_{\alpha\beta}$ a similar tensor composed of the derivatives of the vector $\mathbf{q}/nT$. A more rigorous quantitative calculation of these terms is given in [16, 22a].

Heat Generation. We assume first that the ion mass is infinite and that the ions are at rest on the average: $V_i = 0$. In this case collisions of electrons with ions occur without the exchange of energy. The electron velocities are randomized in the collisions so that the energy associated with the ordered velocity $\mathbf{u} = \mathbf{V}_e - \mathbf{V}_i$ is converted into heat. The ion energy is not changed. In this case the heat generated in the electron gas is equal to the work resulting from the frictional force exerted on the electrons by the ions $-\mathbf{Ru}$. We now assume that the ratio m_i/m_e is large, although finite, and that u = 0. If $T_e = T_i$ the ions and electrons are in thermal equilibrium and no heat is transferred between them. However, if $T_e > T_i$ heat is transferred from the electrons to the ions. It is well known, that when a light particle collides with a heavy fixed particle the order of magnitude of the transferred energy is given by the mass ratio m_1/m_2. For example, the mean transferred fractional energy in isotropic scattering is $2m_1/m_2$. Thus the energy exchanged per unit time between electrons and ions Q_Δ is roughly

$$Q_\Delta \sim \frac{n_e}{\tau_e}\frac{2m_e}{m_i}\frac{3}{2}(T_e - T_i).$$

The calculation of Q_Δ using a collision term was first carried out by Landau [11]. Landau showed that when τ_e is chosen in the form given in Eq. (2.5e) this relation becomes exact.

If $u \neq 0$ and $T_e - T_i \neq 0$ simultaneously, neglecting the fraction $(\sim m_e/m_i)$ of $-\mathbf{Ru}$ acquired by the ions and the $\sim m_e u^2/T_e$ corrections, we can simply add both of these effects so that

$$Q_i = Q_\Delta, \quad Q_e = -\mathbf{Ru} - Q_\Delta = -\mathbf{R}_u\mathbf{u} - \mathbf{R}_T\mathbf{u} - Q_\Delta .$$

The term $-\mathbf{R}_T\mathbf{u}$ is the Joule heat, which can be written in the more familiar form

$$Q_J = \frac{j_\parallel^2}{\sigma_\parallel} + \frac{j_\perp^2}{\sigma_\perp}.$$

This term ($R_T\mathbf{u}$) changes sign when either the direction of current flow or the temperature gradient are reversed and represents a reversible generation of heat. The analogous effect in metals is called the Thomson effect [4].

In formulating the heat balance in a plasma at high temperatures it is necessary to take account of bremsstrahlung and electron synchrotron radiation as well as the heat generated by thermonuclear reactions. Under these conditions Q_e and Q_i must be modified by the addition of appropriate terms.

Conditions of Applicability. The "fluxes" $\mathbf{q}$, $\pi_{\alpha\beta}$, $\mathbf{R}$, and Q that appear in the transport equations are defined under the assumption that the relaxation process, which forces the distribution function to approach a Maxwellian, is not inhibited; thus, these equations apply only when certain requirements are satisfied: essentially, the requirements are that all average quantities in the plasma must change slowly in time and space. The distribution function becomes a Maxwellian in a time of the order of the collision time; hence, if the transport equations are to be used all plasma quantities must not change significantly in a time τ, characteristic of the collisions, or over distances comparable to that traversed by the particles between collisions. The requirement that the time variations must be slow can be written

$$\frac{d}{dt} \ll \frac{1}{\tau}. \qquad (3.4)$$

The requirement that the spatial variations must be slow (for the case in which there is no magnetic field or when the field is weak, i.e., $\omega\tau \lesssim 1$) can be written

$$L \gg l, \qquad (3.5)$$

where L is the characteristic scale length over which all quantities change significantly; $\nabla \sim 1/L$. These two conditions must also be satisfied when the usual kinetic-theory (gas dynamics) equations are used.

In a strong magnetic field ($\omega\tau \gg 1$) the first requirement still applies but the second becomes somewhat more complicated. The motion of particles across the magnetic field is bounded by the Larmor radius r, which is smaller than the mean free path by a factor $\omega\tau$. Thus, in many cases the conditions of applicability are relaxed, becoming

$$L_{\perp} \gg r, \quad L_{\parallel} \gg l, \qquad (3.6)$$

where $L_\perp$ and $L_\parallel$ are the characteristic distances in the directions perpendicular and parallel to the magnetic field: $\nabla_\perp \sim 1/L_\perp$; $\nabla_\parallel \sim 1/L_\parallel$. However, the requirements are relaxed in this way only if the system is highly elongated along the magnetic field and has the required symmetry; typical examples are a long axisymmetric plasma cylinder of radius $\sim L_\perp$ with symmetric magnetic field, or a torus obtained by closing such a cylinder upon itself using a very large radius of curvature R. In an inhomogeneous magnetic field, the particles execute a drift motion with velocity of order $V_c \sim vr\,|\nabla B/B|$ in addition to gyrating around the Larmor circle. This drift represents particle displacement between collisions; if the drift trajectories of various particles pass through regions with different temperature there will be an additional transport of heat and a resulting deviation of the distribution function from a Maxwellian. The condition $L_\perp \gg r$ applies only when this "mixing" mechanism does not operate. In a symmetric system in which the curvature of the lines of force is small (for example a torus with a large radius of curvature $R \gg L_\perp$), the mixing occurs with a characteristic velocity of order vr/R; hence a particle can be displaced over a distance $\sim v_T r/R \sim l r/R$ in one collision time and the requirement $L_\perp \gg l r/R$ must be satisfied in addition to $L_\perp \gg r$. If this special kind of symmetry does not obtain mixing occurs with velocities of the order of $vr/L_\perp$ and the applicability requirement becomes

$$L_\perp \gg \sqrt{lr}, \quad L_\parallel \gg l. \tag{3.7}$$

In computing the transport coefficients we have used the collision term in the Landau form, in which case the effect of the magnetic field on the collision itself is neglected. This approach is valid if the Larmor radius is large compared with the effective dimensions of the region in which the Coulomb interaction occurs, that is to say, if the Larmor radius is large compared with the Debye radius $\delta_D = (T/4\pi e^2 n)^{1/2}$: $r \gg \delta_D$ or $B^2 \ll 8\pi n_e m_e c^2$.

The transport coefficients are changed to some extent if this condition is not satisfied; in practice the change is usually less than one order of magnitude because the importance of collisions characterized by impact parameters smaller than r can at most be $[\ln(\delta_D/r)]^{-1}$ times that of collisions having large impact parameters. The effect of a very strong magnetic field ($r \ll r_D$) on the transport coefficients has been considered in [19].

Let us now consider some numerical examples.

Take $B = 10^4$ G, $m_i = m_p$. Then $\omega_e = 1.8 \cdot 10^{11}\ \text{sec}^{-1}$; $\omega_i = 10^8\ \text{sec}^{-1}$.

With $n = 10^{14}$ cm^{-3} and $T_e = T_i = 30$ eV, using the notation $v = (2T/m)^{1/2}$ we find: $r_e = v_e/\omega_e = 1.8 \cdot 10^{-3}$ cm; $r_i = v_i/\omega_i = 7.7 \cdot 10^{-2}$ cm; $\delta_D = 4.1 \cdot 10^{-4}$ cm. The Coulomb logarithm $\lambda = 11$; $l_e \approx l_i \approx 20$ cm; $\tau_e = 5 \cdot 10^{-8}$ sec; $\tau_i = 3 \cdot 10^{-6}$ sec; $\omega_e \tau_e = 10^4$; $\omega_i \tau_i = 3 \cdot 10^2$.

When $n = 10^{17}$ cm^{-3}, $T_e = T_i = 10^2$ eV, we find $r_e = 3 \cdot 10^{-3}$ cm; $r_i = 1.4 \cdot 10^{-1}$ cm; $\delta_D = 2.4 \cdot 10^{-5}$ cm; $\lambda = 10$; $l_e \approx l_i \approx 0.25$ cm; $\tau_e = 3.5 \cdot 10^{-10}$ sec; $\tau_i = 2.1 \cdot 10^{-8}$ sec; $\omega_e \tau_e = 63$; $\omega_i \tau_i = 2$.

There is one other factor that can limit the applicability of the transport equations that have been used here. This is the presence of any instability in the plasma. An unstable plasma can generate random fluctuating fields which, in turn, can produce strong mixing with a significant enhancement of the transport coefficients. This effect is analogous to turbulence in hydrodynamics. For example, it is well known, that the flow in an ordinary water pipe cannot be computed by means of the stationary solutions of the Navier-Stokes equations because of turbulence effects.

At the present time the theory of plasma turbulence is only in its infancy. This subject will, in fact, be treated in subsequent volumes of the present review series. However, it may be appropriate at this point to make a simple estimate showing the extent to which the transport mechanisms can be enhanced in a magnitized plasma in a turbulent state.

Let us assume that the plasma generates fluctuating electric fields of amplitude $\sim E'$ which become uncorrelated at points separated by distances greater than l'. These fields cause particle drifts with characteristic velocities $V'_c \sim cE'/B$ which change direction randomly after the particle has drifted a distance of order l'. The effective diffusion coefficient appropriate to this mechanism can be estimated from Eq. (3.1) and we find $D_{turb} \sim l'V'_c \sim cE'l'/B$.

We now make the reasonable assumption that the amplitudes of the fluctuating fields are such that the corresponding energy is of the same order as the thermal energy of the particles, i.e., $eE'l' \sim T$. While this relation has obviously not been rigorously justified it can serve as a rough guide. We then have

$$D_{turb} \sim \frac{cT}{eB}. \tag{3.8}$$

Similar results are obtained for the other transport coefficients through the use of Eqs. (3.2) and (3.3). This estimate was first proposed by Bohm, who was one of the first investigators to note the possibility of a strong enhancement of the diffusion coefficient in a plasma as a result of turbulence and the associated fluctuating fields. Bohm published the expression $D = cT_e/16eB$ without formal derivation [23] and this diffusion coefficient is sometimes called the Bohm diffusion coefficient (cf. also [23a]). Comparing this coefficient with the "classical" transverse diffusion coefficient we find

$$\frac{D_{\text{turb}}}{r^2/\tau} \sim \omega\tau. \tag{3.9}$$

Thus, when $\omega\tau \gg 1$ turbulence in a plasma can, in principle, cause strong enhancement of all perpendicular (to the magnetic field) transport processes.

§ 4. Kinetics of a Simple Plasma (Quantitative Analysis)

The local distribution functions for ions and electrons can be determined by a successive-approximation method that is described, for example, in the well-known monograph of Chapman and Cowling [1]. This approach can be described roughly as follows. The distribution function is assumed to be approximately a Maxwellian f^0 with parameters n, **V**, and T, that are slowly varying functions of the coordinates and time, and is expanded in the form

$$f = f^0 + f^1 + f^2 + \cdots \tag{4.1}$$

The important terms in the kinetic equation are assumed to be the collision term and the magnetic term. The other terms, which contain space and time derivatives and the electric field, are assumed to be small. The magnetic term $[\mathbf{v}\boldsymbol{\omega}]\nabla_v f$ vanishes for any spherically symmetric velocity function.

If small terms are neglected the solution will be the function f^0, which is obtained by also setting equal to zero the collisional term and the magnetic term.*

In the next approximation, substituting $f = f^0 + f^1$ in the kinetic equation we only take account of f^0 in the small terms, neglecting f^1; in the

*This statement is not completely accurate and will be modified appropriately below.

collision term $C(f, f)$ we only consider the part that is linear in f^1, i. e., $C(f^0, f^1) + C(f^1, f^0)$; terms quadratic in f^1 are neglected. In the small terms the derivatives over coordinates and time appear only as a consequence of differentiation of the parameters n, **V**, and T; by means of the transport equations, (cf. §1) the time derivatives can then be expressed with the desired accuracy in terms of the coordinate derivatives at a given instant of time. This procedure results in a linear integro-differential equation for the function f^1 in velocity space. Having solved this equation we then find the function $f^1(\mathbf{v})$, which will be a linear function of both the parameters and of the factors that disturb the Maxwellian distribution: ∇T, $\partial V_\alpha/\partial x_\beta$, etc.

This procedure can be extended to take account of second-order perturbation terms in order to find f^2; however, this step leads to extremely complicated calculations. By substituting f^1 in the expressions for the heat flux, momentum flux, etc., it is possible to find these fluxes so that the chain of transport equations can be closed. This procedure requires that the neglected terms must be small compared with those that have been considered in determining the local distribution function, that is to say, the series in (4.1) must converge sufficiently rapidly. To determine the condition of applicability for the first approximation rigorously one should really find the corrections associated with the second approximation f^2 to be convinced that they are in fact small; however, we shall limit ourselves to the qualitative considerations given in §3.

Simplification of the Cross Terms in the Collision Integral. In the further analysis it will be found convenient to make a substitution in the kinetic equation (1.1); we shall replace the velocity **v** by the random velocity $\mathbf{v}_a = \mathbf{v} - \mathbf{V}_a(t, \mathbf{r})$. The function $f_a(t, \mathbf{r}, \mathbf{v}_a)$ is then described by the equation

$$\frac{d_a f_a}{dt} + \mathbf{v}_a \nabla f_a + \left(\frac{e_a}{m_a}\mathbf{E}_a^* - \frac{d_a \mathbf{V}_a}{dt}\right)\nabla_v f_a - \\ - \frac{\partial V_{a\gamma}}{\partial x_\beta} v_{a\beta}\frac{\partial f_a}{\partial v_{a\gamma}} + \frac{e_a}{m_a c}[\mathbf{v}_a \mathbf{B}]\nabla_v f_a = \sum_b C_{ab}(f_a, f_b), \qquad (4.2)$$

where ∇_v is the gradient in velocity space;

$$\frac{d_a}{dt} = \frac{\partial}{\partial t} + (\mathbf{V}_a \nabla), \quad \mathbf{E}_a^* = \mathbf{E} + \frac{1}{c}[\mathbf{V}_a \mathbf{B}].$$

In deriving Eq. (4.2) from (1.1) we have also taken account of the fact that $\nabla_v \mathbf{F} = 0$.

The collisional term is taken in the Landau form [11]:

$$C_{ab}(f_a, f_b) = -\frac{2\pi\lambda e_a^2 e_b^2}{m_a} \frac{\partial}{\partial v_\beta} \int \left\{ \frac{f_a(\mathbf{v})}{m_b} \cdot \frac{\partial f_b(\mathbf{v}')}{\partial v'_\gamma} - \frac{f_b(\mathbf{v}')}{m_a} \frac{\partial f_a(\mathbf{v})}{\partial v_\gamma} \right\} U_{\beta\gamma} d\mathbf{v}'; \tag{4.3}$$

$$U_{\beta\gamma} = \frac{1}{u^3}(u^2\delta_{\beta\gamma} - u_\beta u_\gamma); \quad u_\beta = v_\beta - v_\beta .$$

In collisions between particles it is the relative velocity that is important $\mathbf{v} - \mathbf{v}'$; hence, Eq. (4.3) retains its form in any coordinate system, but obviously the distribution functions in Eq. (4.3) must be expressed in the same coordinate system.

The Coulomb logarithm λ in Eq. (4.3) is equal to the logarithm of the ratio of maximum to minimum impact parameters $\lambda = \ln(p_{max}/p_{min})$. The lower parameter will henceforth be taken to be the impact parameter characterizing a deflection through an angle of $\pi/2$ so that $p_{min} \approx e^2/m\langle v^2\rangle \approx e^2/3T$. The maximum impact parameter is defined in such a way that the Coulomb field of the plasma particles is screened at distances of the order of the Debye length $p_{max} \approx \delta_D$, where $\delta_D = (T_e/4\pi e^2 n)^{1/2}$. At large velocities, in which case $e^2/hv < 1$, where h is Planck's constant (i.e., $v/c < 1/137$), it is necessary to use a smaller value for the maximum impact parameter; specifically, we use the distance for which the scattering angle is of the same order as the quantum uncertainty, in which case $p_{max} \approx \delta_D e^2/hv$. The effect of the magnetic field on the collisions themselves is not considered in Eq. (4.3); this procedure is justified as the fields are weak enough so that the radius of curvature of the particle trajectory is large compared with the Debye length.

The solution of the ion and electron kinetic equations can be simplified by exploiting the fact that the mass ratio of these particles is small. When this is done the cross terms in the collision integral C_{ei} and C_{ie} can be simplified and the equations in (4.2) can be solved separately. This simplification results from the fact that the relative velocity is essentially equal to the electron velocity since the electron velocities are much greater than the ion velocities. Thus, to a high degree of accuracy the collisional cross term $C_{ei}(f_e, f_i)$ is independent of the detailed form of the ion distribution function and can be determined from a knowledge of the mean quantities n_i, $\mathbf{V}_i$, and T_i.

The tensor $U_{\alpha\beta} = (u^2\delta_{\alpha\beta} - u_\alpha u_\beta)u^{-3}$ that appears in C_{ei} depends on the difference between the electron velocity $\mathbf{v}$ and the ion velocity $\mathbf{v}'$ since $\mathbf{u} = \mathbf{v} - \mathbf{v}'$. Let us expand $U_{\alpha\beta}$ in powers of the ion velocity

$$U_{\alpha\beta} = V_{\alpha\beta} - \frac{\partial V_{\alpha\beta}}{\partial v_\gamma} v'_\gamma + \frac{\partial V_{\alpha\beta}}{\partial v_\gamma \partial v_\delta} \frac{v'_\gamma v'_\delta}{2} + \ldots,$$

where

$$V_{\alpha\beta} = U_{\alpha\beta}|_{v'=0} = \frac{1}{v^3}(v^2\delta_{\alpha\beta} - v_\alpha v_\beta),$$

and integrate over $\mathbf{v}'$; an approximate expression is then obtained for C_{ei}. This calculation is convenient in the coordinate system in which the mean ion velocity is zero. As a result we find

$$C_{ei} = \frac{3\sqrt{\pi}}{8}\frac{1}{\tau_e}\left(\frac{2T_e}{m_e}\right)^{3/2}\frac{\partial}{\partial v_\alpha}\left\{V_{\alpha\beta}\frac{\partial f_e}{\partial v_\beta} + \right.$$
$$\left. + \frac{m_e}{m_i}\left(\frac{2v_\alpha}{v^3}f_e + \frac{T_i}{m_e}\frac{3v_\alpha v_\beta - v^2\delta_{\alpha\beta}}{v^5}\frac{\partial f_e}{\partial v_\beta}\right)\right\}. \quad (4.4)$$

Here

$$\tau_e = \frac{3\sqrt{m_e}\,T_e^{3/2}}{4\sqrt{2\pi}\,\lambda e^2 e_i^2 n_i}. \quad (4.5)$$

The electron velocity in Eq. (4.4) is computed from the mean ion velocity $\mathbf{V}_i$ (rather than $\mathbf{V}_e$). The first (principal) term in Eq. (4.4) will be called C'_{ei} below; it is completely independent of the ion distribution function:

$$C'_{ei} = \frac{3\sqrt{\pi}}{8}\frac{1}{\tau_e}\left(\frac{2T_e}{m_e}\right)^{3/2}\frac{\partial}{\partial v_\alpha}\left(V_{\alpha\beta}\frac{\partial f_e}{\partial v_\beta}\right). \quad (4.4')$$

In the integration over $\mathbf{v}'$ in the second term $C''_{ei} \sim m_e/m_i$ we have neglected the difference between the ion pressure tensor and the scalar pressure $n_i T_i$ (i. e., we have neglected $\pi_{i\alpha\beta}$). We compute the friction force $\mathbf{R}^0$ exerted on the electrons by the ions when the electrons have a Maxwellian distribution shifted with respect to the ion distribution by an amount* $\mathbf{U} = \mathbf{V}_e - \mathbf{V}_i$. Assuming that the displacement is small compared with the electron thermal velocity and expanding in U we can write this electron distribution approximately in the coordinate system in which $V_i = 0$:

*Here, in contrast with §2 and 3, the difference of the mean velocities is denoted by a capital letter.

$$f_e = f_e^0\left(1 + \frac{m_e}{T_e}\mathbf{U}\mathbf{v}\right), \text{where } f_e^0 = \frac{n_e}{(2\pi T_e/m_e)^{3/2}}\exp\left(-\frac{m_e v^2}{2T_e}\right).$$

Substituting this expression in Eq. (4.4), using Eq. (1.18), and neglecting m_e/m_i terms we find

$$\mathbf{R}^0 = \frac{3\sqrt{\pi}}{8}\frac{1}{\tau_e}\left(\frac{2T_e}{m_e}\right)^{3/2}\int m_e\mathbf{v}\frac{\partial}{\partial v_\alpha}\left\{V_{\alpha\beta}\frac{m_e}{T_e}U_\beta f_e^0\right\}d\mathbf{v} = -\frac{m_e n_e}{\tau_e}\mathbf{U}. \tag{4.6}$$

Here we have made use of the following property of the tensor $V_{\alpha\beta}$: $v_\alpha V_{\alpha\beta} = V_{\alpha\beta} v_\beta = 0$; thus, C'_{ei} vanishes for any spherically symmetric electron distribution function. The property $\partial V_{\alpha\beta}/\partial v_\alpha = -2v_\beta/v^3$ and $\overline{v_\alpha v_\beta} = (v^2/3)\delta_{\alpha\beta}$ has also been used (the bar denotes an average over direction).

The quantity τ_e derived in Eq. (4.4), which represents the characteristic time between electron-ion collisions, is chosen in such a way that Eq. (4.6) (for $\mathbf{R}^0$) will be of simple form.

The ion-electron collision integral $C_{ie}(f_i, f_e)$ can also be simplified by expanding the tensor $U_{\alpha\beta}$ in powers of the ratio of ion velocity $\mathbf{v}$ to electron velocity $\mathbf{v}'$:

$$U_{\alpha\beta} = V'_{\alpha\beta} - \frac{\partial V'_{\alpha\beta}}{\partial v'_\gamma}v_\gamma + \ldots, \quad V'_{\alpha\beta} = \frac{1}{v'^3}\left(v'^2\delta_{\alpha\beta} - v'_\alpha v'_\beta\right).$$

Here, however, the electron distribution function must be known, in order to actually carry out the integration over electron velocity $\mathbf{v}'$. Let us assume that the electron distribution function is essentially a Maxwellian f_e^0, i. e., assume the form $f_e = f_e^0 + f_e^1$, where f_e^1 is a small correction, in which the difference in mean velocities $\mathbf{U} = \mathbf{V}_e - \mathbf{V}_i$ is small compared with the characteristic electron velocity. Some simple calculations yield the approximate relation

$$C_{ie} = \frac{m_e n_e}{m_i n_i}\frac{1}{\tau_e}\frac{\partial}{\partial v_\alpha}\left(v_\alpha f_i + \frac{T_e}{m_i}\frac{\partial f_e}{\partial v_\alpha}\right) + \frac{1}{m_i n_i}\mathbf{R}_i\nabla_v f_i. \tag{4.7}$$

Here the ion velocity is computed from the mean ion velocity $\mathbf{V}_i$. In accordance with Eq. (1.18) we have used the notation $\mathbf{R}_i = \int m_i\mathbf{v}C_{ie}\,d\mathbf{v} = -\mathbf{R}$ ($\mathbf{R}$ without a subscript denotes $\mathbf{R}_e$). The calculation required for the derivation of Eq. (4.7) can be carried out conveniently in the coordinate system in which the mean electron velocity is zero ($V_e = 0$); we then convert to a system in which the mean ion velocity vanishes ($V_i = 0$) for which $\mathbf{v}$

is replaced by $\mathbf{v}-\mathbf{U}$ and Eq. (4.6) (for $\mathbf{R}^0$) is used. In computing small-correction collisions due to f_e^1 we need consider only the leading term $V'_{\alpha\beta}$ in $U_{\alpha\beta}$.

As is to be expected, Eq. (4.7) is of the same form as the Fokker-Planck collisional term that describes Brownian motion of particles in a moving medium with temperature T_e.

The collisional heat exchange between electrons and ions can be computed neglecting the small deviations from a Maxwellian in the distribution functions. Substituting Eq. (4.7) in Eq. (1.22), for a Maxwellian ion function we find $Q_i = Q_\Delta$ where

$$Q_\Delta = \frac{3m_e}{m_i}\frac{n_e}{\tau_e}(T_e - T_i). \tag{4.8}$$

Similarly, using Eq. (4.5) and taking account of m_e/m_i terms we obtain $Q_e = -Q_\Delta$ if it is assumed that the electrons have a Maxwellian distribution with $\mathbf{V}_e = \mathbf{V}_i$. In the general case it is easiest to compute Q_e using conservation of energy and momentum (1.24) for the collisions: $Q_e + Q_i = -\mathbf{RU}$, whence

$$Q_e = -\mathbf{RU} - Q_\Delta. \tag{4.9}$$

In the remainder of this section we shall only use the variables $\mathbf{v}_a = \mathbf{v} - \mathbf{V}_a(t, \mathbf{r})$, i.e., the random velocities; for reasons of brevity the subscript a will be omitted.

Correction Equations. We now derive the equations for the electron distribution functions. The electron kinetic equation (4.2) can be written

$$C_{ee}(f_e, f_e) + C'_{ei}(f_e, f'_i) - [\mathbf{v}\boldsymbol{\omega}_e]\nabla_v f_e =$$

$$= \frac{d_e f_e}{dt} + \mathbf{v}\nabla f_e + \left(\frac{e_e}{m_e}E_e^* - \frac{d_e\mathbf{V}_e}{dt}\right)\nabla_v f_e - \frac{\partial V_{e\alpha}}{\partial x_\beta} v_\beta \frac{\partial f_e}{\partial v_\alpha} -$$
$$- C'_{ei}(f_e, f_i - f'_i) - C''_{ei}(f_e, f_i). \tag{4.10}$$

Here $\boldsymbol{\omega}_e = (e_e/m_e c)\mathbf{B}$ is a vector whose magnitude is equal to the cyclotron frequency of the electrons and whose direction is antiparallel to the magnetic field since $e_e = -e$.

The terms on the right side of this equation will be small if the gradients are small, if the time variations are slow, and if the shift between the mean velocities of the electrons and ions is small.

In Eq. (4.10) we have added and subtracted the term $C'_{ei}(f_e, f'_i)$ where f'_i is the ion distribution function shifted in such a way that the mean ion velocity coincides with the mean electron velocity. Hence $C'_{ei}(f_e, f'_i)$ represents the quantity C'_{ei} [in accordance with Eq. (4.4)] but with the electron velocity computed from $\mathbf{V}_e$ [as is the case for all terms in Eq. (4.10)]. The term $C'_{ei}(f_e, f_i - f'_i)$ on the right side of the equation is small compared with $C'_{ei}(f_e, f'_i)$ if the relative macroscopic velocity of the electrons and ions $\mathbf{U} = \mathbf{V}_e - \mathbf{V}_i$ is small compared with the thermal velocity of the electrons, a condition that has been assumed.

The zeroth approximation satisfies the equation with the right side set equal to zero. Its solution is a Maxwellian distribution with mean velocity $\mathbf{V}_e$ and arbitrary density and temperature. We take the parameters of this distribution to be the density and temperature of the electrons at a given point in space.

Consider Eq. (4.10); if the entire cross-collisional integral C_{ei} on the left is retained, the solution of the equation without the right side (with the corresponding equation for the ions) is a Maxwellian distribution with $T_e = T_i$ and $\mathbf{V}_e = \mathbf{V}_i$. This is the approach used in the monograph of Chapman and Cowling. However, this approach does not exploit the fact that the ratio m_e/m_i is small. The regrouping in C_{ei} used in Eq. (4.10), in which only $C'_{ei}(f_e, f'_i)$ remains as a principal term is necessary specifically in order to eliminate the effect of small terms on the choice of the zeroth approximation. This feature makes it possible to obtain separate transport equations for the electrons and ions with (different temperatures and different velocities) and to uncouple the electron and ion kinetic equations.

Let us write the electron distribution function in the form $f_e = f_e^0(1 + \Phi)$ where Φ is a small correction. By substituting this expression in Eq. (4.10) and neglecting second-order terms we can obtain an equation for the correction term. As a result of this linearization procedure the left side becomes

$$I_{ee}(\Phi) + I_{ei}(\Phi) - f_e^0 [\mathbf{v}\boldsymbol{\omega}_e] \nabla_v \Phi,$$

where

$$I_{ee}(\Phi) = C_{ee}(f_e^0, f_e^0\Phi) + C_{ee}(f_e^0\Phi, f_e^0), \tag{4.11}$$

$$I_{ei}(\Phi) = C'_{ei}(f_e^0\Phi, f'_i).$$

It is valid to substitute f^0 on the right side of Eq. (4.10) and to omit m_e/m_i terms; then, expanding the integral $C'_{ei}(f_e^0, f_i - f'_i)$ in powers of $U(m_e/T_e)^{1/2}$, it is valid to neglect all terms beyond the first term of the expansion. The time derivatives of n_e, $\mathbf{V}_e$, and T_e on the right side can be replaced by their zeroth approximations. With the right side set equal to zero the equation has the solutions* $\Phi = 1$, v^2; hence, if the equation is to be solved the right side must be orthogonal to this solution.

Multiplying the correction equation by 1, $\mathbf{v}$, and $m_e v^2/2$ and integrating over velocity we obtain an expression for the zeroth time derivatives of n_e, $\mathbf{V}_e$, and T_e which are to be substituted in the right side. These expressions are the same as those derived from the transport equations in the zeroth approximation, i.e., neglecting viscosity, heat flow, etc. The first-approximation correction Φ is thus given by

$$I_{ee}(\Phi) + I_{ei}(\Phi) - f_e^0 [\mathbf{v}\,\omega_e] \nabla_v \Phi = f_e^0 \left\{ \left(\frac{m_e v^2}{2T_e} - \frac{5}{2} \right) \mathbf{v} \nabla \ln T_e + \right.$$

$$+ \left[\frac{3\sqrt{\pi}}{\sqrt{2}} \frac{(T_e/m_e)^{3/2}}{v^3} - 1 \right] \frac{m_e}{T_e \tau_e} \mathbf{U}\mathbf{v} + \frac{1}{n_e T_e} \mathbf{R}^1 \mathbf{v} +$$

$$\left. + \frac{m_e}{2T_e} \left(v_\alpha v_\beta - \frac{v^2}{3} \delta_{\alpha\beta} \right) W_{e\alpha\beta} \right\}, \tag{4.12}$$

where

$$\mathbf{R}^1 = \int m_e \mathbf{v} I_{ei}(\Phi)\, d\mathbf{v}. \tag{4.13}$$

We note that the right side of Eq. (4.12) does not contain terms proportional to ∇n and $\mathbf{g}_e = (e_e \mathbf{E}_e^*/m_e) - d_e \mathbf{V}_e/dt$. This results from the fact that the $f_e^0 \mathbf{v} \nabla \ln n_e$ term is combined with $\mathbf{g}_e \nabla_v f_e^0 = -f_e^0 (m_e/T_e)(\mathbf{v}\mathbf{g}_e)$ and that the sum of these gives terms proportional to ∇T_e and $\mathbf{R} = \mathbf{R}^0 + \mathbf{R}^1 = -(m_e n_e/\tau_e)\mathbf{U} + \mathbf{R}^1$ as follows from the equation of motion $-m_e n_e \mathbf{g}_e = \nabla n_e T_e + \mathbf{R}$.

We now symmetrize the last term on the right side of Eq. (4.12) forming the symmetric tensor with zero trace $W_{\alpha\beta}$

$$W_{\alpha\beta} = \frac{\partial V_\alpha}{\partial x_\beta} + \frac{\partial V_\beta}{\partial x_\alpha} - \frac{2}{3} \delta_{\alpha\beta} \operatorname{div} \mathbf{V}, \tag{4.14}$$

which is called the rate-of-strain tensor.

---

*This follows immediately from the fact that the left side of Eq. (4.10) vanishes for a Maxwellian distribution with arbitrary n and t.

The ion kinetic equation is transformed in similar fashion with the difference that the cross-collisional term C_{ie} (as can be shown by simple estimates) is small compared with the "self" term C_{ii} so that the former is grouped with the small terms and transferred to the right side. The zeroth approximation, which satisfies the equation without the right side, is the Maxwell distribution f_i^0. The ion distribution function is written in the form $f_i = f_i^0(1 + \Phi)$ where the small correction is given by the equation:

$$I_{ii}(\Phi) - f_i^0 [\mathbf{v}\omega_i] \nabla_v \Phi =$$
$$= f_i^0 \left\{ \left(\frac{m_i v^2}{2T_i} - \frac{5}{2} \right) \mathbf{v} \nabla \ln T_i + \frac{m_i}{2T_i} \left(v_\alpha v_\beta - \frac{v^2}{3} \delta_{\alpha\beta} \right) W_{i\alpha\beta} \right\}. \tag{4.15}$$

The terms on the right associated with electron-ion collisions cancel if C_{ie} is written in the form corresponding to Eq. (4.7). Thus, Eq. (4.15) has the same form as for a single-component gas (rather than a mixture). In this approximation the form of the ion distribution function is determined exclusively by ion-ion collisions. On the other hand, the form of the electron distribution function is determined both by self-collisions (electron-electron) and cross-collisions (electron-ion), as follows from Eqs. (4.12) and (4.13).

Equation (4.15) determines the correction Φ to terms of order $c_0 + \mathbf{c}_1 \cdot \mathbf{v} + c_2 v^2$, which causes the left side to vanish. Since the zeroth approximation gives the correct value of the density, mean velocity, and mean energy of the ions, these terms are determined from the requirement that the correction must not change the values of these parameters, i.e.,

$$\int f^0 \Phi d\mathbf{v} = 0, \quad \int \mathbf{v} f^0 \Phi d\mathbf{v} = 0, \quad \int v^2 f^0 \Phi d\mathbf{v} = 0. \tag{4.16}$$

The same conditions must be satisfied by the correction to the electron distribution function. This requirement can obviously be satisfied: the left side of Eq. (4.12) vanishes as an expression of the form $c_0 + c_2 v^2$, while the right side contains a term proportional to the unspecified magnitude $\mathbf{R}^1$ so that a solution can be sought in a form that will satisfy the condition $\int \mathbf{v} f_e^0 \Phi d\mathbf{v} = 0$.

Solution of Eqs. (4.12) and (4.15). Equations (4.12) and (4.15) are linear; this means that the solutions can be written as a sum of terms, each of which corresponds to some single perturbing factor—the temperature gradient ∇T, the velocity shift $\mathbf{U}$, the inhomogeneity in the velocities $W_{\alpha\beta}$.

Considerations of tensor invariance indicate the following form of the solution:

$$\Phi(\mathbf{v}) = \Phi_\alpha(v^2)\, v_\alpha + \Phi_{\alpha\beta}(v^2)\left(v_\alpha v_\beta - \frac{v^2}{3}\,\delta_{\alpha\beta}\right). \qquad (4.17)$$

Here, the first (vector) term corresponds to the vector perturbations ∇T and $\mathbf{U}$ while the second (tensor) term corresponds to $W_{\alpha\beta}$. The first and second terms are obviously orthogonal since averaging over angle in velocity space gives $\overline{v_\alpha} = 0$, $\overline{v_\alpha v_\beta v_\gamma} = 0$. The angular dependence of the first and second terms in velocity space is expressed by spherical functions of first and second order respectively. The heat flux $\mathbf{q}$ and the momentum transfer due to collisions $\mathbf{R}^1$ are specified exclusively by the vector $\mathbf{\Phi}$ while the viscosity $\pi_{\alpha\beta}$ is determined only by the tensor $\Phi_{\alpha\beta}$.

As an example, let us consider how to determine the correction $\Phi_\alpha v_\alpha$ for the electrons connected with ∇T_e and the appropriate parts of $\mathbf{q}_e$ and $\mathbf{R}^1$. The collision integrals are isotropic and do not depend on a specified direction. Hence, in the absence of a magnetic field, the symmetry of the problem indicates that the dependence of the vector $\mathbf{\Phi}(v^2)$ on ∇T_e must be of the form $\mathbf{\Phi}(v^2) = A(v^2)\nabla \ln T_e$, where A is a scalar function. In a magnetic field this dependence is of the form

$$\mathbf{\Phi}(v^2) = A\nabla_\parallel \ln T_e + A'\nabla_\perp \ln T_e + A''[\boldsymbol{\omega}_e \nabla \ln T_e], \qquad (4.18)$$

where $\nabla_\parallel \ln T_e$ and $\nabla_\perp \ln T_e$ are the components of the vector $\nabla \ln T_e$ parallel and perpendicular to the magnetic field. Evidently it is sufficient to consider the case of a transverse gradient since $A(v^2)$ is obtained from $A'(v^2)$ by writing $\omega_e = 0$.

The equation that describes the part of the correction arising from $\nabla_\perp \ln T_e$ is

$$I_{ee}(\Phi) + I_{ei}(\Phi) - f_e^0\,[\mathbf{v}\boldsymbol{\omega}_e]\nabla_v\Phi = f_e^0\left\{\left(\frac{m_e v^2}{2T_e} - \frac{5}{2}\right)\mathbf{v}\nabla_\perp \ln T_e + \right.$$
$$\left. + \frac{1}{n_e T_e}\,\mathbf{R}_T^1\mathbf{v}\right\}. \qquad (4.19)$$

The thermal force $\mathbf{R}_T^1$ can be written in the form

$$\mathbf{R}_T^1 = n_e T_e\left(K'\nabla_\perp \ln T_e + K''[\boldsymbol{\omega}_e \nabla \ln T_e]\right),$$

where K' and K" are functions as yet unknown. Substituting Eqs. (4.18) and

(4.20) and setting the coefficients of $\nabla_\perp \ln T_e$ and $[\omega_e \nabla \ln T_e]$ equal to zero, we obtain two equations for determining A' and A". Introducing the complex quantities

$$A = A' + i(\omega_e \mathbf{h}) A'', \quad K = K' + i(\omega_e \mathbf{h}) K'', \tag{4.20}$$

we can reduce these to a single equation for A:

$$I_{ee}(A\mathbf{v}) + I_{ei}(A\mathbf{v}) - i(\omega_e \mathbf{h}) f_e^0 A\mathbf{v} = f_e^0 \left\{ \frac{m_e v^2}{2T_e} - \frac{5}{2} + K \right\} \mathbf{v}. \tag{4.21}$$

In order to avoid the need for numerical solution of this integral equation, we proceed as in reference [1]. The quantity $A(v^2)$ is expanded in terms of orthogonal functions; in the present case it is convenient to use the Sonine polynomials (sometimes called Laguerre polynomials). These polynomials $L_p^{(m)}(x)$ have the following generating function:

$$(1-\xi)^{-m-1} \exp\left(-\frac{x\xi}{1-\xi}\right) = \sum_{p=0}^{\infty} \xi^p L_p^{(m)}(x). \tag{4.22}$$

The polynomials are orthogonal over the interval 0 to ∞ with respect to the weighting factor $x^m e^{-x}$:

$$\int_0^\infty x^m e^{-x} L_p^{(m)}(x) L_q^{(m)}(x)\, dx = \frac{(p+m)!}{p!} \delta_{pq}. \tag{4.23}$$

The first two polynomials $L_0^{(m)} = 1$; $L_1^{(m)} = m + 1 - x$.

We expand $A(v^2)$ in the form

$$A(v^2) = \tau_e \sum_{k=1}^{\infty} a_k L_k^{(3/2)}(x), \quad x = \frac{m_e v^2}{2T_e}. \tag{4.24}$$

The expansion starts with the k = 1 term rather than the k = 0 term in order to satisfy the condition $\int \mathbf{v} f_e^0 \Phi d\mathbf{v} = 0$. Multiplying Eq. (4.21) by

$$-\frac{4}{15} \frac{1}{n_e} \frac{m_e}{2T_e} \mathbf{v} L_k^{(3/2)} \left(\frac{m_e v^2}{2T_e}\right) d\mathbf{v},$$

integrating over velocity, and using Eq. (4.23), we now find that the integral equation is replaced by an infinite system of algebraic equations for the expansion coefficients:

$$\sum_{l=1}^{\infty}\left(\alpha_{kl}+\alpha'_{kl}\right)a_l+i\,(\omega_e\mathbf{h})\,\tau_e\frac{(k+{}^3/_2)\,!}{k\,!\,({}^5/_2)\,!}\,a_k=\delta_{1k},\quad k=1,\,2,\ldots,\tag{4.25}$$

where α_{kl} and α'_{kl} are the dimensionless matrices:

$$\alpha_{kl}=-\frac{4\tau_e}{15n_e}\frac{m_e}{2T_e}\int L_k^{(^3/_2)}(x)\,v_\beta I_{ee}\left(L_l^{(^3/_2)}(x)\,v_\beta\right)d\mathbf{v};\qquad x=\frac{m_ev^2}{2T_e}:$$

$$\alpha'_{kl}=-\frac{4\tau_e}{15n_e}\frac{m_e}{2T_e}\int L_k^{(^3/_2)}(x)\,v_\beta I_{ei}\left(L_l^{(^3/_2)}(x)\,v_\beta\right)d\mathbf{v}.\tag{4.26}$$

Equations (1.18), (1.21), (4.23) and (4.26) can be used to write the heat flux $\mathbf{q}_T$ and the thermal force $\mathbf{R}_T$ in terms of the expansion coefficients in (4.24):

$$\mathbf{q}_T=-\frac{5}{2}\frac{n_eT_e\tau_e}{m_e}\left(a'_1\nabla_\perp T_e+a''_1[\omega_e\nabla T_e]\right),\tag{4.27}$$

$$\mathbf{R}_T=-\frac{5}{2}n_e\sum_{k=1}^{\infty}\alpha'_{0k}\left(a'_k\nabla_\perp T_e+a''_k[\omega_e\nabla T_e]\right),\tag{4.28}$$

where, by analogy with Eq. (4.20), we write $a_k = a'_k + i(\omega_e\mathbf{h})\,a''_k$. If the expansion of $A(v^2)$ is now limited to the first few terms in the series (4.24) a corresponding cutoff can be introduced in (4.25). Solving the resulting finite system for the first few coefficients we obtain approximate expressions for the heat flux and thermal force by dividing a_k into real and imaginary parts and using Eqs. (4.27) and (4.28).

In completely analogous fashion we can find the contributions to the distribution functions and the contributions to $\mathbf{q}_e$ and $\mathbf{R}^1$ due to the relative velocity $\mathbf{U} = \mathbf{V}_e - \mathbf{V}_i$ as well as the correction to the ion distribution function due to ∇T_i; the ion heat flux can also be found. The appropriate system of equations analogous to (4.25) and the coefficient matrices α_{kl} and α'_{kl} are given in [17].

The calculation of $\Phi_{\alpha\beta}$ and the viscosity tensor proceeds in analogous fashion but the division of the perturbation into independent parts is somewhat more complicated. The tensor $W_{\alpha\beta}$ is divided into three independent parts $W_{\alpha\beta} = W_{0\alpha\beta} + W_{1\alpha\beta} + W_{2\alpha\beta}$ and two new tensors $W_{3\alpha\beta}$ and $W_{4\alpha\beta}$ made up of components of $W_{\alpha\beta}$ are introduced. The correction to the

Maxwellian distribution due to the perturbation $W_{\alpha\beta}$ is written in the form

$$\Phi_{\alpha\beta}v_{\alpha\beta} = -\sum_{p=0}^{4} B_p(v^2) W_{p\alpha\beta}v_{\alpha\beta}, \text{ where } v_{\alpha\beta} = v_\alpha v_\beta - \frac{v^2}{3}\delta_{\alpha\beta} \tag{4.29}$$

The tensors $W_{p\alpha\beta}$ can be chosen so that the magnetic operator $[\mathbf{vh}]\nabla_v$ causes the term $W_{0\alpha\beta}v_{\alpha\beta}$ to vanish and $[\mathbf{vh}]\nabla_v W_{1\alpha\beta}v_{\alpha\beta} = 2W_{3\alpha\beta}v_{\alpha\beta}$; $[\mathbf{vh}]\nabla_v W_{3\alpha\beta}v_{\alpha\beta} = -2W_{1\alpha\beta}v_{\alpha\beta}$; $[\mathbf{vh}]\nabla_v W_{2\alpha\beta}v_{\alpha\beta} = W_{4\alpha\beta}v_{\alpha\beta}$; $[\mathbf{vh}]\nabla_v W_{4\alpha\beta}v_{\alpha\beta} = -W_{2\alpha\beta}v_{\alpha\beta}$. Thus, there are three independent kinds of motion all of which have different effects on the viscosity. The corrections associated with each of these $\Phi_{\alpha\beta}$ can be found independently. The equations for B_1, B_3 and for B_2, B_4 can be combined in pairs by the introduction of appropriate complex quantities. The function $B(v^2)$ is found by the same approximation method as $A(v^2)$. The function $B(v^2)$ can be represented conveniently in a series in the polynomials $L_k^{(5/2)}(mv^2/2T)$ in which an appropriate cutoff is introduced in the chain of algebraic equations for the expansion coefficients. This system of equations is given in [17]. The viscosity tensor is found by means of Eq. (1.17). It depends only on the coefficient of $L_0^{(5/2)}$.

The larger the number of polynomials N used to approximate the correction to the distribution function the more exact the transport coefficients that are obtained by the approximate method we have described. Comparison of the results obtained with different values of N shows that the error in certain coefficients can be comparable with the coefficient itself when N = 1; however, the accuracy increases sharply if N = 2. Further increases in N do not increase the accuracy significantly but do increase the complexity of the expressions greatly. The transport coefficients obtained with two approximation polynomials [17]* are given below.

The results of calculations of the electron fluxes in which a large number of polynomials have been used (up to N = 6) for $0 \leq \omega_e\tau_e \leq 6$ are given in [21]. "Exact" values of the transport coefficients for $\omega_e\tau_e = 0$ have been obtained in [14] by numerical integration of the correction equations.

An accuracy of several percent is obtained when N = 2 and $\omega\tau = 0$. The asymptotic behavior of the transport coefficients for $\omega\tau \to \infty$ is deter-

*We wish to note certain typographical errors in [17]: In Eq. (3.18) for $\mathbf{q}_u$ the minus sign in front of the curly brackets should be replaced by a plus sign. In Eq. (4.14) the quantity b" should read −b", since −b" is a positive number, as follows from Eq. (4.13).

mined by numerical coefficients which are given below in the form of simple rational fractions. These coefficients have been obtained exactly [18]. The largest error (10-20%) in the transport coefficients occurs in the intermediate region $\omega\tau \sim 1$.

Results. The transfer of momentum from the ions to the electrons in collisions $\mathbf{R} = \mathbf{R}^0 + \mathbf{R}^1$ is made up of the frictional force $\mathbf{R}_u = \mathbf{R}^0_u + \mathbf{R}^1_u$ and the thermal force $\mathbf{R}_T = \mathbf{R}^1_T$:

$$\mathbf{R}_u = -\alpha_\parallel \mathbf{u}_\parallel - \alpha_\perp \mathbf{u}_\perp + \alpha_\wedge [\mathbf{h}\mathbf{u}], \tag{4.30}$$

$$\mathbf{R}_T = -\beta_\parallel^{uT} \nabla_\parallel T_e - \beta_\perp^{uT} \nabla_\perp T_e - \beta_\wedge^{uT} [\mathbf{h}\nabla T_e]. \tag{4.31}$$

The electron heat flux $\mathbf{q}_e = \mathbf{q}^e_u + \mathbf{q}^e_T$ consists of two analogous parts:

$$\mathbf{q}^e_u = \beta_\parallel^{Tu} \mathbf{u}_\parallel + \beta_\perp^{Tu} \mathbf{u}_\perp + \beta_\wedge^{Tu} [\mathbf{h}\mathbf{u}], \tag{4.32}$$

$$\mathbf{q}^e_T = -\varkappa^e_\parallel \nabla_\parallel T_e - \varkappa^e_\perp \nabla_\perp T_e - \varkappa^e_\wedge [\mathbf{h}\nabla T_e]. \tag{4.33}$$

Here

$$\left.\begin{aligned} \alpha_\parallel &= \frac{m_e n_e}{\tau_e}\alpha_0, \quad \alpha_\perp = \frac{m_e n_e}{\tau_e}\left(1 - \frac{\alpha_1' x^2 + \alpha_0'}{\Delta}\right), \\ \alpha_\wedge &= \frac{m_e n_e}{\tau_e}\frac{x(\alpha_1'' x^2 + \alpha_0'')}{\Delta}, \end{aligned}\right\} \tag{4.34}$$

$$\beta_\parallel^{uT} = n_e\beta_0, \quad \beta_\perp^{uT} = n_e\frac{\beta_1' x^2 + \beta_0'}{\Delta}, \quad \beta_\wedge^{uT} = n_e\frac{x(\beta_1'' x^2 + \beta_0'')}{\Delta}, \tag{4.35}$$

$$\beta_\parallel^{Tu} = \beta_\parallel^{uT} T_e, \quad \beta_\perp^{Tu} = \beta_\perp^{uT} T_e, \quad \beta_\wedge^{Tu} = \beta_\wedge^{uT} T_e, \tag{4.36}$$

$$\varkappa^e_\parallel = \frac{n_e T_e \tau_e}{m_e}\gamma_0, \quad \varkappa^e_\perp = \frac{n_e T_e \tau_e}{m_e}\frac{(\gamma_1' x^2 + \gamma_0')}{\Delta}, \quad \varkappa^e_\wedge = \frac{n_e T_e \tau_e}{m_e}\frac{x(\gamma_1'' x^2 + \gamma_0'')}{\Delta}, \tag{4.37}$$

where

$$x = \omega_e \tau_e, \quad \Delta = x^4 + \delta_1 x^2 + \delta_0. \tag{4.38}$$

The coefficients α, β, γ, and δ are given in Table 2 for various values of Z.

The exact values of the coefficients as obtained by direct numerical solution of the integral equation for B = 0 and Z = 1 are as follows [14]: $\alpha_0 = 0.5063$; $\beta_0 = 0.7033$; $\gamma_0 = 3.203$. For Z = ∞ an exact solution of the correction equation indicates that

$$\alpha_0 = \frac{3\pi}{32} = 0.2945, \quad \beta_0 = \frac{3}{2}, \quad \gamma_0 = \frac{128}{3\pi} = 13.58.$$

The ion heat flux is

$$\mathbf{q}_i = -\varkappa_{\parallel}^{i}\nabla_{\parallel}T_i - \varkappa_{\perp}^{i}\nabla_{\perp}T_i + \varkappa_{\wedge}^{i}[\mathbf{h}\nabla T_i], \tag{4.39}$$

$$\left.\begin{aligned} \varkappa_{\parallel}^{i} &= 3.906 n_i T_i \tau_i / m_i, \\ \varkappa_{\perp}^{i} &= (n_i T_i \tau_i / m_i)(2x^2 + 2.645)/\Delta, \\ \varkappa_{\wedge}^{i} &= (n_i T_i \tau_i / m_i)\, x \left(\frac{5}{2} x^2 + 4.65\right)/\Delta, \end{aligned}\right\} \tag{4.40}$$

where

$$x = \omega_i \tau_i, \quad \Delta = x^4 + 2.70 x^2 + 0.677.$$

The stress tensor for particles of a given species (the symbols i and e are omitted) is expressed in terms of the corresponding tensor $W_{\alpha\beta}$ [cf. Eq. (4.14)] by means of the five viscosity coefficients:

$$\pi_{\alpha\beta} = -\eta_0 W_{0\alpha\beta} - \eta_1 W_{1\alpha\beta} - \eta_2 W_{2\alpha\beta} + \eta_3 W_{3\alpha\beta} + \eta_4 W_{4\alpha\beta}, \tag{4.41}$$

where $W_{\alpha\beta} = W_{0\alpha\beta} + W_{1\alpha\beta} + W_{2\alpha\beta}$.

Here

$$\left.\begin{aligned} W_{0\alpha\beta} &= \frac{3}{2}\left(h_\alpha h_\beta - \frac{1}{3}\delta_{\alpha\beta}\right)\left(h_\mu h_\nu - \frac{1}{3}\delta_{\mu\nu}\right) W_{\mu\nu}, \\ W_{1\alpha\beta} &= \left(\delta_{\alpha\mu}^{\perp}\delta_{\beta\nu}^{\perp} + \frac{1}{2}\delta_{\alpha\beta}^{\perp} h_\mu h_\nu\right) W_{\mu\nu}, \\ W_{2\alpha\beta} &= \left(\delta_{\alpha\mu}^{\perp} h_\beta h_\nu + \delta_{\beta\nu}^{\perp} h_\alpha h_\mu\right) W_{\mu\nu}, \\ W_{3\alpha\beta} &= \frac{1}{2}\left(\delta_{\alpha\mu}^{\perp}\varepsilon_{\beta\gamma\nu} + \delta_{\beta\nu}^{\perp}\varepsilon_{\alpha\gamma\mu}\right) h_\gamma W_{\mu\nu}, \\ W_{4\alpha\beta} &= \left(h_\alpha h_\mu \varepsilon_{\beta\gamma\nu} + h_\beta h_\nu \varepsilon_{\alpha\gamma\mu}\right) h_\gamma W_{\mu\nu}, \end{aligned}\right\} \tag{4.42}$$

where $\delta_{\alpha\beta}^{\perp} = \delta_{\alpha\beta} - h_\alpha h_\beta$; $\varepsilon_{\alpha\beta\gamma}$ is an antisymmetric unit tensor.

TABLE 2

	$Z=1$	$Z=2$	$Z=3$	$Z=4$	$Z\to\infty$
$\alpha_0 = 1 - (\alpha_0'/\delta_0)$	0.5129	0.4408	0.3965	0.3752	0.2949
$\beta_0 = \beta_0'/\delta_0$	0.7110	0.9052	1.016	1.090	1.521
$\gamma_0 = \gamma_0'/\delta_0$	3.1616	4.890	6.064	6.920	12.471
δ_0	3.7703	1.0465	0.5814	0.4106	0.0961
δ_1	14.79	10.80	9.618	9.055	7.482
α_1'	6.416	5.523	5.226	5.077	4.63
α_0'	1.837	0.5956	0.3515	0.2566	0.0678
α_1''	1.704	1.704	1.704	1.704	1.704
α_0''	0.7796	0.3439	0.2400	0.1957	0.0940
β_1'	5.101	4.450	4.233	4.124	3.798
β_0'	2.681	0.9473	0.5905	0.4478	0.1461
β_1''	3/2	3/2	3/2	3/2	3/2
β_0''	3.053	1.784	1.442	1.285	0.877
γ_1'	4.664	3.957	3.721	3.604	3.25
γ_0'	11.92	5.118	3.525	2.841	1.20
γ_1''	5/2	5/2	5/2	5/2	5/2
γ_0''	21.67	15.37	13.53	12.65	10.23

In the coordinate system in which the z axis is along the magnetic field (x, y, z → 1, 2, 3):

$$h = (0,\ 0,\ 1),\ \delta^{\perp}_{\alpha\beta} = \begin{pmatrix} 1 & 0 & 0 \\ 0 & 1 & 0 \\ 0 & 0 & 0 \end{pmatrix}, \qquad \varepsilon_{\alpha\gamma\beta} h_\gamma = \begin{pmatrix} 0 & -1 & 0 \\ 1 & 0 & 0 \\ 0 & 0 & 0 \end{pmatrix},$$

and the tensors $W_{p\alpha\beta}$ are:

$$W_{0\alpha\beta} = \begin{Vmatrix} \frac{1}{2}(W_{xx} + W_{yy}) & 0 & 0 \\ 0 & \frac{1}{2}(W_{xx} + W_{yy}) & 0 \\ 0 & 0 & W_{zz} \end{Vmatrix}$$

$$W_{1\alpha\beta} = \begin{Vmatrix} \frac{1}{2}(W_{xx} - W_{yy}) & W_{xy} & 0 \\ W_{yx} & \frac{1}{2}(W_{yy} - W_{xx}) & 0 \\ 0 & 0 & 0 \end{Vmatrix} \quad W_{2\alpha\beta} = \begin{Vmatrix} 0 & 0 & W_{xz} \\ 0 & 0 & W_{yz} \\ W_{zx} & W_{zy} & 0 \end{Vmatrix}$$

$$W_{3\alpha\beta} = \begin{Vmatrix} -W_{xy} & \frac{1}{2}(W_{xx} - W_{yy}) & 0 \\ \frac{1}{2}(W_{xx} - W_{yy}) & W_{xy} & 0 \\ 0 & 0 & 0 \end{Vmatrix} \quad W_{4\alpha\beta} = \begin{Vmatrix} 0 & 0 & -W_{yz} \\ 0 & 0 & W_{xz} \\ -W_{zy} & W_{zx} & 0 \end{Vmatrix}$$

It is easily shown that the following orthogonality relation holds:

$$W_{p\alpha\beta} W_{q\alpha\beta} = 0, \text{ when } \ p \neq q. \tag{4.43}$$

The ion viscosity coefficients are

$$\left.\begin{aligned} \eta_0^i &= 0.96 n_i T_i \tau_i, \\ \eta_2^i &= n_i T_i \tau_i \left(\frac{6}{5} x^2 + 2.23\right)/\Delta, \\ \eta_4^i &= n_i T_i \tau_i x (x^2 + 2.38)/\Delta, \end{aligned}\right\} \tag{4.44}$$

where

$$x = \omega_i \tau_i, \quad \Delta = x^4 + 4.03x^2 + 2.33.$$

The coefficients η_1^i and η_3^i are obtained from η_2^i and η_4^i by replacing ω_i by $2\omega_i$:

$$\eta_1^i = \eta_2^i(2x), \quad \eta_3^i = \eta_4^i(2x).$$

The electron viscosity coefficients are (for Z = 1):

$$\left.\begin{aligned} &\eta_0^e = 0{,}733 n_e T_e \tau_e, \\ &\eta_2^e = n_e T_e \tau_e (2.05x^2 + 8.50)/\Delta, \quad \eta_1^e = \eta_2^e(2x), \\ &\eta_4^e = -n_e T_e \tau_e x (x^2 + 7.91)/\Delta, \quad \eta_3^e = \eta_4^e(2x), \end{aligned}\right\} \tag{4.45}$$

where

$$x = \omega_e \tau_e, \qquad \Delta = x^4 + 13.8x^2 + 11.6.$$

Symmetry of the Kinetic Coefficients. We now wish to review briefly certain terminology and results of the thermodynamics of irreversible processes (these are discussed in greater detail, for example, in [9]). The various agencies giving rise to deviations from thermal equilibrium X_m (for example ∇T, $W_{\alpha\beta}$, etc.) are called thermodynamic forces. These produce corresponding fluxes I_m (for example **q**, $\pi_{\alpha\beta}$, etc.). For small deviations from equilibrium the fluxes and forces are related linearly:

$$I_m = \sum_n L_{mn} X_n. \tag{4.46}$$

The irreversible increase of entropy in a nonequilibrium system is called entropy production and is denoted by θ. According to the second law of thermodynamics it is always true that $\theta > 0$. A flux I_m and a force X_n are "conjugate" if the entropy production can be expressed in the form

$$\theta = \sum_m I_m X_m. \tag{4.47}$$

One of the important theorems in the thermodynamics of irreversible processes is the so-called principle of symmetry of the kinetic coefficients, or the Onsager principle. Assume that the fluxes and forces are chosen in such a way that Eq. (4.47) is satisfied. The kinetic coefficients relating these fluxes and forces then satisfy the condition

$$L_{mn}(\mathbf{B}) = L_{nm}(-\mathbf{B}), \tag{4.48}$$

if both forces X_m and X_n are even functions of the particle velocities (for example ∇T) or if both functions are odd in the particles velocities (for example $W_{\alpha\beta}$). However, if one force is odd and the other is even, then the following relation holds:

$$L_{mn}(\mathbf{B}) = -L_{nm}(-\mathbf{B}). \tag{4.48'}$$

The entropy balance for the electrons can be obtained easily through the use of the heat-balance equation (2.3e) and the equation of continuity (2.1e). The entropy per electron is

$$s_e = \frac{3}{2}\ln T_e - \ln n_e + \text{const}. \tag{4.49}$$

The entropy balance is written in the form

$$\frac{\partial n_e s_e}{\partial t} + \operatorname{div}\left(s_e n_e \mathbf{V}_e + \frac{q_e}{T_e}\right) + \frac{Q_\Delta}{T_e} = \theta_e, \tag{4.50}$$

where θ_e is the entropy production per unit volume:

$$T_e\theta_e = -\mathbf{q}_e\nabla\ln T_e - \mathbf{Ru} - \frac{1}{2}\pi_{e\alpha\beta}W_{e\alpha\beta}. \tag{4.51}$$

The left side of Eq. (4.50) contains the change of entropy in time and the loss of entropy into other regions of space and to the ions.

It is evident from Eq. (4.51) that the fluxes $\mathbf{q}_e$, $\mathbf{R}$, $\pi_{\alpha\beta}$, and Q_Δ are conjugate to the forces $\nabla \ln T_e$, $\mathbf{u}$, $1/2\, W_{\alpha\beta}$, and $(T_e - T_i)/T_e T_i$.

Let us now examine the relations (4.30) - (4.33) between the fluxes and forces. Since $\mathbf{B}$ is an axial vector while $\mathbf{q}$, $\mathbf{R}$, ∇T, and $\mathbf{u}$ are polar vectors the coefficients α, β, and γ must be even functions of $\mathbf{B}$. The Onsager principle then leads to the following nontrivial relation for the "cross" effects—the dependence of the thermal force and heat flux on the relative velocity:

$$T_e\beta_{\|}^{uT} = \beta_{\|}^{Tu}, \quad T_e\beta_{\perp}^{uT} = \beta_{\perp}^{Tu}, \quad T_e\beta_{\wedge}^{uT} = \beta_{\wedge}^{Tu}. \tag{4.52}$$

These relations are satisfied automatically when the transport coefficients are derived from the kinetic equation [cf. Eq. (4.36)]. The Onsager principle does not yield a nontrivial relation for the viscosity or for the ion transport coefficients.

Taking account of the symmetry of the transport coefficients and the orthogonality condition (4.43) we can write the entropy production in the form

$$T_e\theta_e = \frac{\varkappa_{\|}^e}{T_e}(\nabla_{\|}T_e)^2 + \frac{\varkappa_{\perp}^e}{T_e}(\nabla_{\perp}T_e)^2 + \frac{j_{\|}^2}{\sigma_{\|}} + \frac{j_{\perp}^2}{\sigma_{\perp}} +$$

$$+ \frac{1}{2}\left\{ \eta_0^e W_{0\alpha\beta}^2 + \eta_1^e W_{1\alpha\beta}^2 + \eta_2^e W_{2\alpha\beta}^2 \right\}. \tag{4.53}$$

Similarly, the entropy production for the ions can be written

$$T_i\theta_i = \frac{\varkappa_{\|}^i}{T_i}(\nabla_{\|}T_i)^2 + \frac{\varkappa_{\perp}^i}{T_i}(\nabla_{\perp}T_i)^2 + \frac{1}{2}\sum_{p=0}^{2}\eta_p^i W_{p\alpha\beta}^2. \tag{4.54}$$

The entropy balance for the entire plasma is

$$\frac{\partial S}{\partial t} + \operatorname{div}\left\{s_e n_e \mathbf{V}_e + s_i n_i \mathbf{V}_i + \frac{\mathbf{q}_e}{T_e} + \frac{\mathbf{q}_i}{T_i}\right\} = \theta_e + \theta_i + \theta_{ei}, \tag{4.55}$$

where $S = s_e n_e + s_i n_i$ is the plasma entropy per unit volume:

$$\theta_{ei} = Q_\Delta\left(\frac{1}{T_i} - \frac{1}{T_e}\right) = \frac{3m_e}{m_i}\cdot\frac{n_e}{\tau_e}\cdot\frac{(T_e - T_i)^2}{T_e T_i}. \tag{4.56}$$

§ 5. Certain Paradoxes

The direct application of the transport equations to a magnetized plasma in which $\omega\tau \gg 1$ frequently leads to apparent contradictions with what might be expected from a cursory examination of individual particle motion in a magnetic field (drift theory). Some of these paradoxes have been analyzed in [6, 26, 27, 28] and a few particular cases are considered in this section.

Let us assume that the electric field and the gradients of all quantities are perpendicular to the magnetic field. We shall also be interested in processes that are so slow that the electron and ion inertia terms can be neglected; similarly, it is assumed that all quantities do not change greatly in the time between collisions. From these conditions and the equations of motion we can obtain explicit expressions for the transverse velocities of the ions and electrons in terms of the gradient. If the ion and electron equations of motion are added (neglecting viscosity and inertia) the plasma equilibrium relation can be written in the form

$$-\nabla(p_e + p_i) + \frac{1}{c}[\mathbf{jB}] = 0.$$

This expression then yields the transverse electric current

$$\mathbf{j}_\perp = -en_e(\mathbf{V}_e - \mathbf{V}_i)_\perp = \frac{c}{B}[\mathbf{h}\nabla(p_e + p_i)] \tag{5.1}$$

Substituting Eq. (5.1) in the expressions for the force **R**, (2.6) and (2.9), and invoking the condition $-e_e n_e = e_i n_i = en$, we have

$$\mathbf{V}_e = \frac{c}{B}[\mathbf{Eh}] - \frac{c}{enB}[\mathbf{h}\nabla p_e] + \mathbf{V}_D, \tag{5.2e}$$

$$\mathbf{V}_i = \frac{c}{B}[\mathbf{Eh}] + \frac{c}{enB}[\mathbf{h}\nabla p_i] + \mathbf{V}_D, \tag{5.2i}$$

where

$$\mathbf{V}_D = -\frac{c^2}{\sigma_\perp B^2}\left\{\nabla(p_e + p_i) - \frac{3}{2}n_e\nabla T_e\right\} =$$

$$= -\frac{m_e c^2}{e^2\tau_e B^2}\left\{(T_e + T_i)\frac{\nabla n}{n} + \nabla T_i - \frac{1}{2}\nabla T_e\right\}. \tag{5.3}$$

Taking account of viscosity would lead to the appearance of terms of order B^{-4}.

Now let us temporarily neglect the collision term in Eq. (5.2) $\mathbf{V}_D$, and compare the remaining terms with those that would be obtained from single-particle motion.

In a strong magnetic field the motion of a charged particle (without collisions) can be described as gyration around a circle whose center (the so-called guiding center) moves with velocity $\mathbf{V}_c$ given by (cf. for example [8, 38])

$$\mathbf{V}_c = \frac{c}{B}\,[\mathbf{E}\mathbf{h}] + \frac{mv_{\perp}^2 c}{2eB}\left[\mathbf{h}\,\frac{\nabla B}{B}\right] + \frac{mv_{\parallel}^2 c}{eB}\,[\mathbf{h}\,(\mathbf{h}\nabla)\,\mathbf{h}] + \\ + \frac{mv_{\perp}^2 c}{2eB}\,\mathbf{h}\,(\mathbf{h}\,\mathrm{rot}\,\mathbf{h}) + v_{\parallel}\mathbf{h}, \tag{5.4}$$

where $\mathbf{h} = \mathbf{B}/B$; $v_{\parallel}$ and $v_{\perp}$ are the projections of the particle velocity (averaged over the gyration) in the direction of the magnetic field and perpendicular to the magnetic field at the location of the guiding center. The first term in Eq. (5.4) is usually called the electric drift, the second term the magnetic drift, and the third the centrifugal drift. If Eq. (5.4) is averaged over a velocity distribution that is approximately Maxwellian we find

$$<\mathbf{V}_c> = \frac{c}{B}\,[\mathbf{E}\mathbf{h}] + \frac{cT}{eB}\left[\mathbf{h},\ \frac{\nabla B}{B} + (\mathbf{h}\nabla)\,\mathbf{h}\right] + \\ + \frac{cT}{eB}\,\mathbf{h}\,(\mathbf{h}\cdot\mathrm{rot}\,\mathbf{h}) + V_{\parallel}\mathbf{h}. \tag{5.5}$$

Here $m<v_{\parallel}^2> = T$; $m<v_{\perp}^2> = 2T$; $<v_{\parallel}> = V_{\parallel} = \mathbf{V}\cdot\mathbf{h}$.

The quantity $n<\mathbf{V}_c>$ is the flux density of guiding centers, and $\int_S n<\mathbf{V}_c>d\mathbf{S}$ is the flux of centers through a surface S, while $n\mathbf{V}$ and $\int_S n\mathbf{V}\,d\mathbf{S}$ represent the flux density and flux of the particles themselves. In general the particle flux can differ from the guiding-center flux and certain paradoxes arise when these two quantities are confused.

Let us compare Eqs. (5.2) and (5.5).

The first term in Eq. (5.2) is easily interpreted—it is the electric drift.

The second term in Eq. (5.2), which we shall call the Larmor term, is associated with the fact that particles intersecting an area in opposite directions arrive from regions characterized by different densities and temperatures, as a result of which the unidirectional fluxes do not balance each other. Particles arrive from a distance $\sim r = mvc/eB$ and "carry" a flux $\sim nv$ so that the resulting difference in flux is of order $(mc/eB)\nabla nv^2 \sim (c/eB)\nabla p$. At first glance the fact that Eq. (5.2) does not contain terms corresponding to the magnetic and centrifugal drifts, i. e., terms explicitly exhibiting the spatial derivatives of the magnetic field, appears to be paradoxical. Actually, however, the absence of such terms is completely natural since the magnetic field, whether it is uniform or not, does not disturb the Maxwellian distribution: $[\mathbf{v}\boldsymbol{\omega}]\nabla_v f^0 = 0$. Hence, if the particle density and temperature are independent of coordinates the particle flux within the plasma (5.2) vanishes although the guiding-center flux (5.5) does not vanish if the magnetic field is inhomogeneous. In this case the magnetic and centrifugal drifts appear as edge effects which produce surface particle fluxes at the interface with the region of constant density and temperature. This is easily shown by simple examples but can also be shown in general form. Introducing the identities

$$\left.\begin{aligned}(\mathbf{h}\nabla)\,\mathbf{h} &= -\,[\mathbf{h}\,\mathrm{rot}\,\mathbf{h}],\\ [\mathbf{h}\cdot(\mathbf{h}\nabla)\,\mathbf{h}] &= \mathrm{rot}\,\mathbf{h} - \mathbf{h}\,(\mathbf{h}\cdot\mathrm{rot}\,\mathbf{h}),\end{aligned}\right\} \tag{5.6}$$

we can write Eq. (5.5) as follows:

$$<\mathbf{V}_c> = \frac{c}{B}\,[\mathbf{E}\mathbf{h}] + \frac{cT}{e}\,\mathrm{rot}\,\frac{\mathbf{h}}{B} + V_{\parallel}\,\mathbf{h}. \tag{5.7}$$

Now, comparing the guiding-center flux with the particle flux (neglecting collisions) for particles of any sort we find

$$n\mathbf{V} = n<\mathbf{V}_c> - \,\mathrm{rot}\left(\frac{cnT}{eB}\,\mathbf{h}\right) \tag{5.8}$$

or

$$\int n\mathbf{V}\cdot d\mathbf{S} = \int n<\mathbf{V}_c>\cdot d\mathbf{S} - \oint \frac{cnT}{eB}\,(\mathbf{h}\cdot d\mathbf{l}). \tag{5.8'}$$

It is evident that the difference between the particle flux and the guiding-center flux through any area as a whole is determined by the values of the quantities at the boundary of the area. This difference arises for the following reason: near the edge of the area in question particles enter and leave whose guiding centers are outside the area. The magnitude of the flux associated with these particles is cnT/eB per unit length of edge along **h**; opposite edges of the area are intersected in opposite directions.

Thus, a magnetized plasma can be regarded as consisting of "quasi-particles" – or "circlets" that move with the drift velocity. It is easily shown that the magnetic moment of a circlet is $\boldsymbol{\mu} = -(mv_\perp^2/2B)\mathbf{h}$; hence, if collisions are neglected the plasma magnetization per unit volume is

$$\mathbf{M} = -\sum_a n_a \frac{m_a < v_\perp^2 >_a}{2B} \mathbf{h}. \tag{5.9}$$

The total current density obtained in this representation is the sum of the drift (convection) current and the magnetization current:

$$\mathbf{j} = \mathbf{j}_c + c \operatorname{rot} \mathbf{M} = \sum_a e_a n_a < V_c >_a - \operatorname{rot} \sum_a \frac{c n_a < v_\perp^2 >_a}{2B} \mathbf{h}. \tag{5.10}$$

When $m_a < v_\perp^2 >_a = 2T_a$ Eq. (5.1) is obtained exactly. As is usually done in macroscopic electrodynamics, we can introduce $\mathbf{H} = \mathbf{B} - 4\pi\mathbf{M}$ in addition to $\mathbf{B}$ and in this case Maxwell's equations are written in the form

$$\operatorname{rot} \mathbf{H} = \frac{4\pi}{c} \mathbf{j}_c + \frac{1}{c} \frac{\partial \mathbf{E}}{\partial t}, \quad \operatorname{div} \mathbf{B} = 0. \tag{5.11}$$

In practice, however, in plasma problems it is usually more convenient to write all currents in explicit form without separating the drift and magnetization currents. When all currents are written explicity $\mathbf{B} \equiv \mathbf{H}$ and Maxwell's equations become

$$\operatorname{rot} \mathbf{B} = \frac{4\pi}{c} \mathbf{j} + \frac{1}{c} \frac{\partial \mathbf{E}}{\partial t}, \quad \operatorname{div} \mathbf{B} = 0. \tag{5.11'}$$

The $\mathbf{V}_D$ terms in Eq. (5.2) stem from particle collisions, specifically, from collisions of electrons with ions. These terms might well be called diffusion terms. They are exactly the same for the ions and electrons and depend only on the gradients of density and temperature but are independent of electric field. At first glance both of these results appear to be paradoxical for the following reason. The diffusion coefficient for diffusion of a charged particle across a magnetic field is approximately $D_\perp \sim r^2/\tau$. For ions, r and τ are larger by a factor of $(m_i/m_e)^{1/2}$ than for electrons. Hence it would appear that the ion diffusion coefficient should be $(m_i/m_e)^{1/2}$ times greater than the electron diffusion coefficient. Actually, however, this is not the case. For example, assume an ion-density gradient along the x axis and take the magnetic field along the z axis. There then arises a Larmor flux of ions along the y axis characterized by the velocity $V_y = (cT/enB)\, dn/dx$. In this case, however, the formula $D \sim r^2/\tau$ cannot be applied directly because the diffusion is taking place in a moving medium and in the collisions the ion obtains some momentum along the y axis (on the average). We then transform to a coordinate system in which $V_y = 0$. In this system there is an electric field $E'_x = (V_y/c)B = (T/e)\,d\ln n/dx$ in which the ions are described by a Boltzmann distribution and in which the ion flux is zero since the flux produced by the electric field compensates the diffusion flux. Thus, collisions between like particles can not produce diffusion across the magnetic field. On the other hand, collisions between electrons and ions do cause diffusion because the Larmor currents of electrons and ions are in opposite directions. The flux along the x axis that results can be regarded as coming from the drift produced by the effect of a frictional force between the electrons and ions which is along the y axis. Since $\mathbf{R}_i = -\mathbf{R}_e$ the velocity is exactly the same for both kinds of particles.

Now let us consider the role of the electric field. Assume an electric field along the x axis. This field produces a particle drift (both charge signs) along the y axis with velocity $V_y = -cE/B$. In the coordinate system in which $V_y = 0$, however, the electric field $E' = 0$; hence there is no flux along the x axis, that is to say, there is no flux in the direction of the applied electric field. In this connection it is sometimes said (erroneously) that the plasma conductivity across the magnetic field is zero.

Now let us consider the heat transport equation. The quantity $v^2_\perp/B$ is conserved for a magnetic field that changes slowly in time, i. e., the energy associated with the transverse motion, $\varepsilon_\perp = mv^2_\perp/2$, is proportional to the field—this is the so-called betatron effect. The heat transport equation does not contain a term proportional to $\partial B/\partial t$. Nevertheless, using some simple examples we can easily show that the equation does take account of the betatron effect.

Let us consider a uniform magnetic field along the z axis that increases in time. Let the plasma occupy a cylindrical volume of infinite length along the z axis. We assume that the plasma density and temperature are constant over the volume (so there is no heat flux); also, for reasons of simplicity we neglect collisions of electrons with ions and the consequent Joule heating. We can also neglect the screening of the external magnetic field by the plasma currents. Under these conditions the induction electric field $E = E_\varphi = -\dot{B}r/2c$. The electric drift leads to plasma compression at a rate $V_r = -\dot{B}r/2B$ so that $\operatorname{div}\mathbf{V} = -\dot{B}/B$. The heat transport equation becomes

$$\frac{3}{2}n\frac{dT}{dt} = -nT\operatorname{div}\mathbf{V} = \frac{nT}{B}\frac{dB}{dt}. \qquad (5.12)$$

This expression is a statement of the betatron effect; actually in betatron heating it is only the energy associated with the transverse motion $d\varepsilon = \varepsilon_{\perp} dB/B$ that increases directly. Collisions then establish an equipartition of energy over the degrees of freedom so that $\varepsilon_{\perp} = (2/3)\varepsilon$ and $(3/2)\, d\varepsilon/dt = (\varepsilon/B)\, dB/dt$. The betatron effect then appears as heating by virtue of adiabatic compression of the plasma. This reversible (in the thermodynamic sense) heating should not be confused with the irreversible gyrorelaxational heating mentioned in §3 which arises as a consequence of an irreversible process: the equipartition of energy over the degrees of freedom. When the magnetic field is reduced to its original value (with the corresponding expansion of the plasma) the adiabatic cooling associated with the expansion is equal to the heating that took place in compression, in accordance with Eq. (5.12); on the other hand, the heat generated in gyrorelaxational heating remains in the plasma since it is proportional to $(\dot{B}/B)^2$.

We now consider the case in which electron-ion collisions precisely equilibrate the electric drift: $cE_{\varphi}/B + V_D = 0$; in this case the plasma remains immobile. Under these conditions heat fluxes will arise in the plasma and we must consider the total increase in energy over the entire plasma volume. If the ion and electron heat transport equations are added and integrated over the volume of the plasma cylinder (unit length along the z axis) we find

$$\frac{3}{2} \cdot \frac{d}{dt} \int (n_e T_e + n_i T_i)\, 2\pi r\, dr = \int E_{\varphi} j_{\varphi} 2\pi r\, dr.$$

Substituting $E_{\varphi} = -\dot{B}r/2c$, $j_{\varphi} = (c/B)\, \partial p/\partial r$, $p = n_e T_e + n_i T_i$, and integrating on the right by parts we have $(3/2)\, d\varepsilon/dt = (\varepsilon/B)\, dB/dt$. In this case the betatron effect appears as the generation of Joule heat.

There is at least one difference between the two examples we have just considered. In the first case the ions and electrons are heated uniformly by the compression. In the second case the heat is generated directly in the electron gas and is then transferred to the ions by means of collisions. It would appear that the ions should obtain as much heat as the electrons in betatron heating. In the absence of ion current a radial electric field arises in the plasma; the magnitude of this field is determined by the ion equilibrium condition $e_i n_i E_r = -\partial p_i/\partial r$. This field causes an ion drift in the azimuthal direction in opposition to the induced electric field. It is easy to show that the work done by this field (negative) on the drift precisely compensates the betatron heating of the ions. The electrons also drift in the radial field and acquire exactly as much energy as is lost by the ions.

The transport of heat (like the transport of particles) can also be interpreted in terms of the motion of guiding centers. If collisions are neglected a formula analogous to Eq. (5.8) is obtained. The total flux density of internal energy is $\mathbf{q}_{\text{total}} = (5/2)\, nT\mathbf{V} + \mathbf{q}$, as follows from Eq. (1.20). We use Eq. (5.8) taking account of the $\mathbf{q}_\wedge$ term in the heat flux, which is independent of collisions; this term is given by Eqs. (2.11) and (2.14): $\mathbf{q}_\wedge = (5/2)(cnT/eB)[\mathbf{h}\nabla T]$. The expression for $\mathbf{q}_{\text{total}}$ can then be written

$$\mathbf{q}_{\text{total}} = \frac{5}{2}\, nT\mathbf{V} + \mathbf{q}_\wedge = \frac{5}{2}\, nT < V_c > - \operatorname{rot}\left(\frac{5}{2}\frac{cnT^2}{eB}\mathbf{h}\right). \tag{5.13}$$

The remarks made above in connection with the derivation of Eq. (5.8) also apply to the derivation of this formula.

§ 6. Hydrodynamic Description of a Plasma

The transport equations correspond to a plasma model consisting of interpenetrating charged gases—the ion gas (one or more species) and the electron gas. It is frequently more convenient to use a single-fluid model for the plasma. In this case, the two equations of motion (for the ions and electrons) are replaced by a single equation of motion for the plasma as a whole; this equation represents an extension of the equation of motion of conventional hydrodynamics while the expression for the electric current is essentially a generalization of the familiar Ohm's law. The single-fluid hydrodynamic model is found to be most useful for the description of low-frequency phenomena because it is then valid to neglect electron inertia and to assume that the plasma remains neutral.

We shall first treat the single-fluid gas dynamic model for a simple plasma; in §7 we discuss certain characteristic features of multicomponent plasmas.

Equations of Continuity and Quasi-Neutrality. We first introduce the mass density ρ and the hydrodynamic velocity $\mathbf{V}$ (the velocity of the mass):

$$\varrho = \sum_a m_a n_a, \tag{6.1}$$

$$\mathbf{V} = \frac{1}{\varrho} \sum_a m_a n_a \mathbf{V}_a. \tag{6.2}$$

Neglecting the electron mass compared with the ion mass we can now make the approximation

$$\varrho = m_i n_i, \tag{6.3}$$

$$\mathbf{V} = \mathbf{V}_i. \tag{6.4}$$

The equation of continuity for the ions is rewritten in the form of a mass conservation relation (it is simply called the equation of continuity):

$$\frac{\partial \varrho}{\partial t} + \operatorname{div}(\varrho \mathbf{V}) = 0. \tag{6.5}$$

Equation (6.5) also holds for the exact definitions (6.1) and (6.2).

The density of electrical charge ρ_e and the density of electric current $\mathbf{j}$ are (we use the notation $\mathbf{u} = \mathbf{V}_e - \mathbf{V}_i$):

$$\varrho_e = \sum_a e_a n_a = e\,(Zn_i - n_e), \tag{6.6}$$

$$\mathbf{j} = \sum_a e_a n_a \mathbf{V}_a = \varrho_e \mathbf{V}_i - e n_e \mathbf{u}. \tag{6.7}$$

The equations of continuity for the electrons and ions yield an equation for the conservation of electric charge:

$$\frac{\partial \varrho_e}{\partial t} + \operatorname{div} \mathbf{j} = 0. \tag{6.8}$$

We shall assume hereinafter that the plasma is quasi-neutral. This does not mean zero space charge in the plasma; rather it means that the space charge is small compared with the quantity en_e so that the difference $Zn_i - n_e$ can be neglected compared with $n = n_e$. The current density is then expressed in the form

$$\mathbf{j} = -en\mathbf{u}. \tag{6.9}$$

We will assume that all processes are slow (in electrodynamics these are called quasi-stationary processes) so that $\partial\rho_e/\partial t$ can be neglected in Eq. (6.8) and the displacement current can be neglected in Maxwell's equations. Under these conditions Eq. (6.8) and Maxwell's equation become

$$\operatorname{div} \mathbf{j} = 0, \tag{6.10}$$

$$\operatorname{rot} \mathbf{E} = -\frac{1}{c}\frac{\partial B}{\partial t}, \tag{6.11}$$

$$\operatorname{rot} \mathbf{B} = \frac{4\pi}{c}\mathbf{j};\ \operatorname{div} \mathbf{B} = 0. \tag{6.12}$$

The neutrality condition provides one relation for the quantities that describe the plasma: $Zn_i = n_e$. Consequently one equation must be omitted from the system of plasma equations; specifically, this is the Poisson equation, in which the space charge appears explicitly:

$$\operatorname{div} \mathbf{E} = 4\pi\varrho_e. \tag{6.13}$$

The quantity $\rho_e = e(Zn_i - n_e)$ is neglected in the remaining equations and no requirement is imposed on div **E**. In this case the rotational electric fields are determined from Eq. (6.11) while the irrotational fields arising from the small differences in positive and negative space charge (although the fields themselves are not small !) are determined from Eq. (6.10) in conjunction with the equations of motion. In other words, the irrotational electric fields in the plasma are automatically chosen in such a way as to avoid too strong a charge separation $Zn_i - n_e$. In this case Poisson's equation only serves as a means of determining ρ_e once the field **E** is known.

It will now be useful to estimate certain quantities. In order-of-magnitude terms, we find from Eq. (6.13) that $\rho_e \sim E/4\pi L$. In a static or slowly moving plasma or in a plasma with no magnetic field we usually find $enE \sim \nabla p$ or $E \sim T/eL$, whence $\rho_e/en \sim \delta_D^2/L^2$ where $\delta_D = (T/4\pi en)^{1/2}$ is the Debye length; the Debye length is always small compared with the characteristic dimensions of the plasma (if this condition is not satisfied the ionized gas cannot properly be called a plasma). The neutrality condition can obviously be violated in layers of thickness $\sim \delta_D$. These departures from neutrality usually occur near the boundaries of the plasma or in high-frequency oscillations. It is also possible for an induction field $E \sim VB/c$ to arise in a plasma moving across a magnetic field. Let us assume that we are dealing with a fast process (see below) in which the velocity of a plasma is determined by its inertia and by the magnetic force. Then $\omega\rho V \sim (1/c)jB$ where ω is the characteristic frequency of the process. In this case the charge density is of order $\rho_e \sim E/4\pi L \sim (c_A^2/c^2)j/\omega L$ where $c_A = B/(4\pi\rho)^{1/2}$ is the so-called Alfvén velocity and the first term in

Eq. (6.8) is of order $\omega\rho_e/(j/L) \sim c_A^2/c^2$ so that Eq. (6.10) can be used if $c_A^2/c^2 = B^2/4\pi\rho c^2$ is small. It will be assumed that this condition is satisfied everywhere below. For example, take $n_i = 10^{14}$ cm^{-3}, $m_i = 1.6 \cdot 10^{-24}$ g, $B = 10^4$ G, in which case $c_A^2/c^2 \sim 10^{-4}$.

The neutrality condition can also be violated in a low density plasma and in a relativistic plasma, in which $V \sim c$ or $u \sim c$.

Equation of Motion. Adding the ion and electron equations of motion and neglecting the electron inertia, we obtain the plasma equation of motion

$$\varrho \frac{d\mathbf{V}}{dt} = -\nabla p + \frac{1}{c}[\mathbf{jB}] + \mathbf{F}, \tag{6.14}$$

where $\mathbf{V} = \mathbf{V}_i$ $d/dt = \partial/\partial t + (\mathbf{V}\nabla)$; p is the total pressure,

$$p = p_e + p_i. \tag{6.14'}$$

In a magnetized plasma under laboratory conditions the principal forces are the pressure gradient and the magnetic force. The term $\mathbf{F}$ represents the sum of the remaining forces acting on a unit volume of plasma. These include the following: the viscous force $F_\alpha^\pi = -\partial\pi_{\alpha\beta}/\partial x_\beta$, where $\pi_{\alpha\beta} = \pi_{i\alpha\beta} + \pi_{e\alpha\beta} \approx \pi_{i\alpha\beta}$ is the stress tensor; the gravitational force $\mathbf{F}_g = \rho\mathbf{g}$, which is important in many astrophysical problems, where $\mathbf{g}$ is the gravitational acceleration. The electric force $\mathbf{F}_E = \rho_e\mathbf{E}$ is usually very small compared with the others.

For greater clarity the magnetic force is frequently expressed in the terms of the Maxwell stress tensor

$$F_\alpha^B = \frac{1}{c}[\mathbf{jB}]_\alpha = \frac{\partial T_{\alpha\beta}^B}{\partial x_\beta}, \quad T_{\alpha\beta}^B = \frac{1}{4\pi}\left(B_\alpha B_\beta - \frac{1}{2}B^2\delta_{\alpha\beta}\right). \tag{6.15}$$

This expression is easily obtained from Eq. (6.12). The tensor $T_{\alpha\beta}^B$ corresponds to the pressure $B^2/8\pi$ across the magnetic lines and the tension along the lines, i.e., this tensor gives the isotropic pressure $B^2/8\pi$ and the longitudinal tension $B^2/4\pi$. For example, if there is a tangential field $\mathbf{B}$ at the plasma boundary and this field is shielded by currents in the surface layer the field pressure $B^2/8\pi$ is transferred to the plasma which shields it. The field normal to the plasma surface cannot transfer tension to the plasma since the magnetic lines of force cannot be cut off (div $\mathbf{B} = 0$) but continue into the plasma. The tension of the magnetic lines can be transferred to the plasma if currents flow in the plasma in such a way as to distort the lines of force. A "straightening" force is produced under these conditions; this force is again across the field lines. If **n** is the principal normal to the line of force and R the radius of curvature,

$$\mathbf{F}_B = -\nabla \frac{B^2}{8\pi} - \frac{B^2}{4\pi} \cdot \frac{\mathbf{n}}{R}. \tag{6.15'}$$

A magnetic pressure $B^2/8\pi$ equal to 1 kg/cm^2 requires a field $B = 5 \cdot 10^3 G$.

The electrical force can also be represented in terms of Maxwell stresses. If rot **E** = 0 we have from Eq. (6.13): *

$$F_\alpha^E = \varrho_e E_\alpha = \frac{\partial T_{\alpha\beta}^E}{\partial x_\beta}, \quad T_{\alpha\beta}^E = \frac{1}{4\pi}\left(E_\alpha E_\beta - \frac{1}{2} E^2 \delta_{\alpha\beta}\right). \tag{6.16}$$

Only the normal component of the electric field can change sharply near the plasma boundary. In this case the lines of force terminate on charges close to the surface and the plasma is not subject to pressure that acts to contain it, as in the case of a magnetic field, but rather is subject to a tension (negative pressure) $E^2/8\pi$. A tension of 1 kg/cm^2 corresponds to $E = 1.5 \cdot 10^6$ V/cm.

If $enE \sim \nabla p$ we find $|\nabla E^2/8\pi| \,/\, |\nabla p| \sim \delta_D^2/L^2$ so that the force F_E can only be large in thin layers. If $E \sim VB/c$ then $E^2/B^2 \sim V^2/c^2$. It is then obvious that the electrical forces in a relativistic plasma can be of the same order as the magnetic forces.

The effect of inertia can be used to classify plasma phenomena as fast or slow. In fast phenomena the inertia term in Eq. (6.14) is of the same order as the other terms—these are phenomena characterized by relatively high frequencies [of order c_S/L or c_A/L where $c_S \sim (p/\rho)^{1/2}$ and

*In the general case, taking account of the displacement current and rot **E** ≠ 0 we find

$$F_\alpha^B + F_\alpha^E = \frac{1}{c}[jB]_\alpha + \varrho_e E_\alpha = \frac{\partial T_{\alpha\beta}^B}{\partial x_\beta} + \frac{\partial T_{\alpha\beta}^E}{\partial x_\beta} - \frac{1}{c^2} \cdot \frac{\partial S_\alpha}{\partial t},$$

where $\mathbf{S} = (c/4\pi)[\mathbf{EB}]$ is the Poynting vector and $\mathbf{S}/c^2$ is the electromagnetic momentum density.

$c_A = (B^2/4\pi\rho)^{1/2}$]. In slow phenomena the inertia term can be neglected as a first approximation—either the plasma is at rest or it moves so slowly that the forces acting upon it are approximately in equilibrium at all times. Fast phenomena include various short-lived and transient processes; for a long-lived plasma magnetohydrodynamic waves are regarded as fast phenomena. Slow phenomena are those in which equilibrium is established in characteristic times appreciably greater than L/c_S. A typical example is the compression of a plasma by a rapidly applied magnetic field—either externally produced or produced by current flowing through the plasma (fast pinch). The characteristic compression velocity in such cases is of order c_A.

To analyze slow phenomena we need retain only the principal terms in Eq. (6.14); thus,

$$\nabla p = \frac{1}{c}[\mathbf{jB}]. \tag{6.17}$$

This equation, together with Eq. (6.12), defines so-called equilibrium magnetohydrodynamic configurations. It is evident from Eq. (6.17) that $\mathbf{B}\nabla p = 0$ and $\mathbf{j}\nabla p = 0$. Consequently, the magnetic lines of force and the current flow lines lie on surfaces of constant pressure which are called magnetic surfaces. A plasma confined by a magnetic field (equilibrium configuration) can be regarded as a series of magnetic surfaces nested within each other.

An important dimensionless parameter that characterizes the effectiveness of a magnetic field for plasma containment is the ratio $8\pi p/B^2$, where p and B are the pressure and field, respectively. In actual laboratory devices used to study slow phenomena this quantity is generally much smaller than unity since the plasma usually loses heat very easily.

Our classification of phenomena as being fast or slow is obviously an arbitrary one and does not exhaust all possibilities. In this review, however, we shall only be interested in making rough estimates for purposes of orientation rather than in the detailed classification of plasma phenomena. In actual problems a more detailed analysis would obviously be required.

Ohm's Law. As it is conventionally stated Ohm's law $\mathbf{j} = \sigma\mathbf{E}$ relates the current density to the electric field at a given instant of time. However, the electric field is actually responsible for the acceleration of electrons rather than their velocity so that in the general case no such relation obtains. In processes in which all quantities vary slowly in time (no significant changes in one electron-ion collision time) the electron inertia is unimportant and the effect of the electric field is balanced by friction due to collisions of electrons with ions, $\mathbf{u} = -\mathbf{j}/en$. This equilibrium condition for an electron gas is called Ohm's law. An Ohm's law can be derived for a plasma in similar fashion.

It is convenient to express the electric field in terms of the current rather than vice versa. In addition to simplifying the formulas, this method of description gives a more accurate picture of the qualitative nature of the effect: in a highly conducting plasma, where the reactance is greater than the real resistance, the current is usually determined by the external conditions while the electric field is determined from the current by Ohm's law.

Neglecting the electron inertia and viscosity in the equations of motion and using Eqs. (2.6) and (2.9) or Eqs. (4.30) and (4.31) for the force $\mathbf{R} = \mathbf{R}_u + \mathbf{R}_T$ we have

$$\mathbf{E}' = \frac{\mathbf{j}_{\parallel}}{\sigma_{\parallel}} + \frac{\mathbf{j}_{\perp}}{\sigma_{\perp}} + \frac{1}{en_e c}[\mathbf{j}\mathbf{B}], \tag{6.18}$$

where $\mathbf{E}'$ is the effective field, given by

$$\mathbf{E}' = \mathbf{E} + \frac{1}{c}[\mathbf{V}\mathbf{B}] + \frac{1}{en_e}(\nabla p_e - \mathbf{R}_T). \tag{6.19}$$

If $\mathbf{j}$ is expressed in terms of $\mathbf{E}'$ then

$$\mathbf{j} = \sigma_{\parallel}\mathbf{E}'_{\parallel} + \frac{\sigma_{\perp}}{1+\omega_e^2\tau_e^2}\{\mathbf{E}'_{\perp} + \omega_e\tau_e[\mathbf{h}\mathbf{E}']\}. \tag{6.20}$$

The quantity $\mathbf{E}'$ contains the electric field $\mathbf{E}^*$ in the coordinate system moving with the matter (with the ions):

$$\mathbf{E}^* = \mathbf{E} + \frac{1}{c}[\mathbf{V}\mathbf{B}]. \tag{6.21}$$

Furthermore, $\mathbf{E}'$ contains the thermolelectric force $-\mathbf{R}_T/en_e$ and the electron pressure term $\nabla p_e/en_e$. The latter is not important in ordinary metal conductors because the electron pressure is uniform. In a plasma, however, the electron pressure can vary sharply and this term can be of great importance.

If there is no magnetic field $\mathbf{E}' = \mathbf{j}/\sigma_{\parallel}$. In a strong magnetic field ($\omega_e\tau_e \gg 1$) the same relation holds for the components along the field

$$E'_{\parallel} = j_{\parallel}/\sigma_{\parallel}, \tag{6.22a}$$

but the transverse components are modified significantly (Fig. 6). The effective field $E'_{\perp}$ is essentially perpendicular to the current $\mathbf{j}_{\perp}$. The projection of the field $\mathbf{E}'_{\perp}$ on the current is related to $\mathbf{j}_{\perp}$ by

$$(E'_{\perp})_j = j_{\perp}/\sigma_{\perp}, \tag{6.22b}$$

and is not very different from Eq. (6.22a). The magnetic field does not have much effect on the friction produced by electron-ion collisions. For example $\sigma_{\perp} \approx \sigma_{\parallel}/2$ when $Z = 1$. However, flow of current across the magnetic field requires a component $\mathbf{E}'$ perpendicular to both it and the magnetic field, the so-called Hall field. This field equilibrates the force acting on the electron $(1/c)[\mathbf{j}\mathbf{B}]$ and is given by

$$\mathbf{E}'_{\text{Hall}} = \frac{1}{en_ec}[\mathbf{j}\mathbf{B}] = \frac{\omega_e\tau_e}{\sigma_{\perp}}[\mathbf{j}\mathbf{h}]. \tag{6.22c}$$

Frequently $\mathbf{E}'_{\text{Hall}}$ arises automatically in a plasma as a consequence of the small charge separation allowed within the framework of quasineutrality, while the external field, which must be applied to the plasma, is determined by Eqs. (6.22a) and (6.22b). In this connection it is sometimes said that the magnetic field does not affect the conductivity of the plasma. This statement is to be understood within the context we have indicated here.

Ohm's law for a plasma can be written in several equivalent forms. Frequently it is convenient to replace the electron equation of motion by the ion equation of motion and to introduce a new effective field $\mathbf{E}''$ defined by

$$\mathbf{E}'' = \mathbf{E} + \frac{1}{c}[\mathbf{V}\mathbf{B}] - \frac{1}{en_e}(\nabla p_i + \mathbf{R}_T) - \frac{m_i}{Ze}\frac{d\mathbf{V}}{dt} + \frac{1}{en_e}\mathbf{F}. \tag{6.23}$$

In this case the resulting expression does not contain the Hall term:

$$\mathbf{E}'' = \frac{\mathbf{j}_{\parallel}}{\sigma_{\parallel}} + \frac{\mathbf{j}_{\perp}}{\sigma_{\perp}}. \tag{6.24}$$

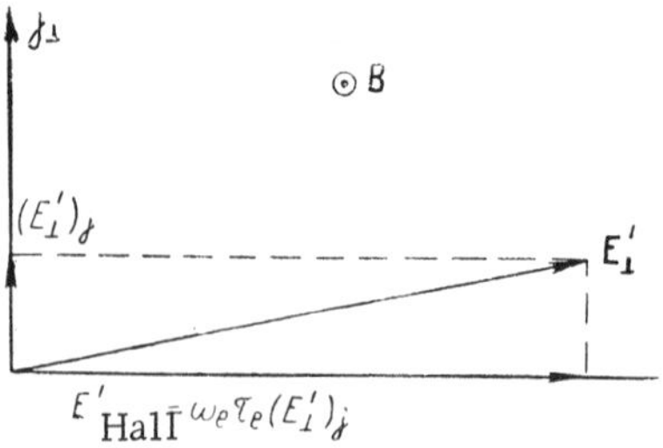

Fig. 6

This expression is also obtained if the $(1/c)[\mathbf{jB}]$ term is eliminated from Eq. (6.18) by means of the equation of motion (6.14). Schlüter has proposed that Ohm's law for a plasma should be written in the form given in (6.24) without the Hall term [24]. This form of the equation is especially convenient in cases in which $d\mathbf{V}/dt$ can be determined easily, in particular, in slow phenomena where this term is small and can be neglected to first approximation.

Although Eqs. (6.18) and (6.24) appear to be different they are actually the same when the equation of motion is taken into account. A peculiar inversion of the equation occurs in a magnetized plasma confined by a magnetic field. The transverse component of the current can be determined from Eq. (6.14). If viscosity is neglected this quantity is

$$\mathbf{j}_\perp = \frac{c}{B}[\mathbf{h}\nabla p]. \tag{6.25}$$

On the other hand, Ohm's law determines the plasma velocity across the magnetic field. Substituting Eq. (6.25) in Eq. (6.24) and omitting $\partial\pi_{\alpha\beta}/\partial x_\beta$ and $d\mathbf{V}/dt$ (neglecting $\mathbf{R}_T$ for simplicity), we find

$$\mathbf{V}_\perp = \frac{c}{B}\left[\left(\mathbf{E} - \frac{\nabla p}{en_e}\right)\mathbf{h}\right] - \frac{c^2}{\sigma_\perp B^2}\nabla_\perp p. \tag{6.26}$$

The second term in the square brackets in Eq. (6.26) is called the rate of diffusion across the magnetic field. We note that according to the generally accepted terminology diffusion means the relative motion of different components of a complex plasma; actually Eq. (6.26) expresses the hydrodynamic velocity of the plasma. For this reason it appears to be desirable to use a different terminology, the "leak" rate. If the current (6.25) is maintained by induction, which is expressed by the term $(1/c)[\mathbf{VB}]$, the leak rate of the plasma across the field is given precisely by the second term in Eq. (6.26), which is proportional to the transverse resistance of the plasma $1/\sigma_{\perp}$.

The order of magnitude of the current and velocity $u = -j/en$ are determined by the equation of motion. According to Eq. (6.12), $B'/L \sim 4\pi j/c$ where B' is the field produced by the currents in the plasma. For fast phenomena, from $\rho V^2 \sim B'^2/4\pi$ we find $u^2/V^2 \sim 1/\Pi$; for slow phenomena from $p \sim B'^2/4\pi$ we find $u^2/c_S^2 \sim 1/\Pi$ where

$$\Pi = \frac{4\pi e^2 n_e^2 L^2}{\varrho c^2} = \frac{4\pi Z e^2 n_e L^2}{m_i c^2}. \qquad (6.27)$$

The dimensionless number Π is proportional to the number of particles nL^2 per unit length of the system.

Thus, in a system containing a large number of particles the electron velocity is "tied" to the ion velocity by the self-consistent magnetic field as well as collisions.

The characteristic frequencies of fast phenomena are of order $c_A/L \sim \omega_i/\Pi^{1/2}$. If $\Pi \gg 1$ these frequencies are small compared with the ion cyclotron frequency.

Estimating the order of magnitude of the various terms in Ohm's law for fast phenomena with $\Pi \gg 1$, $\omega \ll \omega_i$, $L \gg r_i$ we find that the principal terms in the effective field are $\mathbf{E} + (1/c)[\mathbf{VB}]$. When collisions can be neglected we can also neglect $\mathbf{j}/\sigma$, and to a first approximation Ohm's law can be written in the form

$$\mathbf{E} + \frac{1}{c}[\mathbf{VB}] = 0. \qquad (6.28)$$

Eliminating the electric field by means of Eq. (6.28) we obtain the induction equation in the ideal magnetohydrodynamics approximation:

$$\frac{\partial \mathbf{B}}{\partial t} = \operatorname{rot}[\mathbf{VB}]. \qquad (6.29)$$

This equation allows a simple interpretation: the magnetic lines of force behave as though tied to the matter and move with the matter at a velocity $\mathbf{V}$. Equation (6.29) is frequently used in the analysis of plasma oscillations and plasma stability.

When all terms are retained the induction equation obtained from Eq. (6.18) becomes rather complicated:*

$$\frac{\partial \mathbf{B}}{\partial t} = \operatorname{rot}[\mathbf{VB}] - \operatorname{rot}\left[\frac{\mathbf{j}}{en_e}\mathbf{B}\right] - \frac{c}{en}[\nabla n \nabla T] -$$

$$-\frac{c}{e}\operatorname{rot}\frac{\mathbf{R}_T}{n_e} - c\operatorname{rot}\left(\frac{\mathbf{j}_\parallel}{\sigma_\parallel} + \frac{\mathbf{j}_\perp}{\sigma_\perp}\right). \quad (6.30)$$

In place of this equation one frequently makes use of the following simplified equation with isotropic uniform conductivity

$$\frac{\partial \mathbf{B}}{\partial t} = \operatorname{rot}[\mathbf{VB}] + \frac{c^2}{4\pi\sigma}\nabla^2\mathbf{B}. \quad (6.31)$$

Here we have used Eq. (6.12) and the relation rot rot $\mathbf{B} = -\nabla^2\mathbf{B}$. This equation describes the skin effect; it takes account of the fact that the lines of force are not completely entrained but move through the matter with a diffusion coefficient D_m given by

$$D_m = \frac{c^2}{4\pi\sigma}. \quad (6.32)$$

---

*Eliminating [jB] from Eq. (6.30) by means of the equation of motion or by using the relation (6.24), by means of the transformation rot $d\mathbf{V}/dt = \partial$ rot $\mathbf{V}/\partial t$ - rot [$\mathbf{V}$ rot $\mathbf{V}$] we can write the induction equation in the form

$$\frac{\partial}{\partial t}\left(\mathbf{B} + \frac{m_i c}{Ze}\operatorname{rot}\mathbf{V}\right) = \operatorname{rot}\left[\mathbf{V}\left(\mathbf{B} + \frac{m_i c}{Ze}\operatorname{rot}\mathbf{V}\right)\right] +$$

$$+\frac{c}{Zen}[\nabla n \nabla T_i] - (c/en_e)\operatorname{rot}\left(\mathbf{F}_i^\pi + \mathbf{R}_T\right) - c\operatorname{rot}\left(\mathbf{j}_\parallel/\sigma_\parallel + \mathbf{j}_\perp/\sigma_\perp\right), \quad (6.30')$$

where

$$F_{i\alpha}^\pi = -\partial\pi_{i\alpha\beta}/\partial x_\beta.$$

If the last three terms on the right can be neglected the lines $\mathbf{B}$ + $(m_i c/e_i)$ rot $\mathbf{V}$ are tied to the matter; if, however, $\Pi \gg 1$, $\omega \ll \omega_i$ we find $|\operatorname{rot}\mathbf{V}| \ll e_i B/m_i c$ and it may be assumed that the lines $\mathbf{B}$ are tied to the matter. Thus, when B = 0 we obtain the familiar theorem on attachment of the circulation lines of conventional hydrodynamics [3].

The same phenomenon, penetration of plasma through the magnetic field, is described by the last term in Eq. (6.26). When $p \sim B^2/4\pi$ the rate of penetration is of order D_m/L. It is evident from Eq. (6.26) that the rate of penetration is of order $(4\pi p/B^2)\,D_m/L$ when $p \ll B^2/4\pi$. This same result is obviously obtained from Eq. (6.32) since the relative magnitude of the field gradient is of order $B'/LB \sim 4\pi p/B^2L$ where B' is the difference in fields outside and inside the plasma as determined by the plasma equilibrium condition $BB'/4\pi \sim p$; thus, the rate of penetration of the field is $\sim D_m B'/LB \sim (4\pi p/B^2)\,D_m/L$.

If the effective value of $\sigma_\perp$ is reduced as a result of turbulence Eq. (6.26) shows that the penetration of the plasma through the magnetic field is much more rapid; this is the so-called "anomalous diffusion" effect.

Equations of Energy and Heat Transport. When the electron and ion temperatures are very different the individual heat-balance equations given in the preceding sections are used. However, if the thermal coupling between the electrons and ions is strong, the relative temperature difference is small $|T_e - T_i| \ll T$ and one can use the combined equation, writing $T_e = T_i = T$.

The temperatures of the eletron and ion fluids can be very different if much more heat is generated in one than in the other. For example, Joule heat is generated in the electron gas. If Q_{Joule} is equated roughly with the heat transferred to the ions Q_Δ we can obtain the difference of temperatures responsible for this transfer. A rough estimate yields

$$\frac{(T_e - T_i)_{\mathbf{Joule}}}{T} \sim \frac{j^2 m_i}{e^2 n^2 T} \sim \frac{u^2}{v_i^2} \quad \text{or} \quad \frac{(T_e - T_i)_{\mathbf{Joule}}}{T} \sim \frac{1}{\Pi}\frac{B'^2}{4\pi p}.$$

Here we have used the relation $(4\pi/c)\,j \sim B'/L$ where the magnetic field B' is produced by the currents in the plasma. In slow phenomena, in which the main source of heat is Joule heating, the electron temperature tends to exceed the ion temperature.

On the other hand, heat generation by virtue of viscosity effects occurs primarily in the ion gas since the ion viscosity is much greater than the electron viscosity. Equating roughly the quantities $Q_{vis} \sim \eta V^2/L^2 \sim Q_\Delta$ we obtain the appropriate temperature difference. If the "longitudinal" viscosity η_0 is important

$$\frac{(T_i - T_e)_{\mathbf{vis}}}{T} \sim \frac{m_i}{m_e}\frac{V^2\tau_i\tau_e}{L_\parallel^2} \sim \left(\frac{m_i}{m_e}\right)^{1/2}\left(\frac{V\tau_i}{L_\parallel}\right)^2 \sim \left(\frac{m_i}{m_e}\right)^{1/2}\left(\frac{l}{L_\parallel}\frac{V}{v_i}\right)^2,$$

and if the "transverse" viscosity is important $\eta_{1,2} \sim \eta_0/\omega_i^2\tau_i^2$

$$\frac{(T_i - T_e)_{\text{vis}}}{T} \sim \frac{m_i\tau_e}{m_e\tau_i}\left(\frac{m_iVc}{eBL_\perp}\right)^2 \sim \left(\frac{m_i}{m_e}\right)^{1/2}\left(\frac{m_iVc}{eBL_\perp}\right)^2 \sim$$
$$\sim \left(\frac{m_i}{m_e}\right)^{1/2}\left(\frac{r_i}{L_\perp}\frac{V}{v_i}\right)^2.$$

The velocity of strong shock waves in a plasma is greater than the ion thermal velocity but usually smaller than the electron thermal velocity; hence strong heating due to shock waves is experienced only by the ions. When the primary source of heat is the dissipation of energy associated with plasma motion (shock waves, intense plasma oscillations resulting from instabilities, etc.) most of the heat is generated in the ion gas and the ion temperature can be higher than the electron temperature.

If $T_e = T_i = T$ (to the required accuracy) the individual energy equations for the electrons and ions can conveniently be replaced by a general energy balance equation. Combining the energy transport equations for the ions and electrons (1.20), taking account of Eq. (1.24), and neglecting electron inertia, we obtain the plasma energy transport equation:

$$\frac{\partial}{\partial t}\left(\frac{1}{2}\varrho V^2 + \frac{3}{2}p\right) + \frac{\partial}{\partial x_\beta}\left\{\left(\frac{1}{2}\varrho V^2 + \frac{5}{2}p\right)V_\beta + \right.$$
$$\left. + \pi_{\alpha\beta}V_\alpha + q_\beta\right\} = \mathbf{Ej}. \tag{6.33}$$

Here $p = p_e + p_i$,

$$\mathbf{q} = \mathbf{q}_e + \mathbf{q}_i + \frac{5}{2}p_e\mathbf{u}. \tag{6.33'}$$

On the other hand, Maxwell's equations (6.11) and (6.12) provide an energy relation for the field (the Poynting theorem in the approximation $E \ll B$):

$$\frac{\partial}{\partial t}\frac{B^2}{8\pi} + \operatorname{div}\mathbf{S} = -\mathbf{Ej}, \tag{6.34}$$

where $\mathbf{S} = (c/4\pi)[\mathbf{EB}]$ is the Poynting vector.

Combining Eq. (6.33) and Eq. (6.34) we obtain a conservation law for the total energy:

$$\frac{\partial \varepsilon_{\text{total}}}{\partial t} + \operatorname{div} \mathbf{q}_{\text{total}} = 0,$$

$$\varepsilon_{\text{total}} = \frac{1}{2} \varrho V^2 + \frac{3}{2} p + \frac{B^2}{8\pi}, \tag{6.35}$$

$$q_\beta^{\text{total}} = \left(\frac{1}{2} \varrho V^2 + \frac{5}{2} p\right) V_\beta + \pi_{\alpha\beta} V_\alpha + q_\beta + S_\beta.$$

Adding Eq. (1.23) for the electrons andions, taking account of Eq. (1.24) and the relation div ($n_e\mathbf{u}$) = 0, or eliminating the kinetic energy from Eq. (6.33) and using Ohm's law (6.18), we obtain the plasma heat balance equation

$$\frac{3}{2} \frac{\partial p}{\partial t} + \operatorname{div}\left(\frac{3}{2} p \mathbf{V}\right) + p \operatorname{div} \mathbf{V} = -\operatorname{div} \mathbf{q} + \mathbf{u} \nabla p_e + \Sigma Q. \tag{6.36}$$

The right side of this equation contains all heat sources, including the heating due to viscosity: $\Sigma Q = -\mathbf{Ru} + Q_{\text{vis}}$.

Energy is transferred by macroscopic mechanisms (transport with velocity $\mathbf{V}$ and work due to the pressure) and by microscopic mechanisms (thermal conductivity, viscosity, etc.). The microscopic mechanisms and the corresponding terms in the energy and heat equations are called dissipative. These mechanisms increase the entropy of the plasma and result in the conversion of mechanical energy into heat. The entropy of the plasma (per particle), as for any monatomic gas, is equal to $\ln(T^{3/2}/n)$ or $\ln(p^{3/2}/\rho^{5/2})$ (to within an unimportant constant). It is evident from Eq. (6.36) that the entropy is conserved in the absence of dissipative processes.

We note that the left side of Eq. (6.36) can be written in the following form if the equation of continuity is used:

$$\frac{3}{2} \frac{dp}{dt} - \frac{5}{2} \frac{p}{\varrho} \frac{d\varrho}{dt} = \frac{3}{2} p \frac{d}{dt} \ln (p/\varrho^\gamma),$$

where $\gamma = 5/3$ is the adiabaticity index for the monatomic gas.

The relative importance of dissipative processes becomes smaller as the dimensions of the system become larger because the energy transport due to these processes is of a diffusional nature. If the characteristic time of the dissipative processes (L^2/D_m for the electrical resistance, $L^2n/\varkappa$ for the thermal conductivity, $L^2\rho/\eta$ for the viscosity, etc.) is large compared with the reciprocal frequency of the plasma motion $1/\omega$ or L/V, the dissipative terms are small. Under these conditions we can assume that the process is adiabatic and write as a first approximation

$$\frac{d}{dt}\frac{p}{\varrho^{\gamma}} = 0. \tag{6.37}$$

Dissipative processes increase the entropy and result in the damping of any macroscopic motion of the plasma, magnetohydrodynamic waves, and so on.

The plasma entropy balance equation can be obtained by adding Eq. (1.23') for the electrons and ions:

$$\frac{\partial S}{\partial t} + \operatorname{div}\left\{S\mathbf{V} + S_e\mathbf{u} + \frac{\mathbf{q}_e + \mathbf{q}_i}{T}\right\} = \theta, \tag{6.38}$$

$$T\theta = -(\mathbf{q}_e + \mathbf{q}_i)\,\nabla \ln T + \Sigma\, Q. \tag{6.39}$$

Here, $S = S_e + S_i = n_e \ln(T^{3/2}/n_e) + n_i \ln(T^{3/2}/n_i)$ is the plasma entropy per unit volume. The quantity θ is called the entropy production. It is easily shown that this quantity is always positive, that is to say, dissipative processes always cause a monotonic increase in entropy. The quantity $T\theta$ contains the Joule heat $j^2_{\parallel}/\sigma_{\parallel} + j^2_{\perp}/\sigma_{\perp}$ and the viscous heat $-{}^1/_2\pi_{\alpha\beta}W_{\alpha\beta}$, which are always positive.

§ 7. Multicomponent Plasma

Diffusion in a Three-Component Mixture. A simple model of a three-component mixture is an incompletely ionized gas that contains electrons, one ion species, and one species of neutral particles. The motion of these components can be specified by the three velocities $\mathbf{V}_e$, $\mathbf{V}_i$, and $\mathbf{V}_n$ or by a common hydrodynamic velocity $\mathbf{V}$ which is approximately

$$\mathbf{V} = \frac{1}{\varrho}(m_i n_i \mathbf{V} + m_n n_n \mathbf{V}_n), \tag{7.1}$$

and two relative velocities, which can be taken as

$$\mathbf{u} = \mathbf{V}_e - \mathbf{V}_i, \quad \mathbf{w} = \mathbf{V}_i - \mathbf{V}_n. \tag{7.2}$$

In a simple plasma there is one equation for the relative velocity, Ohm's law; in a three-component mixture two equations are required: one for the diffusion velocity **w** and one for the velocity associated with the current $\mathbf{u} = -\mathbf{j}/en_e$.

The determination of the diffusion velocities requires the solution of a system of three kinetic equations and the determination of the local distribution functions for all the components [12]. However, approximate results can be obtained by a simpler technique if the equations of motion for the individual components are used (1.14). The friction force is then obtained from the interaction of particles of one species with the remaining species: $\mathbf{R}_a = \sum_b \mathbf{R}_{ab}$. The forces $\mathbf{R}_{ab} = -\mathbf{R}_{ba}$ can be computed approximately under the assumption that the components a and b have Maxwellian distributions with velocities $\mathbf{V}_a$ and $\mathbf{V}_b$. As a result we find

$$\mathbf{R}_{ab} = -\alpha_{ab}(\mathbf{V}_a - \mathbf{V}_b), \quad \alpha_{ab} = \alpha_{ba}. \tag{7.3}$$

The coefficient of friction α_{ab} is obviously proportional to $n_a n_b$, the reduced mass of the colliding particles $m_{ab} = m_a m_b/(m_a + m_b)$, and the coefficient α'_{ab}, which is of order $v\sigma$ where v and σ are the characteristic values of the relative velocity and the effective cross sections for the colliding particles:

$$\alpha_{ab} = n_a n_b m_{ab} \alpha'_{ab}. \tag{7.4}$$

The calculation of α_{ab} is shown in the Appendix and can also be found in [1]. Suppose that $T_a = T_b = T$. If the scattering cross section [here the so-called transport cross section $\sigma' = \int(1 - \cos\vartheta)\, d\sigma(\vartheta)$ is the important factor] is inversely proportional to the relative velocity $\sigma'_{ab}(v) = \alpha'_{ab}/v$ Eq. (7.4) is obtained directly. For solid smooth spheres of radius r_a and r_b the cross section is $\sigma_{ab} = \pi(r_a + r_b)^2$. For this case

$$\alpha'_{ab} = \frac{4}{3}\sigma_{ab}\left(\frac{8}{\pi}\frac{T}{m_{ab}}\right)^{1/2}. \tag{7.5}$$

For ions of charge e_a and e_b [compare Eq. (2.5e)]

$$\alpha'_{ab} = \frac{4\sqrt{2\pi}\lambda e_a^2 e_b^2}{3\sqrt{m_{ab}}T^{3/2}}. \tag{7.6}$$

The relation in (7.3) does not take account of the possible anisotropy of the coefficient of friction in a magnetic field and also neglects the thermal force, so that it does not give thermal diffusion. In simple cases these effects can be estimated as in §3.

The component equations of motion, [using (7.2) and (7.3) and neglecting electron inertia] can be written in the form

$$-\nabla p_e - en_e\left(\mathbf{E} + \frac{1}{c}[\mathbf{V}_e\mathbf{B}]\right) = -\alpha_e\frac{\mathbf{j}}{en_e} + \alpha_{en}\,\mathbf{w}, \qquad (7.7e)$$

$$-m_i n_i\frac{d_i\mathbf{V}_i}{dt} - \nabla p_i + en_e\left(\mathbf{E} + \frac{1}{c}[\mathbf{V}_i\mathbf{B}]\right) = \alpha_{ei}\frac{\mathbf{j}}{en_e} + \alpha_{in}\mathbf{w}, \qquad (7.7i)$$

$$-m_n n_n\frac{d_n\mathbf{V}}{dt} - \nabla p_n = \alpha_{en}\frac{\mathbf{j}}{en_e} - \alpha_n\,\mathbf{w}. \qquad (7.7n)$$

Here we use the substitution $\mathbf{u} = -\mathbf{j}/en_e$ and the notation

$$\alpha_e = \alpha_{ei} + \alpha_{en} = m_e n_e/\tau_e; \qquad \tau_e = \left(\frac{1}{\tau_{ei}} + \frac{1}{\tau_{en}}\right)^{-1}, \qquad (7.8)$$

$$\alpha_n = \alpha_{en} + \alpha_{in} = \alpha_{in}/(1-\varepsilon); \; \varepsilon = \alpha_{en}/\alpha_n. \qquad (7.9)$$

Actually, we should take account of the viscosity in Eq. (7.7) writing $\partial P_{a\alpha\beta}/\partial x_\beta = \partial p_a/\partial x_\alpha + \partial \pi_{a\alpha\beta}/\partial x_\beta$ in place of $\nabla p_a (a = e, i, n)$. In the present analysis viscosity will be neglected.

The coefficient of friction between the plasma and neutral gas α_n depends primarily on the collisions between heavy particles because such collisions result in large momentum transfer; thus, one usually writes

$$\alpha_n \approx \alpha_{in}, \quad \varepsilon = \alpha_{en}/\alpha_n \approx (m_e/m_{in})(\alpha'_{en}/\alpha'_{in}) \ll 1.$$

Adding Eqs. (7.7e) and (7.7i) we obtain the equation of motion for the ionized particles; the electric field vanishes in the equation:

$$-m_i n_i\frac{d_i\mathbf{V}_i}{dt} - \nabla(p_e + p_i) + \frac{1}{c}[\mathbf{jB}] = -\alpha_{en}\frac{\mathbf{j}}{en_e} + \alpha_n\mathbf{w}. \qquad (7.7p)$$

The sum of equations (7.7n) and (7.7p) gives the general equation of motion.

If the collision frequency is low it is more convenient to use the individual equations of motion for the neutral and ionized particles since the velocities are no longer "tied together" by collisions (strictly speaking the kinetic equation should be used in the low-collision case). On the other hand, the hydrodynamic description applies at high collision frequencies and it is more convenient to use the general equation of motion for **V** and the relative-velocity equations. We shall be interested in the second case. In the inertia terms we replace $d_i\mathbf{V}_i/dt$ and $d_n\mathbf{V}_n/dt$ by $d\mathbf{V}/dt$; this corresponds to neglecting terms of order $d\mathbf{w}/dt$ compared with terms of order $\mathbf{w}/\tau$ which are contained in the friction force. Viscosity is also neglected.

Various authors, for example [7, 25, 29], transform Eq. (7.7) by different methods and different expressions are obtained for the various relative velocities convenient for particular problems. The plasma diffusion rate with respect to the neutrals **w** can be determined, for example, from Eqs. (7.7n) and (7.7p). Eliminating the inertia term from these two equations we write **w** in the form

$$\mathbf{w} = \frac{1}{\alpha_n}\left\{ -\mathbf{G} + \frac{\xi_n}{c}[\mathbf{jB}]\right\} + \frac{\varepsilon \mathbf{j}}{en_e}, \tag{7.10}$$

where

$$\mathbf{G} = \xi_n \nabla (p_e + p_i) - \xi_i \nabla p_n. \tag{7.11}$$

Here we have introduced the relative densities

$$\xi_n = m_n n_n/\rho, \quad \xi_i = m_i n_i/\rho, \quad \xi_n + \xi_i = 1.$$

If $T_i = T_n = T$, $m_i = m_n$ then $\mathbf{G} = \xi_n \nabla p_e + (p_i + p_n)\nabla \xi_i$; $p_i + p_n = T\rho/m_i$.

For example Ohm's law can be obtained by eliminating **w** from the electron equation of motion (7.7e) by means of Eq. (7.10):

$$\mathbf{E} + \frac{1}{c}[\mathbf{V}_i\mathbf{B}] + \frac{1}{en_e}(\nabla p_e - \varepsilon \mathbf{G}) = \frac{\mathbf{j}}{\sigma} + \frac{1 - \varepsilon\xi_n}{en_e c}[\mathbf{jB}], \tag{7.12}$$

where

$$\sigma = e^2 n_e^2 \left(\alpha_{ei} + \frac{\alpha_{en}\alpha_{in}}{\alpha_{en} + \alpha_{in}}\right)^{-1} \approx \frac{e^2 n_e \tau_e}{m_e}. \tag{7.13}$$

Equation (7.12) is very similar to Eq. (6.18) since $\varepsilon \ll 1$ but it contains the resistance $1/\sigma$, which is determined by the total electron collision frequency $1/\tau_e$. If the [jB] term is eliminated from Eq. (7.12) by means of the general equation of motion, Ohm's law is obtained in the form given by Schlüter [25].

Sometimes in writing Ohm's law it is convenient to retain the electric field $\mathbf{E}^* = \mathbf{E} + (1/c)[\mathbf{VB}]$ in the coordinate system moving with the velocity of the common mass $\mathbf{V}$. Using the relation $\mathbf{V}_i = \mathbf{V} + \xi_n \mathbf{w}$ and Eq. (7.10) we have from Eq. (7.12)

$$\mathbf{E} + \frac{1}{c}[\mathbf{VB}] + \frac{1}{en_e}(\nabla p_e - \varepsilon \mathbf{G}) - \frac{\xi_n}{\alpha_n c}[\mathbf{GB}] = \frac{\mathbf{j}_\parallel}{\sigma_\parallel} + \frac{\mathbf{j}_\perp}{\sigma^*_\perp} + \frac{1-2\varepsilon\xi_n}{en_e c}[\mathbf{jB}], \tag{7.14}$$

where

$$\sigma_\parallel = \sigma, \quad \frac{1}{\sigma^*_\perp} = \frac{1}{\sigma} + \frac{\xi_n^2 B^2}{\alpha_n c^2}. \tag{7.15}$$

When $m_i = m_n$, $\varepsilon \ll 1$, we find $\sigma/\sigma^*_\perp = 1 + 2\xi_n \omega_e \tau_e \omega_i \bar{\tau}_{in}$, where

$$1/\bar{\tau}_{in} = \alpha'_{in}(n_i + n_n).$$

Proceeding in the same way as in the derivation of Eq. (6.26) and using Eq. (7.12), we find that in the presence of neutrals the rate at which a plasma moves across the magnetic surfaces (the corresponding term in $\mathbf{V}_i$) is $(c^2/\sigma B^2)\nabla p$ where σ is expressed by Eq. (7.13) and p is the total pressure.

Ohm's law in the form given in (7.14) was derived by Cowling [7]. It contains the effective transverse resistance $1/\sigma^*_\perp$; in a strong magnetic field this can be much greater than the longitudinal resistance. This effect is explained by the fact that the motion of a plasma across the magnetic field means motion of the plasma with respect to the neutral gas; because of the large coefficient of friction between the ions and neutrals this implies a high rate of energy dissipation. It should be noted, however, that in certain cases (especially in slow phenomena, where the plasma pressure is almost always in equilibrium with the magnetic force) the terms in the curly brackets in Eq. (7.10) can almost balance each other; in such cases the last term on the left in Eq. (7.14) will almost balance the $j_\perp/\sigma^*_\perp$ term.

We wish to emphasize the great difference between Eq. (7.12) and Eq. (7.14) which contain $\mathbf{E} + (1/c)[\mathbf{V}_i\mathbf{B}]$ and $\mathbf{E} + (1/c)[\mathbf{VB}]$ respectively; in evaluating an electric field in the presence of a magnetic field it is of paramount importance to specify the coordinate system in which the electric field is being determined. A marked change in electric field occurs for even a small change in the velocity of the coordinate system.

We now consider the energy dissipation caused by friction in a mixture e, i, n. The total heat generated as a result of friction is $Q_{fr} = Q_e + Q_i + Q_n$. Taking account of the general relation (1.24) this expression can be written in the form $Q_{fr} = -\mathbf{R}_{ei}\mathbf{u} - \mathbf{R}_{en}(\mathbf{u} + \mathbf{w}) - \mathbf{R}_{in}\mathbf{w}$. Using Eq. (7.3) we find

$$Q_{fr} = \alpha_{ei}u^2 + \alpha_{en}(\mathbf{u} + \mathbf{w})^2 + \alpha_{in}w^2 = \\ = \alpha_e u^2 + \alpha_n w^2 + 2\alpha_{en}\mathbf{u}\mathbf{w}. \quad (7.16)$$

Using Eqs. (7.10) and (7.13) we now transform Eq. (7.16) as follows:

$$Q_{fr} = \frac{j^2}{\sigma} + \frac{1}{\alpha_n}\left(\frac{\xi_n}{c}[\mathbf{jB}] - \mathbf{G}\right)^2. \quad (7.17)$$

If the current flows along the magnetic field (or $B = 0$), we find $w \sim \varepsilon u \ll u$ because of the high coefficient of friction for the heavy particles so that the dissipation due to heavy-particle friction is small: $\alpha_n w^2 \sim \varepsilon\alpha_e u^2$. However, if the current flows across the magnetic field the dissipation can be larger because of collisions between ions and neutrals.

For example, when $\mathbf{G}$ can be neglected, if the plasma is cold or weakly ionized we find from Eq. (7.17) $Q_{fr} = j^2_{\parallel}/\sigma + j^2_{\perp}/\sigma^*_{\perp}$.

A fully ionized plasma consisting of electrons ($a = e$) and two ion species ($a = 1, 2$) represents another important example of a three-component mixture. Typical mixtures of this kind are a hydrogen plasma containing impurity ions, an ionized mixture of deuterium and tritium, and so on.

In such a plasma the density and hydrodynamic velocity are approximately

$$\varrho = m_1 n_1 + m_2 n_2, \quad \mathbf{V} = \frac{1}{\varrho}(m_1 n_1 \mathbf{V}_1 + m_2 n_2 \mathbf{V}_2). \quad (7.18)$$

The current density is expressed as the sum of the electron and ion components:

$$\mathbf{j} = -en_e\mathbf{u}_e + \left(\frac{e_1}{m_1} - \frac{e_2}{m_2}\right) \varrho\xi_1\xi_2\mathbf{w}, \tag{7.19}$$

where we have introduced the notation

$$\mathbf{u}_e = \mathbf{V}_e - \mathbf{V}, \quad \mathbf{w} = \mathbf{V}_1 - \mathbf{V}_2, \tag{7.20}$$

and the relative densities $\xi_1 = m_1n_1/\rho$ and $\xi_2 = m_2n_2/\rho$ which appear in the expressions $\mathbf{V}_1 = \mathbf{V} + \xi_2\mathbf{w}$ and $\mathbf{V}_2 = \mathbf{V} - \xi_1\mathbf{w}$.

The component equations are

$$m_1n_1\frac{d\mathbf{V}}{dt} = -\nabla p_1 + e_1n_1\left(\mathbf{E} + \frac{1}{c}[\mathbf{V}_1\mathbf{B}]\right) - \alpha_{12}\mathbf{w} - \\ - \alpha_{1e}(\xi_2\mathbf{w} - \mathbf{u}_e), \tag{7.21}$$

$$m_2n_2\frac{d\mathbf{V}}{dt} = -\nabla p_2 + e_2n_2\left(\mathbf{E} + \frac{1}{c}[\mathbf{V}_2\mathbf{B}]\right) + \alpha_{12}\mathbf{w} + \\ + \alpha_{2e}(\xi_1\mathbf{w} + \mathbf{u}_e), \tag{7.22}$$

$$0 = -\nabla p_e - en_e\left(\mathbf{E} + \frac{1}{c}[\mathbf{V}_e\mathbf{B}]\right) + (\alpha_{e1}\xi_2 - \alpha_{e2}\xi_1)\,\mathbf{w} - \alpha_e\mathbf{u}_e. \tag{7.23}$$

Here we have replaced $d_a\mathbf{V}_a/dt$ by $d\mathbf{V}/dt$, $\partial P_{a\alpha\beta}/\partial x_\beta$ by $\partial p_a/dx_\alpha$ and have introduced the notation

$$\alpha_e = \alpha_{e1} + \alpha_{e2} = m_en_e/\tau_e, \quad 1/\tau_e = 1/\tau_{e1} + 1/\tau_{e2}. \tag{7.24}$$

Using this system of equations we can find the relative velocity and obtain Ohm's law and an expression for **w** which is rather complicated in the general case [10a, 10b].

If T_i is not very much greater than T_e, we have $\alpha_{12} \gg \alpha_{e1}, \alpha_{e2}$. For example when $T_i \sim T_e$, $\alpha_{12} \sim (m_i/m_e)^{1/2}\alpha_e$.

When $B = 0$, because of the large value of α_{12} we find $w \ll u_e$ so that the current is transported primarily by electrons and Ohm's law can be written approximately in the form

$$\mathbf{E} + \frac{1}{en_e} \nabla p_e = \frac{\mathbf{j}}{\sigma}, \tag{7.25}$$

$$\sigma = \frac{e^2 n_e \tau_e}{m_e}. \tag{7.26}$$

The same relation holds for the component along the magnetic field.

Because of their greater mass ions can move across a strong magnetic field much more easily than can electrons; hence the ion component of the current across the magnetic field can be larger, esspecially in fast phenomena. Let us consider certain relations that hold between the transverse components when $\omega_i\tau_i$ is large. In this case, to a first approximation, we neglect collisions and then introduce them as a small correction. For example one can write $\mathbf{w} = \mathbf{w}^{(1)} + \mathbf{w}^{(2)}$ where $\mathbf{w}^{(1)}$ can be found neglecting collisions. We divide Eq. (7.21) by e_1n_1 and Eq. (7.22) by e_2n_2 and subtract one from the other. Neglecting the friction forces and writing $\mathbf{w}$ we find:

$$\mathbf{w}^{(1)} = \frac{c}{B}\left[\mathbf{h}\left(\frac{\nabla p_1}{e_1n_1} - \frac{\nabla p_2}{e_2n_2}\right)\right] + \frac{c}{B}\left(\frac{m_1}{e_1} - \frac{m_2}{e_2}\right)\left[\mathbf{h}\frac{d\mathbf{V}}{dt}\right]. \tag{7.27}$$

The electric field then vanishes. The $\perp$ symbol has been omitted. Now, taking account only of the friction between the ions and substituting Eq. (7.27) in the $\alpha_{12}\mathbf{w}$ term, we have

$$\mathbf{w}^{(2)} = -\frac{m_{12}c^2\alpha_{12}n_e}{e_1e_2B^2}\left\{\left(\frac{\nabla p_1}{Z_1n_1} - \frac{\nabla p_2}{Z_2n_2}\right) + \left(\frac{m_1}{Z_1} - \frac{m_2}{Z_2}\right)\frac{d\mathbf{V}}{dt}\right\}, \tag{7.28}$$

where $Z_1 = e_1/e$; $Z_2 = e_2/e$.

The quantity $\mathbf{u}_e = \mathbf{u}_e^{(1)} + \mathbf{u}_e^{(2)}$ can be expressed in similar fashion using Eq. (7.23) and eliminating the electric field $\mathbf{E}^* = \mathbf{E} + c^{-1}[\mathbf{VB}]$.

Let us consider a slow steady-state process in a plasma confined by a magnetic field; inertia effects will be neglected.

An estimate of the terms in Eq. (7.28) shows that the diffusion velocity $\mathbf{w}^{(2)}$ is $\sim(\alpha_{12}/\alpha_e) \sim (m_i/m_e)^{1/2}$ times greater than the penetration velocity for a simple plasma (6.26). The following question then arises: is the penetration velocity of a plasma with different ion species increased by a factor of $\sim(m_i/m_e)^{1/2}$ as compared with a simple plasma as a result of the friction between ions. In a steady state this process does not actually occur since the electron velocity across a magnetic surface $\mathbf{u}_e^{(2)}$ remains of order $c^2p/\sigma B^2L$, where σ is given by Eq. (7.26). The current across the magnetic surface vanishes so that $w^{(2)} \sim u_e^{(2)}$. Consequently the ion distribution that is established in the plasma must satisfy the condition

$$\frac{\nabla p_1}{e_1 n_1} - \frac{\nabla p_2}{e_2 n_2} \sim \frac{\alpha_e}{\alpha_{12}} \approx 0. \tag{7.29}$$

The equilibration process proceeds at a rate $\sim(m_i/m_e)^{1/2}$ times faster than the penetration rate, after which $w^{(1)}$ becomes small $w^{(1)} \sim (\alpha_e/\alpha_{12})u_e^{(1)}$ and there is no large frictional force between ions. It is evident from Eq. (7.29) that in this case the ions with higher charge will be concentrated in plasma regions of higher density; for example with $T_1 = T_2 = T$ and $\nabla T = 0$ the Boltzmann distribution $(1/e_1)\nabla \ln n_1 = (1/e_2)\nabla \ln n_2$ obtains.

Diffusion in a Weakly Ionized Gas. We denote by $\mathbf{u}_a$ the diffusion velocity of the a component; then

$$\mathbf{u}_a = \mathbf{V}_a - \mathbf{V}, \quad \sum_a m_a n_a \mathbf{u}_a = 0, \tag{7.30}$$

where $\mathbf{V}$ is given by Eq. (6.2). Using Eq. (1.14), replacing $d_a\mathbf{V}_a/dt$ by dV/dt and $dP_{a\alpha\beta}/dx_\beta$ by $\partial p_a/\partial x_\alpha$, the equation of motion for the a component can be written in the form

$$m_a n_a \frac{dV}{dt} = -\nabla p_a + e_a n_a \left(\mathbf{E}^* + \frac{1}{c}[\mathbf{u}_a \mathbf{B}]\right) - \sum_b \alpha_{ab}(\mathbf{u}_a - \mathbf{u}_b). \tag{7.31}$$

We shall consider the case in which the number of ionized particles is much smaller than the number of neutrals (weakly ionized plasma) so that the friction force is due to the $\mathbf{R}_{an}$ term associated with the neutral gas. The electron-ion collision cross section is much larger than the electron-neutral cross section (for example, in hydrogen at $T_e = 1$ eV we find $\alpha_{ei}/\alpha_{en} \sim 10^2 n_i/n_n$). Hence, electron-ion collisions can only be neglected when the neutral particle density is several orders of magnitude greater than the ion density (the exact values depend on the electron temperature and the nature of the gas). In this case the hydrodynamic velocity can be taken to be the velocity of the neutral gas $\mathbf{V} \approx \mathbf{V}_n$, $\mathbf{u}_n \approx 0$. Equation (7.31) will then be treated for particles of all species a in addition to the basic neutral component. The same statement holds for the summations over a used below. The velocity $\mathbf{V}$ is determined from the general equation of motion, with viscosity taken into account. The frictional force in Eq. (7.31) can be written in the form $\mathbf{R}_a = -\alpha_{an}\mathbf{u}_a$.

Let B = 0. Then from Eq. (7.31) we have

$$\mathbf{u}_a = b_a(e_a\mathbf{E} - \mathbf{G}_a/n_a) = b_a\left(e_a\mathbf{E} - m_a\frac{d\mathbf{V}}{dt}\right) - D_a\nabla \ln p_a, \quad (7.32)$$

where

$$\mathbf{G}_a = \nabla p_a + m_a n_a \frac{d\mathbf{V}}{dt}. \quad (7.33)$$

The mobility b_a and diffusion D_a are

$$b_a = \frac{n_a}{\alpha_{an}} = \frac{\tau_a}{m_{an}}, \quad D_a = \frac{\tau_a}{m_{an}} T_a, \text{ where } \tau_a = \frac{\alpha'_{an}}{n_n}. \quad (7.34)$$

These coefficients obey the well-known Einstein relation

$$D_a = b_a T_a. \quad (7.34')$$

The last term in Eq. (7.32) is proportional to $\nabla n_a/n_a + \nabla T_a/T_a$ but the thermal force can affect the coefficient of ∇T_a (cf. footnote on page 227).

The current density $\mathbf{j} = \Sigma e_a n_a \mathbf{u}_a$, where the neutrality condition has been used. According to Eq. (7.32)

$$\mathbf{j} = \sigma\mathbf{E} - \sum_a e_a b_a \mathbf{G}_a, \quad (7.35)$$

where

$$\sigma = \sum_a e_a^2 n_a b_a. \quad (7.36)$$

In the presence of a magnetic field vector quantities parallel to **B**, i. e., $\mathbf{u}_\parallel$, $\mathbf{j}_\parallel$, $\mathbf{E}_\parallel$, $\mathbf{G}_\parallel$ satisfy the same relations as for B = 0. The perpendicular components are obtained from Eq. (7.31):

$$\mathbf{u}_{a\perp} = b_{a\perp}(e_a\mathbf{E}^* - \mathbf{G}_a/n_a)_\perp + b_{a\wedge}[(e_a\mathbf{E}^* - \mathbf{G}_a/n_a)\mathbf{h}], \quad (7.37)$$

where

$$b_{a\perp} = \frac{b_a}{1 + \omega_{an}^2\tau_a^2}, \quad b_{a\wedge} = \omega_{an}\tau_a b_{a\perp}. \quad (7.38)$$

Here we have used the notation

$$\omega_{an} = e_a B / m_{an} c, \quad \omega_{en} \approx -\omega_e.$$

The current density across the magnetic field is

$$\mathbf{j}_\perp = \sigma_1 \mathbf{E}^*_\perp + \sigma_2 [\mathbf{E}^* \mathbf{h}] - \sum_a e_a b_{a\perp} \mathbf{G}_{a\perp} - \sum_a e_a b_{a\wedge} [\mathbf{G}_a \mathbf{h}], \quad (7.39)$$

where

$$\sigma_1 = \sum_a e_a^2 n_a b_{a\perp}, \quad \sigma_2 = \sum_a e_a^2 n_a b_{a\wedge}. \quad (7.40)$$

In order to use Eq. (7.39) to express $\mathbf{E}^*_\perp = \mathbf{E}_\perp + (1/c)[\mathbf{VB}]$ in terms of $\mathbf{j}_\perp$ we multiply (7.39) by $\sigma_1/(\sigma_1^2 + \sigma_2^2)$, take the vector product with $\mathbf{h}\sigma_2/(\sigma_1^2 + \sigma_2^2)$, and then add the results. In this way we obtain

$$\mathbf{E}^*_\perp = \frac{1}{\sigma_\perp} \mathbf{j}_\perp + \frac{1}{\sigma_\wedge} [\mathbf{jh}] + \sum_a \beta_{a\perp} \mathbf{G}_{a\perp} + \sum_a \beta_{a\wedge} [\mathbf{G}_a \mathbf{h}], \quad (7.41)$$

where $1/\sigma_\perp$ is the perpendicular resistance; $\mathbf{h}/\sigma_\wedge$ is the so-called Hall vector:

$$\frac{1}{\sigma} = \frac{\sigma_1}{\sigma_1^2 + \sigma_2^2}, \quad \frac{1}{\sigma_\wedge} = -\frac{\sigma_2}{\sigma_1^2 + \sigma_2^2},$$

$$\beta_{a\perp} = e_a \left(\frac{b_{a\perp}}{\sigma_\perp} - \frac{b_{a\wedge}}{\sigma_\wedge} \right), \quad \beta_{a\wedge} = e_a \left(\frac{b_{a\wedge}}{\sigma_\perp} + \frac{b_{a\perp}}{\sigma_\wedge} \right). \quad (7.42)$$

If gravity is important, $d\mathbf{V}/dt$ must be replaced by $d\mathbf{V}/dt - \mathbf{g}$ in all equations. If necessary this term can be eliminated by means of the general equation of motion.

Equations (7.39) and (7.41) can be simplified if the $\mathbf{G}_a$ terms can be neglected. In this case the frictional heat can also be expressed simply: $Q_{fr} = \mathbf{E}^*\mathbf{j} = j_\parallel^2/\sigma_\parallel + j_\perp^2/\sigma_\perp$.

We now consider what is called ambipolar diffusion of a plasma. Assume that all gradients and the electric field are parallel and in the x direction, and let $j_x = 0$. This is the case, for example, of a plasma in a long tube with insulating walls; the axial gradients can be neglected and we shall be concerned with plasma diffusion in the radial direction only (the role of x is played by r) with $j_r = 0$. This joint diffusion of electrons and ions is called ambipolar diffusion.

Suppose that the plasma contains ions of one species (for simplicity $Z = 1$) and let $\nabla T_e = \nabla T_i = \mathbf{V} = d\mathbf{V}/dt = 0$.

If $B = 0$, we have from Eq. (7.32)

$$nu_{ex} = -b_e enE - D_e \nabla n, \quad nu_{ix} = b_i enE - D_i \nabla n.$$

From $j_x = nu_{ex} - nu_{ix} = 0$ we have

$$E_x = -\frac{D_e - D_i}{b_e + b_i} \frac{1}{en} \frac{dn}{dx}.$$

Eliminating the electric field we can express the plasma flux $nu_{ex} = nu_{ix}$ in terms of one of the density gradients:

$$nu_{ex} = nu_{ix} = -D_A \nabla n, \tag{7.43}$$

where D_A is the so-called ambipolar diffusion coefficient

$$D_A = \frac{b_i D_e + b_e D_i}{b_e + b_i} = (T_e + T_i) \frac{b_e b_i}{b_e + b_i}. \tag{7.44}$$

This same expression can be obtained immediately from Eq. (7.10) if it is assumed that $\xi_n \approx 1$; $V \approx V_a = 0$; $w_x = u_{ix} = u_{ex}$; $G_x \approx (T_e + T_i)\, dn/dx$ and use is made of Eqs. (7.9) and (7.34).

If there is a magnetic field $B = B_z$, Eq. (7.43) becomes $nu_{ex} = nu_{ix} = -D_{A\perp}\nabla n$ where $D_{A\perp}$ is obtained from Eq. (7.44) by replacing b_a with $b_{a\perp}$:

$$D_{A\perp} = \frac{D_A}{1 + \omega_e \tau_e \omega_{in} \tau_i}. \tag{7.44'}$$

This same result can be obtained from Eq. (7.10) if we write $V = 0$, express j_y by means of Eq. (7.14), $j_y = (\sigma^*_\perp \xi_n B_z / \alpha_n c)\, G_x$ and take $\xi_n \approx 1$.

Diffusion has been considered above using an approximate expression (7.3) for the frictional force. A more exact analysis of diffusion and the calculation of thermal conductivity require the use of the kinetic equation.

A kinetic analysis of diffusion and thermal conductivity of electrons in a weakly ionized gas in the presence of a magnetic field has been carried out by Davydov [30]. It is shown in this work that the electron distribution function can be approximated in the form $f(t, \mathbf{r}, \mathbf{v}) = f_0(t, \mathbf{r}, v) + \mathbf{f}_1(t, \mathbf{r}, v) \cdot \mathbf{v}/v$; then, averaging the kinetic equation (multiplied by 1 and $\mathbf{v}/v$) over angle in velocity space a system of equations is obtained for f_0 and $\mathbf{f}_1$:

$$\frac{\partial f_0}{\partial t} + \frac{v}{3} \operatorname{div} \mathbf{f}_1 + \frac{e}{3m_e v^2} \frac{\partial (v^2 \mathbf{f}_1)}{\partial v} \cdot \mathbf{E} = C_{en}(\mathbf{f}_0), \tag{7.45}$$

$$\frac{\partial \mathbf{f}_1}{\partial t} + v \nabla f_0 - \frac{e}{m_e} \mathbf{E} \frac{\partial f_0}{\partial v} - \frac{e}{m_e c} [\mathbf{f}_1 \mathbf{B}] = - \frac{\mathbf{f}_1}{\tau_e}, \tag{7.45'}$$

where $1/\tau_e = \alpha'_{en} n_n$ and $C_{en}(f_0)$ is the collision term averaged over angle. Here we have written $V = 0$.

Since it is assumed that electrons collide with neutrals but not with themselves there is no reason to assume that the spherically symmetric part of the distribution function f_0 will be Maxwellian. If $\partial/\partial t \ll 1/\tau_e$, Eq. (7.45') can be used to express $\mathbf{f}_1$ in terms of f_0 so that an equation for f_0 can be obtained from Eq. (7.45). This equation has been solved in [30], for various $\tau_e(v)$; the function f_0 has been obtained together with the corresponding expressions for the particle and energy fluxes. Flux expressions for the case of a Maxwellian function f_0 are also given in [30].

Multicomponent Plasma. In the laboratory and under geophysical and astrophysical conditions one is frequently concerned with a multicomponent plasma. A fully ionized plasma may contain ions of various kinds while a gas that is not fully ionized can contain various molecules, atoms, excited atoms, etc. If collisions between particles are sufficiently frequent the hydrodynamic description can still be applied to such a plasma. The plasma density and hydrodynamic velocity are determined by Eqs. (6.1) and (6.2) where the summation is carried out over all components; as in the case of a simple plasma the electrons can be neglected. In addition to the mass conservation equations (6.5) we now require equations for the components that describe the change of state of the plasma. If the rate of production per unit volume of particles of species a is Γ_a, these equations can be written in the form

$$\begin{gathered} \frac{\partial n_a}{\partial t} + \operatorname{div}(n_a \mathbf{V}_a) = \Gamma_a, \\ \varrho \frac{d\xi_a}{dt} + \operatorname{div}(m_a n_a \mathbf{u}_a) = m_a \Gamma_a, \end{gathered} \tag{7.46}$$

where $\mathbf{u}_a = \mathbf{V}_a - \mathbf{V}$ is the diffusion velocity and $\xi_a = m_a n_a/\rho$ is the relative concentration of the a component. From conservation of mass and charge we have $\sum_a m_a \Gamma_a = 0, \ \sum_a e_a \Gamma_a = 0.$

The equation of motion of the plasma, which describes the total momentum balance, is obtained by adding the momentum transport equations (1.12) for all components, taking account of momentum conservation in collisions. Using the equation of continuity this is reduced to the form of (6.14) where $p = \sum_a p_a, \ \pi_{\alpha\beta} = \sum_a \pi_{a\alpha\beta}$ *.

The diffusion velocities $\mathbf{u}_a$ can be determined approximately from Eq. (7.31) but in the general case this procedure leads to rather complicated expressions. Certain particular cases have been treated in the earlier sections.

In accordance with Eqs. (1.24) and (7.3), the total frictional heat is

$$Q_{\text{fr}} = \sum_a Q_a = \sum_{a,\,b} Q_{ab} = \sum_{a>b} \alpha_{ao} (u_a - u_b)^2. \tag{7.47}$$

Multiplying Eq. (7.31) by $\mathbf{u}_a$ and summing over all components, taking account of Eq. (7.47), we have

$$Q_{\text{fr}} = \mathbf{E}^* \mathbf{j} - \sum_a \mathbf{u}_a \nabla p_a. \tag{7.48}$$

*It should be noted that these expressions are obtained if we adopt new definitions of the quantities p_a and $\pi_{a\alpha\beta}$ which are somewhat different than those used in §1; these definitions are frequently used in the analysis of gas mixtures. The difference lies in the fact that here, in defining the temperature in terms of the random velocity of component a we take $\mathbf{v}' = \mathbf{v} - \mathbf{V}$ rather then $\mathbf{v}_a = \mathbf{v} - \mathbf{V}_a$ as in §1. The "new" and "old" quantities are related by

$$T_a^{\text{new}} = T_a^{\text{old}} + \frac{m_a u_a^2}{3}, \quad p_a^{\text{new}} = p_a^{\text{old}} + m_a n_a u_a^2,$$

$$\pi_{\alpha\beta\gamma}^{\text{new}} = \pi_{\alpha\beta\gamma}^{\text{old}} + m_a n_a u_{a\beta} u_{a\gamma}.$$

This difference is not important because u_a is small when collisions dominate and the hydrodynamic description applies, in which case the quadratic term can be neglected. Taking account of the difference between the "old" and "new" quantities increases the accuracy of the hydrodynamic description.

The energy balance equation for a multicomponent plasma is obtained by summing the energy balances for all components and is formally similar to Eqs. (6.33) or (6.35), where the heat flux is*

$$\mathbf{q} = \Sigma \mathbf{q}_a + \Sigma \frac{5}{2} p_a \mathbf{u}_a .$$

It should be noted, however, that Eqs. (6.33) and (6.35) apply only for a plasma consisting of monatomic components in which case it may be assumed that the kinetic energy of all particles is associated with the translational motion if, for example, the plasma is fully ionized. The internal energy of the plasma (per unit volume) is then $\varepsilon = \Sigma \varepsilon_a = (3/2)p$. In the general case, $(3/2)p$ must be replaced by the internal energy ε in the expression for the energy while $(5/2)p$ must be replaced by $\varepsilon + p$ in the expression for the energy flux. For example, in a diatomic molecule, which has five effective degrees of freedom, $\varepsilon_a = (5/2) T_a n_a = (5/2) p_a$; $\varepsilon_a + p_a = (7/2) p_a$.

The heat balance equation (the internal energy transport equation) is obtained for a multicomponent plasma in the same way as Eq. (6.36) and is of the form

$$\frac{\partial \varepsilon}{\partial t} + \operatorname{div}(\varepsilon \mathbf{V}) + p \operatorname{div} \mathbf{V} = -\operatorname{div} \mathbf{q} + \sum_a u_a \nabla p_a + \Sigma Q =$$

$$= -\operatorname{div} \mathbf{q} + \mathbf{E}^* \mathbf{j} + Q_{\text{vis}}, \tag{7.49}$$

where $\Sigma Q = Q_{fr} + Q_{vis}$. Other sources (loss) of heat can also appear.

If the plasma can be assumed to be approximately in local thermodynamic equilibrium the entropy balance equation is obtained in the general case by the methods of irreversible thermodynamics [9, 10a]. This equation is of the same form as Eq. (6.38) except that $\mathbf{q}_e + \mathbf{q}_i$ is replaced by $\Sigma \mathbf{q}_a$ and $S_e \mathbf{u}$ by $\Sigma S_a \mathbf{u}_a$.

The heat flux and the viscous stresses of a plasma consisting of monatomic components can be obtained in general form and relevant orders

*More precisely, $\mathbf{q} = \Sigma q_a^{new} + \Sigma(5/2) p_a \mathbf{u}_a$ where $q_{a\beta}^{new} = q_{a\beta}^{old} + (m_a/2) n_a u_a^2 u_{a\beta} + \pi_{a\beta\gamma}^{old} u_{a\gamma}$ but this difference is unimportant (see preceding footnote). The quantity Σq_a is sometimes called the reduced heat flux.

of magnitude can be estimated using the qualitative considerations of § 3 and the results for a simple plasma. In a weakly ionized plasma the thermal conductivity and the viscosity are determined primarily by the neutral gas. These can be estimated for a monatomic gas using the expressions given by Chapman and Cowling [1].

New effects appear in gases that have rotational or internal degrees of freedom (excitation, ionization, dissociation). For example, an additional heat flux arises if particles are ionized or dissociate at one point and if they recombine at another point, liberating a corresponding energy [10a]. The stress tensor for a gas with internal degrees of freedom contains terms of the form $\zeta\delta_{\alpha\beta}$ div $\mathbf{V}$ where ζ is the so-called second viscosity [3]. Radiation can also play a role in the heat flux.

The electron temperature is frequently very different from the temperatures of the heavy particles—ions and neutrals in a gas that is not fully ionized; for this reason the individual energy equations are generally used. If ionization is by electron impact, T_e is determined primarily by the ionization potential of the gas and usually stabilizes at a level corresponding to a small fraction of the ionization potential so that the fastest electrons are capable of ionization. In this case energy obtained by electrons is dissipated primarily in excitation radiation and in ionization by electron impact. The ionization rate is very sensitive to T_e which, on the other hand, is a relatively weak function of the various parameters and is of the order of electron volts. If the gas density is not very high the transfer of heat from the electrons to the ions or neutrals is strongly inhibited because the ratio m_e/m_i is so small. Thus, if the neutral gas is cooled and there is no other source of heat it is easy for a large temperature difference to arise between the electrons and heavy particles; this difference can reach two orders of magnitude. In gases that are not fully ionized it is frequently found that the important factor is not the plasma dynamical situation, but rather the maintenance of ionization, excitation of atoms, energy loss by radiation, interaction of the plasma with the walls, and so on. When an electric current flows through a gas a host of new characteristic effects appear; these are the subject of study of the physics of electrical discharges in gases. A very good elementary introduction to this field is contained in the small volume by Penning [10].

§ 8. Examples

Pinch Effect. The magnetic field produced by a current flowing through a plasma tends to constrict the plasma because the current filaments which comprise the total current tend to attract each other. This

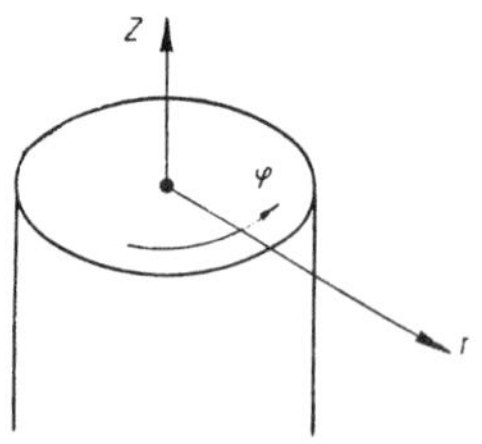

Fig. 7

phenomenon is called the pinch effect. For reasons of brevity a plasma contracted by its own magnetic field will simply be called a pinch.

As a simple example let us consider an infinitely long plasma cylinder contained by a magnetic field; this is the so-called linear pinch (Fig. 7). We assume that all quantities vary in the r direction only ($\partial/\partial z = \partial/\partial\varphi = 0$), that the plasma as a whole does not move along z, and that it does not rotate. Under these conditions the magnetic field and the current have only z and φ components and the magnetic surfaces are cylinders (r = const).

The equilibrium condition for the pinch is [cf. Eq. (6.17)]

$$-\frac{\partial p}{\partial r} = \frac{1}{c}(j_z B_\varphi - j_\varphi B_z) = B_\varphi \frac{\partial r B_\varphi}{r\partial r} + B_z \frac{\partial B_z}{\partial r}. \qquad (8.1)$$

We now multiply Eq. (8.1) by r^2 and integrate with respect to r from 0 to a, where a is the radius of the pinch. Integrating by parts and taking $p(a) = 0$, $B_\varphi(a) = 2J/ca$, where J is the total current, we obtain the equilibrium condition for the pinch in integral form [31]:

$$2c^2(N_e\overline{T}_e + N_i T_i) = J^2 + \frac{a^2c^2}{4}\left[B_z^2(a) - \overline{B_z^2}\right], \qquad (8.2)$$

where $\overline{B_z^2} = \int_0^a B_z^2 2\pi r\, dr/\pi a^2$; N_e and N_i are the numbers of electrons and ions per unit length of the pinch; $\overline{T}_e$ and $\overline{T}_i$ are the mean temperatures. The self-magnetic field of the current J always acts to constrict the plasma. The longitudinal magnetic field constricts the plasma if the external field $B_z(a)$ is greater than the internal field, and tends to expand it if the external field is smaller than the internal field.

Now let us consider the application of Ohm's law to the linear pinch. From Eqs. (6.18) and (6.19) we have

$$\mathbf{E}_\parallel = \mathbf{j}_\parallel/\sigma_\parallel, \quad \mathbf{E}_\wedge + \frac{1}{c}[\mathbf{VB}] - \frac{1}{en_e}\mathbf{R}_\perp = \mathbf{j}_\perp/\sigma_\perp, \qquad (8.3)$$

where $\mathbf{E}_\wedge$ is the component of the electric field perpendicular to the magnetic field and tangent to the magnetic surface r = const. From Eq. (6.24) we find $E_r'' = 0$. If inertia and the radial viscous stress are neglected compared with $\partial p_i/\partial r$,

$$E_r = \frac{1}{en_e}\frac{\partial p_i}{\partial r}. \tag{8.4}$$

At equilibrium the radial electric field automatically assumes the value given in (8.4) and balances the ion pressure; the ions exhibit a Boltzmann distribution in this field if T_i = const. Then the Hall field will automatically assume the required value in accordance with Eq. (6.18)

$$E_r' = E_r + \frac{1}{en_e}\frac{\partial p_e}{\partial r} = \frac{1}{c}[\mathbf{jB}]_r. \tag{8.5}$$

In a fast pinch, in which ion inertia is important, Eq. (8.5) still holds but Eq. (8.4) does not.

The transverse current component $\mathbf{j}_\perp = (c/B)[\mathbf{h}\nabla p]$. Substituting this in the second equation in (8.3) we obtain an equation for the velocity:

$$V_r = \frac{c}{B}(h_z E_\varphi - h_\varphi E_z) - \frac{c^2}{\sigma_\perp B^2}\left(\frac{\partial p}{\partial r} - \frac{3}{2} n_e \frac{\partial T_e}{\partial r}\right). \tag{8.6}$$

If the electric field corresponding to Eq. (8.4) is not established for any reason (for example if the pinch is of finite length and if the ends exert a strong effect) in accordance with Eq. (6.26) there will be a plasma velocity V_φ component

$$V_\varphi = \frac{c}{B}\left(E_r - \frac{1}{en_e}\frac{\partial p_i}{\partial r}\right) h_z.$$

The nonuniformity in V_φ means that the ions feel the effect of a φ projection of the viscous stress $F_\alpha^\pi = -\partial \pi_{i\alpha\beta}/\partial x_\beta$; in accordance with Ohm's law [cf. Eq. (6.24)] an additional term must now appear in the expression V_r,

$$V_{r\,\mathrm{vis}} = \frac{c}{en_e B} F_\varphi^\pi h_z. \tag{8.7}$$

This velocity is sometimes called the diffusion velocity due to ion collisions [20] although it is proportional to the third radial derivative of the density rather than the first. In order-of-magnitude terms $V_{r\,\mathrm{vis}} \sim (r_i^4/\tau_i a^3) \sim 1/B^4$ and can be comparable with the Joule rate of penetration $\sim r_e^2/\tau_i a$ for $r_i^2/a^2 \sim (m_e/m_i)^{1/2}$.

If the plasma current or the external magnetic field increase very rapidly the equilibrium condition (8.2) is not satisfied and the magnetic field causes the plasma to become constricted rapidly. Because of the skin effect the magnetic field cannot penetrate to the inside in zero time, but compresses the plasma in piston-like fashion while moving in from the outer edge; thus, a strong shock wave moves from the outer edge to the axis. Because of its elasticity the pinch rebounds after contraction and expands again; in fact, it has been shown experimentally, that the pinch executes several oscillations before breaking up as a consequence of various instabilities.

A detailed analysis of the oscillations of a pinch requires the solution of a complex system of magnetohydrodynamic equations [34]; however, the time required for total compression can be estimated rather simply [32, 33]. For example, assume that $J = \dot{J}t$ and $B_z = 0$. The skin effect becomes important when the current in the pinch increases rapidly. The current flows along the surface of the pinch and the force due to the magnetic pressure acts in the surface layer. The layer thickness is determined by the specific resistance $1/\sigma^*_\perp$ associated with ion-neutral collisions [cf. Eq. (7.15)] which can be appreciably greater than the resistance due to electron-ion collisions $1/\sigma$; this effect is sometimes described as the movement of the magnetic lines with the ions [33]. Because of the skin effect and the formation of the strong shock wave initially the plasma "rakes" the field away from the edge and gradually more and more layers are accelerated. Let us assume that the entire mass of the gas in motion is concentrated at the point $a(t)$ and is equal to $\rho_0 \pi (a_0^2 - a^2)$ where a_0 is the initial radius of the pinch and ρ_0 is the initial density; the equation of motion for this mass can be written in the form

$$\frac{d}{dt}\left\{\varrho_0\pi\left(a_0^2 - a^2\right)\frac{da}{dt}\right\} = -\frac{B_\varphi^2}{8\pi}2\pi a = -\frac{J^2}{c^2 a} = -\frac{\dot{J}^2 t^2}{c^2 a}. \quad (8.8)$$

We integrate this expression approximately, taking the value of $a(t)$ at the upper limit outside of the integral sign on the right in the first integration over time. As a result we obtain

$$a^2 = a_0^2\left(1 - t^2/t_0^2\right), \quad (8.9)$$

$$t_0 = (3\pi\varrho_0 c^2)^{1/4} a_0 \dot{J}^{-1/2}. \quad (8.10)$$

Total compression corresponds approximately to the time t_0 and current $J_0 = \dot{J}t_0$. It is evident that $1/t_0 \sim a_0/c_A$, where $c_A = B_0/(4\pi\rho_0)^{1/2}$ and $B_0 \sim J_0/ca_0$.

The compression time of a pinch compressed by a B_z field can be estimated in completely analogous fashion.

If small perturbations that disturb the equilibrium are produced rapidly in an equilibrium pinch the pinch will execute small oscillations. In the next section we shall analyze oscillations for the case of an infinite plasma; however, the order of magnitude of the quantities obtained in that analysis applies to the finite pinch.

If changes in an equilibrium pinch occur slowly (frequencies small compared with the characteristic frequencies of these magnetohydrodynamic oscillations) the pinch remains in a quasi-equilibrium state at all times and inertia does not play a role—this is in fact the description of a slow process.

All of the considerations given above will obviously hold only when the pinch is stable; however, stability will not be discussed in this review.

Magnetohydrodynamic Waves. We wish to consider small oscillations of a uniform plasma in a uniform magnetic field. A plasma is, in fact, capable of executing a large variety of oscillations. At this point, however, we shall be interested only in the relatively low-frequency and large-scale oscillations in which the motion of matter plays an important role and which can be described by a hydrodynamic analysis §6 (the neutrality conditions $c_A^2 \ll c^2$, etc., are satisfied). An analysis of these oscillations will give us an idea of the "elastic" properties of a plasma. Because an ordinary gas only exhibits longitudinal elasticity, it can support the propogation of only one kind of wave; this is the sound wave. As pointed out by Alfvén [4, 5], however, a conducting fluid in a magnetic field exhibits a peculiar kind of elasticity with respect to transverse displacements; this elasticity results from the fact that the magnetic lines of force behave as though they were stretched rubber bands. The resulting oscillations are called magnetohydrodynamic waves.

Let us write

$$\varrho = \varrho_0 + \varrho', \quad p = p_0 + p', \quad \mathbf{B} = \mathbf{B}_0 + \mathbf{B}', \qquad (8.11)$$

where the zeros denote unperturbed equilibrium values and the primes denote small perturbations. The velocity $\mathbf{V}$ is also regarded as a small quantity.

At the outset we neglect all dissipative processes, assuming that the plasma conductivity is very large and that the viscosity is small, etc. (more exact criteria will be given in the following section). The adiabaticity condition (6.37) then gives $p/\rho^\gamma = \text{const} = p_0/\rho_0^\gamma$ where $\gamma = 5/3$ is the adiabaticity index. Using Eq. (8.11) and expanding in terms of the small quantities we have

$$p = p_0\left(\frac{\varrho}{\varrho_0}\right)^\gamma = p_0 + \frac{\gamma p_0}{\varrho_0}\varrho' + \frac{p_0\gamma(\gamma-1)}{2}\left(\frac{\varrho'}{\varrho_0}\right)^2 + \cdots =$$

$$= p_0 + c_s^2\varrho' + \frac{\gamma-1}{2\varrho_0}c_s^2\varrho'^2 + \ldots, \tag{8.12}$$

where c_s is the velocity of sound, which is defined by the relation

$$c_s = \left(\frac{\partial p}{\partial \varrho}\right)_s^{1/2} = \left(\frac{\gamma p_0}{\varrho_0}\right)^{1/2}. \tag{8.13}$$

Neglecting all powers of the small perturbations higher than the first in the equations of continuity, motion, and induction we obtain the following linearized system:

$$\frac{\partial \varrho'}{\partial t} + \varrho_0 \operatorname{div} \mathbf{V} = 0, \tag{8.14a}$$

$$\varrho_0 \frac{\partial \mathbf{V}}{\partial t} = -c_s^2 \nabla p' - \frac{1}{4\pi}[\mathbf{B}_0 \operatorname{rot} \mathbf{B}'], \tag{8.14b}$$

$$\frac{\partial \mathbf{B}'}{\partial t} = \operatorname{rot}[\mathbf{V}\mathbf{B}_0]. \tag{8.14c}$$

We have also neglected the Hall term in the induction equation in accordance with the estimate in §6, which applies when $\Pi \gg 1$. The characteristic dimension can be taken to be the wavelength of the oscillation λ or, better still, the reciprocal wave number $1/k = \lambda/2\pi$ so that Eq. (8.14c) is valid when

$$\Pi = \frac{4\pi e^2 n_e^2}{\varrho c^2 k^2} \gg 1. \tag{8.15}$$

We now seek a solution of Eq. (8.14) in which all perturbed quantities are proportional to $e^{i(\mathbf{kr} - \omega t)}$, that is to say, we seek plane wave solutions characterized by a frequency ω and wave vector $\mathbf{k}$. An arbitrary

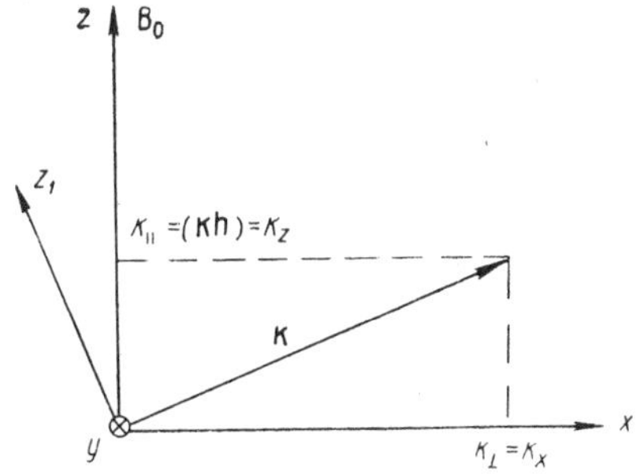

Fig. 8

perturbation can be expanded in a Fourier series and represented as a superposition of these component waves. Writing $\partial/\partial t \to -i\omega$, $\nabla \to i\mathbf{k}$ we find

$$-\omega\varrho'/\varrho_0 + (\mathbf{k}\mathbf{V}) = 0, \tag{8.16a}$$

$$-\omega\mathbf{V} = -\mathbf{k}c_s^2\varrho'/\varrho_0 - [\mathbf{B}_0[\mathbf{k}\mathbf{B}']]/4\pi\varrho_0, \tag{8.16b}$$

$$-\omega\mathbf{B}' = [\mathbf{k}[\mathbf{V}\mathbf{B}_0]]. \tag{8.16c}$$

The condition div $\mathbf{B}' = 0$ indicates that the variable magnetic field is perpendicular to the wave vector. We choose the z axis along $\mathbf{B}_0 = \mathbf{B}_{0z}\mathbf{h}$ and take the y axis to be perpendicular to both $\mathbf{B}_0$ and $\mathbf{k}$ (Fig. 8). Projecting Eq. (8.16) on these axes we see that the system of equations divides into two independent sets for the variables V_y, B'_y and for the variables ρ', V_x, V_z, B'_x, B'_z. The imaginary unit disappears in Eq. (8.16) indicating that ρ', $\mathbf{V}$, and $\mathbf{B}$ in each wave are in phase, that is to say, all are proportional, for example, to the factor cos $(\mathbf{kr} - \omega t)$.

Let us consider the first set. Since $\mathbf{k}\cdot\mathbf{V} = 0$, then $\rho' = 0$ and consequently $p' = 0$. From Eq. (8.16) we find

$$-\omega V_y = k_\parallel B'_y B_0/4\pi\varrho_0, \tag{8.17a}$$

$$-\omega B'_y = k_\parallel V_y B_0. \tag{8.17b}$$

The condition that must be satisfied in order for this system to yield a nontrivial solution yields a relation between the frequency and the wave vector:

$$\omega^2 = c_A^2 k_\parallel^2 = \frac{(\mathbf{B}_0 \mathbf{k})^2}{4\pi\varrho_0}, \tag{8.18}$$

where c_A is the so-called Alfvén velocity:

$$c_A = \frac{B_0}{(4\pi\varrho_0)^{1/2}}. \tag{8.19}$$

This wave is called the Alfvén wave. The velocity and variable field for this wave are perpendicular to $\mathbf{B}_0$ and $\mathbf{k}$ and are related by

$$V_y = B_y' (4\pi\varrho_0)^{-1/2}, \tag{8.20}$$

while the density and pressure do not oscillate; hence the wave can propagate in either a compressable or an incompressible fluid.

The group velocity of the Alfvén waves $\partial\omega/\partial\mathbf{k} = \mathbf{B}_0 (4\pi\rho_0)^{-1/2} = c_A \mathbf{h}$. This velocity is independent of $\mathbf{k}$, meaning that appropriate perturbations of any (but obviously not too small) scale size at any point of the plasma are propagated with the velocity c_A along the magnetic lines of force.

We now consider the second set of equations for $\mathbf{V}$ and $\mathbf{B}'$; these lie in the plane of $\mathbf{B}_0$ and $\mathbf{k}$. The magnetic field is perpendicular to $\mathbf{k}$ and is along the z_1 axis (cf. Fig. 8). We denote this projection by B'. Projecting Eq. (8.16c) along z_1 and Eq. (8.16b) along x and z we have

$$\omega\varrho'/\varrho_0 = k_\parallel V_z + k_\perp V_x, \tag{8.21a}$$

$$\omega B' (4\pi\varrho_0)^{-1/2} = c_A k V_x, \tag{8.21b}$$

$$\omega V_x = c_s^2 k_\perp \varrho'/\varrho_0 + c_A k B' (4\pi\varrho_0)^{-1/2}, \tag{8.21c}$$

$$\omega V_z = c_s^2 k_\parallel \varrho'/\varrho_0. \tag{8.21d}$$

Eliminating ρ' and B' we find

$$\left(\omega^2 - c_s^2 k_\perp^2 - c_A^2 k^2\right) V_x = c_s^2 k_\parallel k_\perp V_z, \tag{8.22a}$$

$$\left(\omega^2 - c_s^2 k_\parallel^2\right) V_z = c_s^2 k_\parallel k_\perp V_x. \tag{8.22b}$$

The condition that must be satisfied for this system to yield a nontrivial solution gives

$$\omega^4 - \omega^2 \left(c_A^2 k^2 + c_s^2 k^2\right) + c_A^2 c_s^2 k^2 k_\parallel^2 = 0. \tag{8.23}$$

Thus, we find the two roots:

$$\frac{\omega^2}{k^2} = \frac{1}{2}\left(c_A^2 + c_s^2\right) \pm \left[\frac{1}{4}\left(c_A^2 + c_s^2\right)^2 - c_A^2 c_s^2 k_\parallel^2 / k^2\right]^{1/2} \tag{8.24}$$

These waves are called magnetoacoustic or magnetosonic waves: the plus sign corresponds to the fast magnetoacoustic wave. When $c_A \ll c_s$ one of these waves becomes the usual acoustic wave with frequency $\omega = c_s k$ while the other behaves like the Alfvén wave with frequency $\omega = c_A k$. An incompressible conducting fluid, for which $c_s \to \infty$, can thus support the propagation of two Alfvén waves with different polarizations.

Now let us consider the case $c_s \ll c_A$ in greater detail. The frequency of the fast wave is

$$\omega = c_A k. \tag{8.25}$$

The group velocity is equal to the phase velocity and is in the direction of **k**. In this wave the motion occurs primarily along the x axis and the density perturbation is small. From Eqs. (8.21) and (8.22) we find

$$V_x = \frac{B'}{(4\pi\varrho_0)^{1/2}}, \quad V_z = \frac{c_s^2}{c_A^2} \frac{k_\parallel k_\perp}{k^2} V_x, \quad \frac{\varrho'}{\varrho_0} = \frac{k_\perp}{k} \frac{V_x}{c_A}. \tag{8.26}$$

When $c_s \ll c_A$ the slow wave represents the acoustic wave distorted by the magnetic field. The frequency of this wave is

$$\omega = c_s k_\parallel . \tag{8.27}$$

The motion in this wave occurs primarily along the z axis and the perturbation of the magnetic field is small:

$$\frac{\varrho'}{\varrho_0} = \frac{V_z}{c_s}, \quad V_x = -\frac{c_s^2}{c_A^2} \frac{k_\parallel k_\perp}{k^2} V_z, \quad \frac{B'}{(4\pi\varrho_0)^{1/2}} = -\frac{c_s}{c_A} \frac{k_\perp}{k} V_z. \tag{8.28}$$

The group velocity is also directed along the z axis and not along **k** as in ordinary sound waves: $\partial\omega/\partial\mathbf{k} = c_s\mathbf{h}$. These perturbations are carried along the lines of force as though the latter were rails.

The temperature oscillations can be expressed in terms of ρ':

$$\frac{T'}{T_0} = \frac{p'}{p_0} - \frac{\varrho'}{\varrho_0} = (\gamma - 1)\frac{\varrho'}{\varrho_0}. \tag{8.29}$$

The electric field is determined by Ohm's law. According to Eq. (6.28), $E = E_x = -V_y B_0/c$ in the Alfvén wave; in the fast wave $E = E_y = V_x B_0/c$. These expressions can be refined by using Eq. (6.18) without the dissipative terms and taking $p'_e/n_e = \gamma T_0 \rho'/\rho_0$. Thus

$$\mathbf{E} = -\frac{1}{c}[\mathbf{V}\mathbf{B}_0] + \frac{1}{en_e c}[\mathbf{j}\mathbf{B}_0] + \frac{\nabla p_e}{en_e} =$$

$$= -\frac{1}{c}[\mathbf{V}\mathbf{B}_0] + \frac{i[[\mathbf{k}\mathbf{B}']\mathbf{B}_0]}{4\pi e n_e} + \frac{i\mathbf{k}\gamma T_0 \varrho'}{e\varrho_0}. \tag{8.30}$$

Here, the second term (the Hall term) is smaller than the first by a factor of $\sim\Pi$. The third term (irrotational field) vanishes in the Alfvén wave but is of order $(c_s^2/c_A^2)/\Pi$ in the fast wave. In the acoustic wave the irrotational field can be smaller or greater than the induction field but does not affect the induction equation since rot **E** appears in this equation.

The energy in the wave can be found by substituting Eq. (8.11) in the general expression (6.35) and retaining second-order terms. Using the expansion in (8.12) we have

$$\varepsilon_{\text{total}} = \left(\frac{p_0}{\gamma - 1} + \frac{B_0^2}{8\pi}\right) + \left(\frac{c_s^2\varrho'}{\gamma - 1} + \frac{\mathbf{B}_0\mathbf{B}'}{4\pi}\right) + $$

$$+ \left(\frac{\varrho_0 V^2}{2} + \frac{c_s^2\varrho'^2}{2\varrho_0} + \frac{B'^2}{8\pi}\right) \tag{8.31}$$

The first bracket here represents the energy of the unperturbed plasma. The second bracket contains oscillating terms which vanish when integrated over the volume of the wave or when averaged in time. The third term gives the energy associated with the wave. The energy of the electric field is omitted since it is much smaller than the magnetic energy:

$$E^2/B'^2 \sim (VB_0/c)^2/4\pi\varrho_0 V^2 \sim c_A^2/c^2,$$

and it is assumed that this ratio is small. The wave energy per unit volume is equal to the mean value of the third bracket:

$$\bar{\varepsilon} = \frac{\varrho_0 \overline{V^2}}{2} + \frac{c_s^2 \overline{\varrho'^2}}{2\varrho_0} + \frac{\overline{B'^2}}{8\pi}. \tag{8.32}$$

Using Eq. (8.14) it is easily shown that the quantity $\bar{\varepsilon}$ averaged over the volume of the wave is conserved in the oscillations. In accordance with Eq. (8.20), the energy of the Alfvén wave is

$$\bar{\varepsilon} = \varrho_0 \overline{V_y^2} = \overline{B'^2_y}/4\pi. \tag{8.33}$$

The energy of the fast magnetoacoustic wave (when $c_s \ll c_A$) is approximately

$$\bar{\varepsilon} = \varrho_0 \overline{V_x^2} = \overline{B'^2}/4\pi. \tag{8.34}$$

Here we have omitted the energy associated with the pressure and V_z^2.

When $c_s \ll c_A$ the energy of the acoustic wave is approximately

$$\bar{\varepsilon} = \varrho_0 \overline{V_z^2} = c_s^2 \overline{\varrho'^2}/\varrho_0. \tag{8.35}$$

Here we have omitted the magnetic energy and V_x^2.

In the general case of arbitrary c_s/c_A, using Eq. (8.24) it is easily shown that the following relation holds:

$$\bar{\varepsilon} = \varrho_0 \overline{V^2} = \overline{B'^2}/4\pi + c_s^2 \overline{\varrho'^2}/\varrho_0. \tag{8.36}$$

Damping of Magnetohydrodynamic Waves. Dissipative effects, which we have neglected so far, cause wave damping. The energy associated with the waves diminishes in time and is converted into heat. For this reason ω becomes complex $\omega = \omega_1 - i\omega_2$, and the amplitude is damped in time in proportion to $e^{-\omega_2 t}$. Repeating the foregoing calculations taking account of dissipative effects would lead to extremely complicated expressions; in the case of greatest interest, in which the damping is small ($\omega_2 \ll \omega_1$), the damping can be found more directly and simply (cf. [3] §77).

We use the following notation: $\omega_1 = \omega$ is the real part of the frequency; $\omega_2 = \omega\delta$, where δ is the logarithmic damping decrement. The energy of the wave (integrated over the volume) is proportional to the square of the amplitude and, consequently with damping, $\bar{\varepsilon} = \bar{\varepsilon}_1 e^{-2\omega\delta t}$ where $\bar{\varepsilon}_1 = \bar{\varepsilon}(t = 0)$. Because part of the plasma energy (the wave energy) is in "organized" form, the entropy of the plasma must have some negative part $\overline{\Delta S}$; in the course of time this negative entropy damps out together with the wave energy: $-\overline{\Delta S} = -(\overline{\Delta S})_1 e^{-2\omega\delta t}$. When all of the wave energy has been dissipated the plasma entropy has been increased by an amount $\bar{\varepsilon}_1/T_0$ so that $(\overline{\Delta S})_1 = \bar{\varepsilon}_1/T_0$. Using this relation it is easy to express the damping decrement in terms of $d\overline{\Delta S}/dt$:

$$\delta = \frac{1}{2\omega}\,\frac{T_0}{\bar{\varepsilon}}\,\frac{d\overline{\Delta S}}{dt} = \frac{1}{2\omega\bar{\varepsilon}}\,T_0\theta. \tag{8.37}$$

The quantity $d\overline{\Delta S}/dt$ can easily be computed by means of Eq. (6.38). For the case of weak damping, as a first approximation we can use the expressions obtained for all wave quantities with damping neglected. Both the entropy production (6.39) and the damping decrement (8.37) will then be expressed in the form of a sum, each term of which gives the damping corresponding to a particular dissipative effect:

$$\delta = \delta_{\text{Joule}} + \delta_{\text{vis}} + \delta_{\text{ther}} + \delta_{\text{dif}} + \cdots \tag{8.38}$$

If these calculations are to apply and if the expressions for the frequency and polarization given above are to hold (neglecting dissipative effects) the condition $\delta \ll 1$ must be satisfied.

We first consider wave damping in a simple plasma.

Alfvén Wave. Taking $Q_{\text{Joule}} = j^2_{\parallel}\sigma_{\parallel} + j^2_{\perp}/\sigma_{\perp}$ and $\mathbf{j} = (c/4\pi)\,i[\mathbf{k}\mathbf{B}']$, for the Alfvén wave we have

$$\overline{Q}_{\text{Joule}} = (c^2/4\pi)\left(k^2_{\parallel}/\sigma_{\perp} + k^2_{\perp}\sigma_{\parallel}\right)\overline{B'^2_y}/4\pi.$$

Thus, using Eq. (8.37) and the expression $\bar{\varepsilon} = \overline{B'^2_y}/4\pi$ we find

$$2\omega\delta_{\text{Joule}} = \frac{c^2}{4\pi\sigma_{\parallel}}\,k^2_{\perp} + \frac{c^2}{4\pi\sigma_{\perp}}\,k^2_{\parallel}. \tag{8.39}$$

In viscous damping, $Q_{\text{vis}} = (1/2)\ \pi_{\alpha\beta} W_{\alpha\beta} = (1/2) \sum_{p=0}^{2} \eta_p W^2_{p\alpha\beta}$; the following are important: $\partial V_y/\partial x = W_{xy} = ik_\perp V_y$; $\partial V_y/\partial z = W_{yz} = ik_\parallel V_y$. The tensors $W_{1\alpha\beta}$ and $W_{2\alpha\beta}$ are nonvanishing; only the transverse viscosity is of importance. Simple calculations made on the basis of Eqs. (4.42) or (2.21) yield:* $\overline{Q}_{\text{vis}} = (\eta_1 k^2_\perp + \eta_2 k^2_\parallel)\overline{V^2_y}$.

Taking $\overline{\varepsilon} = \rho \overline{V^2_y}$, we find

$$2\omega\delta_{\text{vis}} = \frac{1}{\varrho_0}\left(\eta_1 k_\perp^2 + \eta_2 k_\parallel^2\right). \tag{8.40}$$

Since the density and temperature do not oscillate in the Alfvén wave, $\rho_{\text{ther}} = 0$.

Fast Magnetoacoustic Wave. In this wave the current is directed along the y axis (across the magnetic field) so that $Q_{\text{Joule}} = j^2/\sigma_\perp = (c^2/4\pi\sigma_\perp)k^2(B'^2/4\pi)$. Thus, taking account of Eq. (8.34) we have

$$2\omega\delta_{\text{Joule}} = \frac{c^2}{4\pi\sigma_\perp} k^2. \tag{8.41}$$

The velocity in this wave is directed primarily along the x axis and has derivatives with respect to x and z so that all three viscosity coefficients are important: η_0, η_1, η_2. Computing $\overline{Q}_{\text{vis}}$ by means of Eqs. (8.34) and (8.37) we have

$$2\omega\delta_{\text{vis}} = \frac{1}{\varrho_0}\left[\left(\frac{\eta_0}{3} + \eta_1\right)k_\perp^2 + \eta_2 k_\parallel^2\right]. \tag{8.42}$$

The entropy production due to the thermal conductivity is

$$\overline{\theta}_{\text{ther}} = -\overline{\mathbf{q}\nabla T}/T_0^2 = Q_{\text{ther}}/T_0,$$

where

$$\overline{Q}_{\text{ther}} = \frac{\varkappa_\parallel^e}{T_0}\overline{(\nabla_\parallel T_e)^2} + \frac{\varkappa_\perp^e}{T_0}\overline{(\nabla_\perp T_e)^2} + \frac{\varkappa_\parallel^i}{T_0}\overline{(\nabla_\parallel T_i)^2} + \frac{\varkappa_\perp^i}{T_0}\overline{(\nabla_\perp T_i)^2}.$$

---

*Here, in computing the viscous dissipation we have used the notation of §4. It is also possible to use Eq. (2.21) directly but this procedure is not as convenient.

Taking $T'_e = T'_i = T'$, determining T'/T_0 from Eq. (8.29) and using Eqs. (8.26) and (8.34), (with the notation $\varkappa = \varkappa^e + \varkappa^i$) we find

$$2\omega\delta_{\text{ther}} = \frac{(\gamma - 1)^2 T_0 k_\perp^2}{\varrho_0 c_A^2 k^2} \left(\varkappa_\parallel k_\parallel^2 + \varkappa_\perp k_\perp^2\right). \tag{8.43}$$

Acoustic Wave. Using the same method, by means of Eqs. (8.28) and (8.35), taking $V \approx V_z$ we find

$$2\omega\delta_{\text{Joule}} = \frac{c^2}{4\pi\sigma_\perp} k_\perp^2 \frac{c_s^2}{c_A^2}, \tag{8.44}$$

$$2\omega\delta_{\text{vis}} = \frac{1}{\varrho_0}\left(\frac{4}{3}\eta_0 k_\parallel^2 + \eta_2 k_\perp^2\right), \tag{8.45}$$

$$2\omega\delta_{\text{ther}} = \frac{(\gamma - 1)^2 T_0}{\varrho c_s^2}\left(\varkappa_\parallel k_\parallel^2 + \varkappa_\perp k_\perp^2\right). \tag{8.46}$$

The temperature vanishes from Eq. (8.46) if we substitute $c_s^2 = \gamma p_0/\rho_0 = \gamma(Z + 1)T_0/m_i$. If the thermal conductivity of the electrons is very large Eqs. (8.43) and (8.46) must be modified. When $\varkappa_e \to \infty$ the electron motion is isothermal rather than adiabatic hence we must assume that the electron adiabaticity index is $\gamma_e = 1$. In this case the electron terms vanish from Eqs. (8.43) and (8.46) and the acoustic velocity is modified: $c_s^2 = (p_e + \gamma p_i)/\rho = (Z + \gamma)T_0/m_i$.

Collisions with Neutrals. The presence of a neutral gas causes the heat of friction to increase because the electrons collide with neutrals as well as ions; what is more important, heat is generated because of the friction between the ions and neutrals. This effect has been considered in [29, 35, 36]. Furthermore, the expressions for δ_{vis} and δ_{ther} now contain the coefficients of viscosity and thermal conductivity modified appropriately to take account of the neutral gas; these are isotropic in weakly ionized plasmas.

Frictional damping in a three-component mixture e, i, and n can be computed using Eq. (7.17). In the expressions calculated above for δ_{Joule} we now substitute σ in accordance with Eq. (7.13). The damping decrement now contains an additional term which we shall call the diffusion term δ_{dif}. It results from collisions of ions with neutrals and arises as a result of the second term in Eq. (7.17):

$$Q_{\text{dif}} = \frac{1}{\alpha_n}\left\{\frac{\xi_n}{c}[\mathbf{jB}] - \mathbf{G}\right\}^2, \quad \mathbf{G} = \xi_n \nabla (p_e + p_i) - \xi_i \nabla p_n.$$

In the Alfvén wave $\mathbf{G} = 0$; in the fast magnetoacoustic wave the ratio of G to the first term in the curly brackets is of order $\xi_i c_s^2/c_A^2$. Neglecting G we find $Q_{\text{dif}} = (\xi_n^2 B^2/\alpha_n c^2)\, j_\perp^2$. This expression has the same form as the Joule heat; thus, without repeating the calculations we can immediately find the damping by means of Eqs. (8.39) and (8.41) simply by substituting $1/\sigma^*_\perp = 1/\sigma + \xi_n^2 B^2/\alpha_n c^2$ in place of $1/\sigma$. In this case collisions of ions with neutrals simply increase the effective perpendicular resistance.

We now write the diffusion damping for the Alfvén wave and for the fast magnetoacoustic wave

$$2\omega\delta_{\text{dif}} = \frac{c^2 k_\parallel^2}{4\pi}\frac{\xi_n^2 B^2}{\alpha_n c^2} \text{ (Alfvén wave),} \tag{8.47a}$$

$$2\omega\delta_{\text{dif}} = \frac{c^2 k^2}{4\pi}\frac{\xi_n^2 B^2}{\alpha_n c^2} \text{ (fast wave).} \tag{8.47b}$$

Let $m_i = m_n$ and assume that α_{en} can be neglected compared with α_{in}. The diffusion damping is then larger than the Joule damping by a factor $2\xi_n\omega_e\tau_e\omega_i\bar{\tau}_{in}$ where $1/\bar{\tau}_{in} = \alpha'_{in}(n_i + n_n)$. Both expressions (8.47a) and (8.47b) then reduce to the form

$$\delta_{\text{dif}} = \omega\bar{\tau}_{in}(n_n/n_i). \tag{8.48}$$

Estimating the magnitude of the diffusion velocity we find $\omega/V \sim \omega\bar{\tau}_{in}\xi_i$ and this quantity must be small if the expressions we have obtained are to apply.

Both terms in Q_{dif} are of the same order for the acoustic wave. Let $m_i = m_n$, in which case $\mathbf{G} = \xi_n \nabla p_e$. Calculations made with Eq. (8.28) give $\nabla p_e = i\mathbf{k}(n_e/n_0)\rho_0 c_s V_z$, where $n_0 = n_e + n_i + n_n$; $[\mathbf{jB}]/c = i\mathbf{k}_\perp \rho_0 c_s V_z$ and, in the usual way, we find

$$2\omega\delta_{\text{dif}} = \frac{\rho_0 c_s^2 \xi_n^2}{\alpha_n}\left\{k_\parallel^2 \frac{n_e^2}{n_0^2} + k_\perp^2 \frac{(n_i+n_n)^2}{n_0^2}\right\} \approx$$

$$\approx \omega^2 \bar{\tau}_{in}\frac{2n_n}{n_i}\left\{\frac{n_e^2}{n_0^2} + \frac{k_\perp^2 (n_i+n_n)^2}{k_\parallel^2 n_0^2}\right\}. \tag{8.49}$$

In the second relation we have neglected α_{en}/α_{in} and substituted $\omega = c_s k_{\parallel}$.

In the presence of a neutral gas δ_{dif} frequently can make the largest contribution to the damping.

Collisions Between Different Ions. If the plasma contains ions with different e/m ratios, these ions move with somewhat different velocities, and friction between them can also cause wave damping.

Consider the case $\omega_i \tau_i = e_i B/m_i c \gg 1$. Here we can take Eqs. (7.27) for the diffusion velocity of the ions. For the Alfvén wave and the fast magnetoacoustic wave, neglecting the pressure we have

$$\mathbf{w} = \frac{c}{B}\left(\frac{m_1}{e_1} - \frac{m_2}{e_2}\right)\left[\mathbf{h}\,\frac{d\mathbf{V}}{dt}\right] = -\frac{i\omega}{B}\left(\frac{m_1}{e_1} - \frac{m_2}{e_2}\right)[\mathbf{hV}].$$

Substituting the frictional heat $\overline{Q}_{fr} = \alpha_{12}\overline{w}^2$ (we only consider collisions between ions), for both of these waves we find

$$2\omega\delta_{dif} = \frac{\alpha_{12}}{\varrho_0}\frac{c^2}{B^2}\left(\frac{m_1}{e_1} - \frac{m_2}{e_2}\right)^2\omega^2 \tag{8.50}$$

or, in order-of-magnitude terms, $\delta_{dif} \sim \omega/\omega_i^2\tau_i$. This damping is weaker than the damping due to collisions with neutrals because the primary ion velocity is the velocity due to the electric drift, which is the same for both species.

APPENDIX

The collision term for elastic collisions is of the form [1, 2, 3]

$$C_{ab}(f_a, f_b) = \int \left\{ f_a(\mathbf{v}') f_b(\mathbf{v}_b') - f_a(\mathbf{v}) f_b(\mathbf{v}_b) \right\} u\, d\sigma\, d\mathbf{v}_b. \tag{A.1}$$

Here $d\sigma = \sigma(u, \vartheta)\, do$ is the differential cross section for scattering into the element of solid angle $do = \sin\vartheta\, d\vartheta\, d\varphi$ for collisions of particles with relative velocity $u = |\mathbf{v} - \mathbf{v}_b|$. Before particle a collides with particle b it has a velocity $\mathbf{v}$ while the b particle has a velocity $\mathbf{v}_b$. The post-collision velocities $\mathbf{v}'$ and $\mathbf{v}_b'$ are related to $\mathbf{v}$ and $\mathbf{v}_b$ by the laws of elastic collisions (conservation of momentum and energy). The second term in the curly brackets gives the loss of a particles out of the element of volume $d\mathbf{v}$ in velocity space around $\mathbf{v}$ resulting from collisions with b particles; the first term corresponds to the influx into this elementary volume. Collisions of a and b particles with velocities v_a and v_b can be analyzed most simply in the coordinate system in which the total momentum vanishes: $m_a\mathbf{v}_a + m_b\mathbf{v}_b = 0$. Introducing the relative velocity $\mathbf{u} = \mathbf{v}_a - \mathbf{v}_b$, in this system we have $\mathbf{v}_a = m_b(m_a + m_b)^{-1}\mathbf{u}$; $\mathbf{v}_b = -m_a(m_a + m_b)^{-1}\mathbf{u}$; $m_a v_a^2/2 + m_b v_b^2/2 = m_{ab}u^2/2$, where $m_{ab} = m_a m_b(m_a + m_b)^{-1}$ is the reduced mass. As a consequence of the conservation of energy the relative velocity cannot change in magnitude in the collision $u = |\mathbf{v}_a - \mathbf{v}_b| = |\mathbf{v}_a' - \mathbf{v}_b'|$ but can only be deflected through some angle ϑ.

Strictly speaking, the Boltzmann form of the collision term (A.1) does not apply for Coulomb collisions. This results from the fact that substitution of the Rutherford cross section in the place of $d\sigma$ leads to a divergent integral. However, if this integral is cut off, as indicated in §4, the expression in (A.1) gives the same results as the collision term in the Landau form.

We now compute the friction force $\mathbf{R}_{ab}$ experienced by a gas of a particles in collisions with b particles, assuming that both particle species have Maxwellian distributions at the same temperature but with different mean velocities $\mathbf{V}_a$ and $\mathbf{V}_b$. We use the notation $\mathbf{U} = \mathbf{V}_a - \mathbf{V}_b$ and assume that the velocity shift is small compared with the relative velocities of the particles $U \ll (T/m_{ab})^{1/2}$. The friction force is

$$\mathbf{R}_{ab} = \int m_a \mathbf{v} C_{ab}(f_a, f_b)\, d\mathbf{v}.$$

This force is independent of the coordinate system and will be computed in the system in which $\mathbf{V}_a = 0$, $\mathbf{V}_b = -\mathbf{U}$. In this coordinate system $f_a = f_a^0$, and f_b can be expanded in powers of U to give the expression

$$f_b = f_b^0 - (m_b/T)(\mathbf{U}\mathbf{v}_b) f_b^0.$$

Substitution of f_a^0 and f_b^0 in $\mathbf{R}_{ab}$ obviously gives zero, so that

$$R_{ab\alpha} = -\frac{m_a m_b}{T} U_\beta \int v_\alpha C_{ab}\left(f_a^0,\ f_b^0 v_{b\beta}\right) d\mathbf{v}$$

Here, C_{ab} is given by (A.1) and represents a vector that depends on $\mathbf{v}$ (on $\mathbf{v}_b$ in the integration). Since this vector does not contain any vector parameters other than the velocity $\mathbf{v}$, it is of the form $\mathbf{v}A(v)$; in component form: $v_\beta A(v)$ where $A(v)$ is a scalar function of the speed. Averaging over angle under the integral sign and using the relation $\overline{v_\alpha v_\beta} = (v^2/3)\,\delta_{\alpha\beta}$ we find

$$R_{ab} = -\frac{m_a m_b}{3T} U \int v_\beta C_{ab}\left(f_a^0, f_b^0 v_{b\beta}\right) d\mathbf{v}.$$

We now substitute C_{ab} in accordance with Eq. (A.1) and use the relation $f_a^0(v_a')f_b^0(v_b') = f_a^0(v_a)f_b^0(v_b)$ which follows from the conservation of energy in collisions (we write $\mathbf{v}_a$ in place of $\mathbf{v}$ to obtain a symmetric expression). Then

$$R_{ab} = -\frac{m_a m_b}{3T} U \int f_a^0 f_b^0 v_{a\beta}\left\{v'_{b\beta} - v_{b\beta}\right\} u\,d\sigma\,d\mathbf{v}_a d\mathbf{v}_b.$$

To compute the integral we convert from the variables $\mathbf{v}_a$ and $\mathbf{v}_b$ to the velocity of the center of mass $\mathbf{v}_c$ and the relative velocity $\mathbf{u}$:

$$\mathbf{v}_a = \mathbf{v}_c + \frac{m_b}{m_a + m_b}\mathbf{u}, \qquad \mathbf{v}_b = \mathbf{v}_c - \frac{m_a}{m_a + m_b}\mathbf{u}. \tag{A.2}$$

It is easily shown that $d\mathbf{v}_a d\mathbf{v}_b = d\mathbf{v}_c d\mathbf{u}$ and that $f_a^0 f_b^0 = n_a n_b f_c^0 f_u^0$, where

$$f_c^0 = \left(\frac{m_a + m_b}{2\pi T}\right)^{3/2} e^{-\frac{(m_a+m_b)v_c^2}{2T}}, \qquad f_u^0 = \left(\frac{m_{ab}}{2\pi T}\right)^{3/2} e^{-\frac{m_{ab}u^2}{2T}}. \tag{A.3}$$

The integration over $d\mathbf{v}_c$ is easily performed and the $\mathbf{v}_c$ term drops out of $\mathbf{v}_a$; integration of f_c^0 gives unity. Figure 9 shows directly that $u_\beta(u_\beta - u_\beta') = u^2(1-\cos\vartheta)$ and finally we have

$$R_{ab} = -n_a n_b m_{ab} \alpha'_{ab} U, \tag{A.4}$$

where

$$\alpha'_{ab} = \frac{m_{ab}}{3T}\int u^3 \sigma'_{ab} f_u^0 d\mathbf{u}, \tag{A.5}$$

$$\sigma'_{ab}(u) = \int (1 - \cos\vartheta)\, d\sigma(u, \vartheta). \tag{A.6}$$

When $\sigma'_{ab} = \alpha'_{ab}/u$ we obtain Eq. (7.4); if σ'_{ab} = const we obtain Eq. (7.5). Substituting the Rutherford cross section in (A.6) we obtain a divergent integral in which the artificial cutoff gives Eq. (7.6).

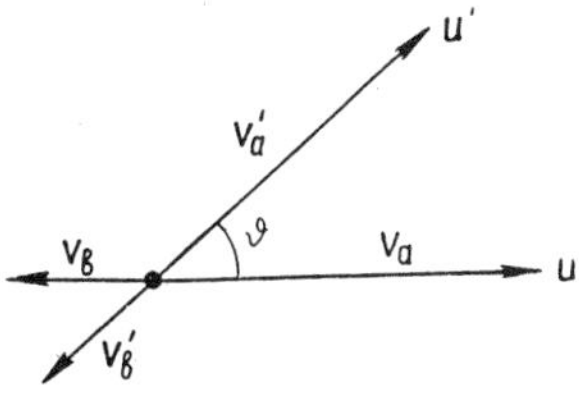

Fig. 9

Similarly, it is possible to compute the frictional heat Q_{ab} generated in a gas of a particles in collisions with b particles when both particle species have Maxwellian distributions at the same temperature but with small shifts **U**. In the expression

$$Q_{ab} = \int \frac{m_a v_a^2}{2} C_{ab}\left(f_a^0, f_b\right) d\mathbf{v}_a$$

we carry out an expansion up to the quadratic terms in the shift:

$$f_b = f_b^0 \left[1 - \frac{m_b}{T}(\mathbf{U}\mathbf{v}_b) - \frac{m_b}{2T}U^2 + \frac{m_b^2}{2T^2}(\mathbf{U}\mathbf{v}_b)^2\right].$$

Only the last term gives a nonvanishing contribution:

$$Q_{ab} = \frac{m_a m_b^2}{4T^2} U_\alpha U_\beta \int f_a^0 f_b^0 v_a^2 \left\{v_{ba}' v_{b\beta}' - v_{ba} v_{b\beta}\right\} u d\sigma d\mathbf{v}_a d\mathbf{v}_b.$$

Carrying out the substitution $\mathbf{v}_a, \mathbf{v}_b \to \mathbf{v}_c, \mathbf{u}$, after some simple calculations we find

$$Q_{ab} = \frac{m_b}{m_a + m_b} n_a n_b m_{ab} \alpha_{ab}' U^2. \tag{A.7}$$

The expression for Q_{ba} is obtained by interchange of the subscripts. It is evident that $Q_{ab} + Q_{ba} = -\mathbf{R}_{ab}\mathbf{U}$, where the total heat generated by friction is distributed between the components in inverse proportion to their masses.

LITERATURE CITED

1. Chapman and Cowling, Mathematical Theory of Nonuniform Gases, Cambridge University Press, 1953.
2. A. Sommerfeld, Thermodynamics and Statistical Mechanics, Academic Press, New York, 1949.
3. Landau and Lifshits, Fluid Mechanics, Addison-Wesley, Reading, Mass., 1959.
4. Landau and Lifshits, Electrodynamics of Continuous Media, Addison-Wesley, Reading, Mass., 1960.
5. H. Alfvén, Cosmical Electrodynamics, Oxford, The Clarendon Press, 1953.
6. L. Spitzer, Jr., Physics of Fully Ionized Gases, Interscience, New York, 1962.
7. T. G. Cowling, Magnetohydrodynamics, Interscience, New York, 1957.
8. Bogolyubov and Mitropolskii, Asymptotic Methods in the Theory of Nonlinear Oscillations, (translated from the Russian) Gordon and Breach, New York, 1961.
9. S. R. de Groot, Thermodynamics of Irreversible Processes, Interscience, New York, 1951.
10. F. M. Penning, Electrical Discharges in Gases, Macmillian, New York, 1957.
10a. W. Finkelnburg and H. Maecker, Elektrische Bogen und thermisches Plasma, Flügge, Encyclopedia of Physics, XXII.
10b. R. V. Polovin and K. P. Cherkasova, ZhTF, 32, 649 (1962), Soviet Phys. Technical Physics 7, 475 (1962).
11. L. D. Landau, ZhETF (J. Exptl. Theoret. Phys. USSR), 7, 203 (1937).
12. G. T. Cowling, Proc. Roy. Soc. (London) A183, 453 (1945).
13. R. K. M. Landshoff, Phys. Rev., 76, 904 (1949).
14. L. Spitzer, Jr. and R. Härm, Phys. Rev., 89, 977 (1953).
15. I. E. Tamm, Plasma Physics and the Problem of Controlled Thermonuclear Reactions (translated from the Russian) Pergamon Press, New York, 1959, Vol. I.
16. E. S. Fradkin, ZhETF, 32, 1176 (1957), Soviet Phys. JETP, 5, 956 (1957).
17. S. I. Braginskii, ZhETF, 33, 459 (1957), Soviet Phys. JETP, 6, 358 (1958).
18. S. I. Braginskii, Plasma Physics and the Problem of Controlled Thermonuclear Reactions (translated from the Russian) Pergamon Press, New York, 1959, Vol. I.

19. S. T. Belyaev, Plasma Physics and the Problem of Controlled Thermonuclear Reactions (translated from the Russian) Pergamon Press, New York, 1959, Vol. I.
20. C. L. Longmire and M. N. Rosenbluth, Phys. Rev., 103, 507 (1956).
21. S. J. Kanenko, J. Phys. Soc. Japan 15, 1685 (1960).
22. A. N. Kaufman, Phys. Fluids, 3, 610 (1960).
22a. R. Herdan and B. S. Liley, Revs. Modern Phys., 32, 731 (1960).
22b. B. B. Robinson and I. B. Bernstein, Ann. Phys., 18, 110 (1962).
23. D. Bohm, in: The Characteristics of Electrical Discharges in Magnetic Fields, ed. by A. Guthrie and R. K. Wakerling, McGraw-Hill, New York, 1949.
23a. L. Spitzer, Jr., Phys. Fluids, 3, 600 (1960).
24. A. Schlüter, Z. Naturforsch. 5a, 72 (1950).
25. A. Schlüter, ibid. 6a, 73 (1951).
26. A. Schlüter, Ann. Physik, 10, 422 (1952).
27. L. Spitzer, Jr., Astrophys. J. 116, 299 (1952).
28. S. I. Braginskii, ZhETF, 33, 645 (1957), Soviet Phys. JETP, 6, 494 (1958).
29. B. Lehnert, Nuovo cimento, Supplement No. 1, 13, 1959.
30. B. I. Davydov, ZhETF (J. Exptl. Theoret. Phys. USSR), 7, 1069 (1937).
31. S. I. Braginskii and V. D. Shrafranov, Plasma Physics and the Problem of Controlled Thermonuclear Reactions (translated from the Russian) Pergamon Press, New York, 1959, Vol. II.
32. M. A. Leontovich and S. M. Osovets, Atomnaya energiya (Atomic Energy), 3, 81 (1956).
33. S. I. Braginskii and S. I. Migdal, Plasma Physics and the Problem of Controlled Thermonuclear Reactions (translated from the Russian) Pergamon Press, New York, 1959, Vol. II.
34. Braginskii, Gelfand, and Fedorenko, Plasma Physics and the Problem of Controlled Thermonuclear Reactions (translated from the Russian) Pergamon Press, New York, 1959, Vol. IV.
35. J. H. Piddington, Monthly Notices Roy. Astron. Soc., 94, 638 (1954); ibid. 94, 651 (1954).
36. D. A. Frank-Kamenetskii, ZhTF, 30, 893 (1960), Soviet Phys. Technical Physics, 5, 842 (1961).
37. B. B. Kadomtsev, ZhETF, 33, 151 (1957), Soviet Phys. JETP, 6, 117 (1958).
38. D. V. Sivukhin, Reviews of Plasma Physics (translated from the Russian) Consultants Bureau, New York, 1965, Vol. 1, p. 1.
39. B. A. Trubnikov, Reviews of Plasma Physics (translated from the Russian) Consultants Bureau, New York, 1965, Vol. 1, p. 105.

THERMODYNAMICS OF A PLASMA

A. A. Vedenov

In this review we shall be concerned with the statistical thermodynamics of a plasma, i.e., a system of particles characterized by Coulomb interactions. The central problem of statistical thermodynamics is that of computing the thermodynamic functions for a system of interacting particles in thermal equilibrium. This problem is solved most simply when the interaction between the particles is weak, i. e., when the particles constitute an ideal gas.

In practice it is impossible to determine the thermodynamic quantities of nonideal systems if there is no small physical parameter in terms of which the quantities of interest can be expanded. For this reason we shall only study weakly nonideal Coulomb gases. The small parameter in this problem is the ratio f/r, i.e., the ratio of the mean Coulomb scattering amplitude $f \sim e^2/E$ (E is the mean energy of the plasma particles) to the mean distance between particles $r \sim n^{-1/3}$ (n is the plasma particle density). The thermodynamic potential of the plasma can be expanded in terms of this small parameter and we shall be interested in the leading terms in this "virial" expansion.

§ 1. Classical Coulomb System

Let us consider the thermodynamic functions of a system of Coulomb particles in the classical case. By classical we mean the system obeys Boltzmann statistics (i.e., the effects of degeneracy can be neglected) and the particle motion in the system can be described within the framework of classical mechanics.

This description is valid if two conditions are satisfied: $\lambda \ll r$ and $\lambda \ll f$ where $\lambda \sim \hbar/mv$ is the mean de Broglie wavelength of the particles (v is the mean thermal velocity) and r is the mean distance between particles, while f is the mean scattering amplitude (which is of the order of the square root of the mean scattering cross section). The first of these conditions implies that quantum statistical effects are small while the second indicates the applicability of a classical description for the collisions, i.e., the particle interactions.

As noted above, we shall consider the case in which the system is essentially ideal, i.e., the corrections to the thermodynamic quantities due to the interaction are small compared with the quantities themselves.

It should be pointed out that in classical Coulomb systems the particle interaction is a Coulomb interaction at large distances only. At small distances the interaction potential of the particles V must deviate from the Coulomb potential. In fact, the statistical integral

$$\int e^{-\beta \sum_{i,k} V_{ik}} \prod_{l} dx_l$$

diverges strongly because the integrand increases at small distances if the force is attractive and inversely proportional to the square of the distance. This means that a purely classical analysis of a system in which $V \sim 1/r$ is not correct (cf. §2). Hence in using the classical analysis here we shall assume that a repulsive force acts between the particles at small distances and that this force is converted into the Coulomb attractive force (or a Coulomb repulsive force depending on the sign of the particle charges) at larger distances.

The problem we are considering has three characteristic lengths: the range of the repulsive force a, the mean scattering amplitude of the Coulomb field e^2/T, and the mean distance between particles r.*

If a and e^2/T, which characterize the interaction, are small compared with the mean interparticle distance r, the system is essentially ideal. In this case, the gas density $n \sim r^{-3}$ is the formal small parameter of the problem; we then try to expand the thermodynamic functions of the Coulomb system in terms of the small parameter n. If both characteristic interaction lengths are neglected as a first approximation (setting the ratios a/r and e^2/Tr equal to zero) we obtain the thermodynamic functions for an ideal gas. We shall be interested in the first-order terms in the expansion of these thermodynamic functions in a/r and e^2/Tr, i.e., first-order terms in the density n.

In solving this problem we shall find it useful to introduce the two-particle correlation function $K(\mathbf{x}_1, \mathbf{x}_2)$ which represents the probability of

*In the classical case the mean de Broglie wavelength λ can be set equal to zero.

finding particle 2 at point $\mathbf{x}_2$ when particle 1 is at point $\mathbf{x}_1$. Using the function $K(\mathbf{x}_1, \mathbf{x}_2)$ which, for central forces depends only on the distance $|\mathbf{x}_1 - \mathbf{x}_2|$ between particles 1 and 2, we can find the thermodynamic functions for an arbitrary classical system characterized by binary interactions. For example, it is possible to use one of the two following formulas:* the free energy per unit volume F

$$F = F_0 + \frac{n^2}{2} \int_0^1 d\lambda \int d\mathbf{x} V(\mathbf{x}) K^{\lambda V}(\mathbf{x}) \tag{1.1}$$

or the pressure P

$$P = nT - \frac{1}{6} \int d\mathbf{x}\, \mathbf{x} \frac{\partial V(\mathbf{x})}{\partial \mathbf{x}} K(\mathbf{x}). \tag{1.2}$$

For a gas mixture with densities n_α Eq. (1.1) becomes

$$F = F_0 + \frac{1}{2} \int_0^1 d\lambda \int d\mathbf{x} \sum_{\alpha\beta} n_\alpha n_\beta V_{\alpha\beta}(\mathbf{x}) K_{\alpha\beta}^{\lambda V}(\mathbf{x}). \tag{1.1a}$$

Here, F_0 is the free energy of the ideal gas while the superscript λV on the function K means that it is to be taken for the case in which the interaction potential between the particles is λV. The second term in Eq. (1.1) represents the change in system energy when the interaction is switched on adiabatically. The second term in Eq. (1.2) also derives from the interaction forces: it expresses the deviation of the equation of state for the system (with the interaction) from the Clapeyron equation.

If the interparticle distance $\mathbf{x}$ is small, the correlation function $K(\mathbf{x})$ is equal to the Boltzmann distribution function for a field characterized by a potential $V(x)$:

$$K_s = e^{-V/T}. \tag{1.3}$$

If Eq. (1.3) is used to find the correction to the pressure or free energy in accordance with Eqs. (1.1) or (1.2) a meaningless infinite expression is obtained; this divergence arises because the quantity

$$K_s - 1 \simeq e^2/Tx$$

*See Problems 1 and 2 at the end of this section.

falls off slowly at large distances (this quantity represents the interaction correction to the correlation function of an ideal gas, which is identically equal to unity). In order to avoid this divergence we introduce the so-called "Debye shielding" of the potential e^2/x at large distances (cf. Problem 3). To determine this shielding potential U we supplement the equations

$$K_l - 1 = e^{-\beta U} - 1 \simeq -\beta U \tag{1.4}$$

by Poisson's equation, which relates the potential U to the density of the particles that produce it: a point charge e at the origin of coordinates and a probable distribution of charges with density eK_l

$$\Delta U = 4\pi e(-e\delta(\mathbf{x}) - \sum eK_l)^*. \tag{1.5}$$

Now, substituting K_l from Eq. (1.4) we obtain the following relation for U:

$$\Delta U - U/D^2 = -4\pi e^2 \delta(\mathbf{x}) \tag{1.6}$$

(where the Debye radius D is $\sqrt{T/4\pi\, \Sigma n e^2}$ and is much greater than the mean interparticle distance). We then find the screened potential

$$U = \frac{e^2}{x} e^{-x/D} \tag{1.7}$$

and the correlation function at large distances ($x \gg a$, $x \gg e^2/T$)

$$K_{l,\alpha\beta} \simeq 1 - \beta U_{\alpha\beta} + \frac{\beta^2 U^2_{\alpha\beta}}{2}, \tag{1.8}$$

$$U_{\alpha\beta} = \frac{e_\alpha e_\beta}{x} e^{-x/D}. \tag{1.9}$$

It should be noted that Eqs. (1.3) and (1.8) coincide in the region in which $a \ll x \ll D$; here, on the one hand the potential U is already a Coulomb potential and on the other the Debye screening is not important. Thus, Eqs. (1.3) and (1.8) for K_s and K_l determine the correlation function completely in the approximation needed here.

---

*The sum is taken over the various charge species.

We can now use Eqs. (1.1) or (1.2) to determine the various thermodynamic functions of the system using the two-particle correlation function K. For example, using Eq. (1.2) we obtain the first terms in the expansion of the pressure of a rarefied classical Coulomb system in the particle density n. In Eq. (1.2) we divide the region of integration over x into two parts: from zero to some value R, and from R to infinity. The quantity R satisfies the condition

$$a \ll R \ll D. \tag{1.10}$$

Equation (1.3) can now be used for the correlation function K in the first region and the function in (1.8) can be used in the second region (large distances). Substituting these expressions in Eq. (1.1a) we have

$$F = F_0 + \frac{1}{2}\int_0^1 d\lambda \sum_{\alpha\beta} n_\alpha n_\beta \left(\int_{|\mathbf{x}|<R} \mathbf{dx} V_{\alpha\beta} K_{s,\,\alpha\beta}^{(\lambda V)} + \right.$$
$$\left. + \int_{|\mathbf{x}|>R} \mathbf{dx} V_{\alpha\beta} K_{l,\,\alpha\beta}^{(\lambda V)} \right). \tag{1.11}$$

Carrying out the integration in the last term on the right side of Eq. (1.11) and assuming, in accordance with (1.10), that the ratio R/D is small compared with unity, we find

$$F = F_0 + \frac{T}{2}\sum_{\alpha\beta} n_\alpha n_\beta \int_{|\mathbf{x}|<R} \mathbf{dx}\left(\mathrm{e}^{-\beta U_{\alpha\beta}} - 1\right) - \frac{T}{8\pi D^3}\left(\frac{2}{3} - \frac{R}{2D}\right) +$$
$$+ \left(\sum_\alpha n_\alpha e_\alpha^3\right)^2 4\pi \int_0^1 \frac{d\lambda}{2} \lambda^2 \frac{\beta^2}{2} \ln\frac{D}{R}. \tag{1.12}$$

We now note that when R changes from values satisfying the inequality (1.10) to $R = \infty$, Eq. (1.12), which is a function of R, changes only by an amount of order $n^2 T(\beta e^2)^3$, and remains finite. Hence, neglecting terms of this order in the expansion of F in the density n we can remove the uncertainty in the choice of R in Eq. (1.12) by going to the limit $R \to \infty$:

$$F = F_0 - \frac{T}{12\pi D^3} + \lim_{R\to\infty}\left\{-2\pi T\int_0^R r^2dr\sum_{\alpha\beta} n_\alpha n_\beta\left(e^{-\beta V_{\alpha\beta}} - 1\right) + \right.$$

$$\left. + \frac{TR}{16\pi D^4} + \frac{\pi}{3}\left(\sum_\alpha n_\alpha e_\alpha^3\right)^2 \frac{1}{T^2}\ln\frac{D}{R}\right\}. \quad (1.13)$$

We have now obtained the first terms in the density expansion for a classical Coulomb system:

$$F - F_0 = An^{3/2} + Bn^2 \ln n + Cn^2. \quad (1.14)$$

This expansion is analogous to the well-known virial expansion for a gas with short-range forces:

$$F - F_0 = B_2 n^2 T + \cdots \quad (1.15)$$

Here, $\mathbf{F}_0$ is the free energy of the ideal gas (neglecting the interaction) while the term $An^{3/2}$ is the so-called Debye correction to the free energy.

A characteristic difference of the expansion in (1.14) from the usual virial expansion is the fact that it contains a factor ln n, in which the density appears as the argument of a logarithm, in addition to fractional powers of n. For a system of changed particles in which

$$\sum_\alpha n_\alpha e_\alpha^3 = 0^*,$$

the logarithmic term in the density expansion vanishes so that

$$F - F_0 = An^{3/2} + Cn^2.$$

We can use Eqs. (1.13) and (1.14) for short-range forces by writing $e = 0$ and then taking $R \to \infty$. In this case we obtain the first terms in the expansion in (1.15) and the value of the second virial coefficient

$$B_2 = -2\pi\int_0^\infty r^2dr\left(e^{-\beta V(r)} - 1\right).$$

*A Coulomb system for which $\sum_\alpha n_\alpha e_\alpha^3 = 0$ is called symmetric.

PROBLEMS

1. Express the free energy of a classical system of N particles characterized by a central binary interaction $V(|\mathbf{x}_1 - \mathbf{x}_2|)$ in terms of the two-particle correlation function $K(|\mathbf{x}_1 - \mathbf{x}_2|)$.

Differentiating the expression for the free energy of a system with the interaction $\lambda V(|\mathbf{x}_1 - \mathbf{x}_2|)$,

$$F(\lambda) = -T \ln \int \cdots \int e^{-\lambda\beta \sum\limits_{i>k} V(|\mathbf{x}_i - \mathbf{x}_k|)} d\mathbf{x}_1 \cdots d\mathbf{x}_N,$$

with respect to the parameter λ, we have

$$\frac{\partial F(\lambda)}{\partial \lambda} = \frac{\int \cdots \int \sum\limits_{i>k} V(|\mathbf{x}_i - \mathbf{x}_k|) e^{-\lambda\beta \sum\limits_{i>k} V_{ik}} d\mathbf{x}_1 \cdots d\mathbf{x}_N}{\int \cdots \int e^{-\lambda\beta \sum\limits_{i>k} V_{ik}} d\mathbf{x}_1 \cdots d\mathbf{x}_N} =$$

$$= \frac{N^2}{2\omega^2} \int\int d\mathbf{x}_1 d\mathbf{x}_2 V(|\mathbf{x}_1 - \mathbf{x}_2|) K^{(\lambda V)}(\mathbf{x}_1 - \mathbf{x}_2), \qquad (1.16)$$

where ω is the volume while

$$K^{(\lambda V)}(\mathbf{x}_1 - \mathbf{x}_2) = \frac{\int \cdots \int e^{-\lambda\beta \sum\limits_{i>k} V_{ik}} d\mathbf{x}_3 \cdots d\mathbf{x}_N}{\int \cdots \int e^{-\lambda\beta \sum\limits_{i>k} V_{ik}} d\mathbf{x}_1 \cdots d\mathbf{x}_N}$$

is the two-particle correlation function for the interaction λV.

Integrating Eq. (1.16) with respect to λ from 0 to 1 assuming that $F(0)$ is the free energy of the ideal gas (because when $\lambda = 0$ the interaction is turned off) and $N/\omega = n$, we obtain Eq. (1.1).

2. Obtain the equation of state for a classical system if the two-particle correlation function $K(|\mathbf{x}_1 - \mathbf{x}_2|)$ is known.

We use the well-known virial theorem

$$2\langle t \rangle = \langle \Sigma \mathbf{f}\mathbf{x} \rangle$$

(where the symbol $\langle \cdots \rangle$ denotes an average, **f** is the force, and t is the kinetic energy) in a system of N interacting particles within a closed volume ω. In this case

$$<t> = N\frac{3}{2}T,$$

while the virial $\sum_{k=1}^{N} \mathbf{f}(\mathbf{x}_k)\,\mathbf{x}_k$ is made up of the virial of the interaction forces

$$\sum_{k>l} \frac{\partial V_{kl}}{\partial \mathbf{x}_{kl}} \mathbf{x}_{kl}$$

(where $\mathbf{x}_{kl} = \mathbf{x}_k - \mathbf{x}_l$) and the virial for the pressure forces exerted on the particles by the walls of the container

$$\int P\mathbf{n}\mathbf{x}\,d\sigma = 3P\omega$$

(where $\mathbf{n}$ is the normal to the wall while P is the pressure), so that

$$2N\frac{3}{2}T = 3P\omega + \left\langle \sum_{i>k} \mathbf{x}_{ik} \frac{\partial V_{ik}}{\partial \mathbf{x}_{ik}} \right\rangle. \tag{1.17}$$

Taking the average in Eq. (1.17) by means of the relation

$$<\Psi> = \frac{\int \Psi e^{-\beta \Sigma V_{ik}}\, d\mathbf{x}_1 \cdots d\mathbf{x}_N}{\int e^{-\beta \Sigma V_{ik}}\, d\mathbf{x}_1 \cdots d\mathbf{x}_N},$$

we obtain Eq. (1.2):

$$\frac{P}{nT} = 1 - \frac{n}{6T}\int d\mathbf{x}\,\mathbf{x}\cdot\frac{\partial V}{\partial \mathbf{x}} K(\mathbf{x}).$$

3. Find an expression for the two-particle correlation function for a nearly-ideal classical Coulomb system starting with the Gibbs distribution

$$W(\mathbf{x}_1 \cdots \mathbf{x}_N) = e^{-\beta \sum_{i>k} V_{ik}}, \quad V_{ik} = \frac{e_i e_k}{|\mathbf{x}_i - \mathbf{x}_k|}. \tag{1.18}$$

Differentiating Eq. (1.18) with respect to β and integrating the relation that is obtained with respect to $\mathbf{dx}_{s+1}\ldots\mathbf{dx}_N$, we obtain the following system of equations for the correlation functions:

$$\left.\begin{aligned} &F_s(\mathbf{x}_1\cdots\mathbf{x}_s) = \int W\,\mathbf{dx}_{s+1}\cdots\mathbf{dx}_N,\\ &\frac{\partial F_s}{\partial\beta} + V_s F_s + N\int\sum_{k=1}^{s} V_{k,\,s+1}F_{s+1}\mathbf{dx}_{s+1} + \\ &+\frac{N^2}{2}\int V_{s+1,\,s+2}F_{s+2}\mathbf{dx}_{s+1}\mathbf{dx}_{s+2} = 0. \end{aligned}\right\} \tag{1.19}$$

where $V_s = \sum\limits_{1\leqslant i<k\leqslant s} V_{ik}$, N is the number of particles (the volume of the system is taken to be unity): $N \gg 1$, $N \gg s$.

We seek a solution of the system in (1.19) assuming that the correlation between particles is small. This means that to obtain the first approximation to the correlation function for an ensemble of s particles F_s we need only take account of the two-particle correlations: hence, in this approximation

$$\begin{aligned} &F_1 - 1 = 0,\\ &F_{12} - 1 = G_{12},\\ &F_{123} - 1 = G_{12} + G_{13} + G_{23} + G_{12}G_{13} + \cdots\\ &F_{1234} - 1 = G_{12} + G_{13} + G_{14} + G_{23} + G_{24} + G_{34} + G_{12}G_{13} + G_{12}G_{14} + \cdots\\ &\cdots\cdots\cdots\cdots\cdots\cdots\cdots\cdots\cdots \end{aligned}$$

Substituting these expressions in one of the equations in (1.19) with $s \geq 2$ (for example the $s = 2$ equation) we obtain an equation for the function G:

$$0 = \frac{\partial G_{ab}}{\partial\beta} + V_{ab} + 2\int\sum_c n_c G_{ac}V_{cb}\mathbf{dx}_c + \int\sum_{c,\,d} n_c n_d G_{ac}G_{bd}V_{cd}\mathbf{dx}_c\mathbf{dx}_d, \tag{1.20}$$

where the sum is taken over the various charge species. We seek a solution in the form $G_{ab} = (e_a e_b/\Sigma n e^2)\,G(|\mathbf{x}_a - \mathbf{x}_b|)$. An equation for the Fourier component $g(\mathbf{k}, \beta)$ of the function $G(\mathbf{x}, \beta)$ can then be obtained using Eq. (1.20):

$$\frac{\partial g}{\partial\beta} + 4\pi\sum n e^2(1+g)^2/k^2 = 0.$$

Solving this equation with the boundary condition $g(\mathbf{k}, 0) = 0$,* we find

$$g(\mathbf{k}, \beta) = -\frac{\varkappa^2}{\varkappa^2 + k^2}$$

and

$$F_{ab} = 1 - \frac{\beta e_a e_b e^{-\frac{|\mathbf{x}_a - \mathbf{x}_b|}{D}}}{|\mathbf{x}_a - \mathbf{x}_b|},$$

where

$$\varkappa^2 = D^{-2} = 4\pi\beta \sum_c n_c e_c^2 .$$

§ 2. Quantum Coulomb System

As we have indicated in the preceding section, an ideal Coulomb gas cannot be analyzed within the framework of classical statistical thermodynamics (this is evident immediately from the divergence of the statistical integral for the Coulomb attraction case). This situation arises because the relative motion of two Coulomb particles in close proximity should be described quantum mechanically rather than classically; for this reason, and to determine the thermodynamic functions for a Coulomb system, we must compute the quantum-mechanical partition function rather than the statistical integral.

It is true, however, that the first terms in the expansion of the thermodynamic potentials for a nonsymmetric plasma ($\Sigma n e^3 \neq 0$) in terms of n can be based on the classical calculation because these terms are weak functions of the quantum parameter of the problem, which contains Planck's constant $\hbar$.

As in the classical case, there are again three characteristic lengths: the mean distance between particles r, the mean Coulomb scattering amplitude e^2/T, and the length λ, which contains Planck's constant. The quantity λ can be taken to be the mean De Broglie wavelength of the particles $\hbar/mu$ where u is the mean thermal velocity of the particles.

*This condition corresponds to the total disappearance of correlation at an infinite temperature.

We shall be interested in the case of a rarefied plasma in which $r \gg e^2/T$, $r \gg \lambda$. The ratio $e^2/T\lambda \sim e^2/\hbar u$, which is the usual parameter in the quantum-mechanical problem of particle motion in a Coulomb field, is taken to be of order unity.

The possibility of using the classical method for finding the first terms in the expansion of the thermodynamic functions in n stems from the long-range nature of the Coulomb force. Actually the two-particle correlation function differs appreciably from unity up to distances of the order of the Debye radius D which, in a rarefied plasma, is appreciably greater than the lengths λ and e^2/T. Hence there is a large region of x

$$\lambda \ll x \lesssim D,$$

which makes an important contribution to the integrals in (1.1) or (1.2) in which quantum effects can be neglected. However, quantum effects can be introduced as follows: the correlation function obtained in the preceding section (1.8) does not apply at distances $x \sim \lambda$ so that the integration over x in Eq. (1.1) should not be taken from $x = 0$ but rather from $x \sim \lambda$.

Substituting the two-particle correlation function (1.8) in Eq. (1.1a) and integrating, we obtain (keeping $\sim n^2 \ln n$ terms and neglecting n^2 terms):

$$F = F_0 - \frac{T}{12\pi D^3} + \frac{\pi}{3T^2}\left(\sum_\alpha n_\alpha e_\alpha^3\right)^2 \ln\frac{D}{\lambda}. \tag{2.1}$$

In a nonsymmetric plasma the first terms in the density expansion of F evidently contain the quantum length λ only as the argument of a logarithm; hence, in our approximation, in which only terms of order $n^{3/2}$ and $n^2 \ln n$ are considered, the exact value of λ is unimportant.

As we have indicated above, quantum effects appear in two ways in a many-body problem: first, if the de Broglie wavelength of the particle λ is not small compared with the scattering amplitude the particle interaction must be described quantum mechanically; second, if λ is comparable with the mean interparticle distance r, quantum statistics must be used to take account of the degeneracy.

Up to this point in §2 we have only been considering quantum effects of the first kind. We now consider the expansion of the thermodynamic potentials when degeneracy becomes important.

As λ increases degeneracy effects first become important for the electrons. Because the ion mass is large the ion wavelengths are very short and degeneracy effects can be neglected. The correction to the thermodynamic potential for an idealized plasma Ω,* arising from the interaction of the plasma charges consists of two terms in this case; we shall call these the "Debye" term and the "exchange" term.

The Debye term is due to the interaction of charges at distances larger than the mean scattering amplitude. In both a classical Coulomb system and a rarefied plasma the Debye correction to the thermodynamic potential is

$$-\frac{T}{12\pi D^3}, \tag{2.2}$$

where D is the Debye radius. It should be remembered, however, that when degeneracy is important the Debye radius is given by

$$\left(\sum 4\pi \frac{\partial n}{\partial \mu} e^2\right)^{-1/2}, \tag{2.3}$$

which goes over to the classical form $(4\pi\beta \Sigma ne^2)^{-1/2}$ only in a rarefied gas (in which case $\lambda \ll r$ and Boltzmann statistics apply).

The exchange correction to the thermodynamic potential can be obtained by averaging the electrostatic interaction energy of the electrons; the average is carried out for an ideal gas since we are interested in small corrections to the thermodynamic potential:

---

*The thermodynamic potential Ω appears in the Gibbs' formulation for a variable number of particles and is given by the following formula (cf. for example, Landau and Lifshits, Statistical Physics, 1951):

$$\Omega(\mu, T, \omega) = -T \ln \mathrm{Sp} \exp -\left(\hat{\mathbf{H}} - \hat{\mathbf{N}}\mu\right)/T,$$

where $\hat{\mathbf{H}}$ is the Hamiltonian of the system, $\hat{\mathbf{N}}$ is the operator that specifies the total number of particles, and μ is the chemical potential. Knowing Ω we can find the equation of state, the heat capacity, etc., by means of the relations

$$\frac{\partial \Omega}{\partial \mu} = -N,\ P = -\frac{\Omega}{\omega},\ \frac{\partial \Omega}{\partial T} = -S.$$

$$\frac{\mathrm{Sp}\, e^{-\beta(\hat{H}_0 - \hat{N}\mu)} \sum_{pp'q} \frac{1}{2} V_q a_p^+ a_{p'}^+ a_{p'-q} a_{p+q}}{\mathrm{Sp}\, e^{-\beta(\hat{H}_0 - \hat{N}\mu)}}, \tag{2.4}$$

where

$$V_q = \frac{4\pi e^2}{q^2}.$$

Since the kinetic energy operator has the form $\hat{H}_0 = \sum_p \varepsilon_p a_p^+ a_p$, where $\varepsilon_p = p^2/2m$, in the average in (2.4) only those terms in the sum will make contributions for which $p' = p + q$. Carrying out a statistical average by means of the expression

$$\frac{\mathrm{Sp}\, e^{-\beta(\hat{H}_0 - \hat{N}\mu)} a_p^+ a_p}{\mathrm{Sp}\, e^{-\beta(\hat{H}_0 - \hat{N}\mu)}} = n_p = \frac{1}{e^{\beta(\varepsilon_p - \mu)} + 1} \tag{2.5}$$

we find the expression for the exchange correction:

$$-\frac{1}{2}\int V_q n_p n_{p+q} \mathbf{dpdq}. \tag{2.6}$$

By adding the Debye and exchange terms we now obtain an expression for the correction to the thermodynamic potential Ω due to the Coulomb interaction in a degenerate electron plasma:

$$\Delta\Omega = \Omega - \Omega_0 = -\frac{1}{2}\int V_q n_p n_{p+q} \mathbf{dpdq} - \frac{T}{12\pi D^3}. \tag{2.7}$$

In the limiting case of a strong degeneracy, for which $\lambda \sim r$, the exchange correction is of order e^2/r (per particle) and is much greater than the Debye correction. It should be pointed out that in this limiting case Eq. (2.7) applies only for a high density plasma. This limitation arises from the fact that the exchange correction e^2/r must only be a small part of the kinetic energy (order $\hbar^2/mr^2$) and this is possible only when the mean interparticle distance is appreciably smaller than the Bohr radius

$$r \ll \frac{\hbar^2}{me^2}.$$

In the almost nondegenerate plasma, where $\lambda \ll r$, the basic contribution in Eq. (2.7) comes from the Debye term; under these conditions the exchange term is reduced, being of order $e^2 \lambda^2/r^3$.

Thus, we see that in addition to the reduction in plasma energy associated with the long-range nature of the Coulomb force [Debye correction in Eq. (2.7)] there is an additional energy reduction due to the exchange effect in a quantum plasma.

§ 3. Degree of Ionization of a Plasma

When the temperature of a neutral gas is increased the gas becomes partially ionized. If this partially ionized gas is in thermodynamic equilibrium the degree of ionization can be found from the condition that the free energy of the system must be a minimum. We consider the case in which the mean de Broglie wavelength of the plasma electrons is appreciably smaller than the mean distance between electrons so that the electrons can be described by Boltzmann statistics. The mean energy of the plasma particles is assumed to be much smaller than the ionization energy:

$$T \ll I.$$

Under these conditions the ratio of the number of atoms in the first (or higher) excited state to the number of atoms in the ground state is always small. Thus, we assume, that the plasma comprises a mixture consisting of neutral atoms in the ground state (with density N) and ionized components—an equal number of ions and electrons ($n_+ = n_- \equiv n$).

We consider a rarefied plasma in which the mean distance between particles is large compared with the scattering amplitude, in which case the plasma can be regarded as a mixture of three ideal gases: the neutral atoms, the ions, and the electrons. The free energy of such a mixture (per unit volume) is equal to the sum of the free energies of the components:

$$F = -NT \ln\left[\frac{e}{N}\left(\frac{M+m}{2\pi\hbar^2}T\right)^{3/2} e^{I/T}\right] - \\ - 2nT \ln\left[\frac{e}{n}\left(\frac{\sqrt{Mm}}{2\pi\hbar^2}T\right)^{3/2}\right], \qquad (3.1)$$

where M and m are the ion and electron masses respectively. In thermodynamic equilibrium the quantity F is a minimum, i. e.,

$$\frac{\partial F}{\partial n} = 0, \tag{3.2}$$

subject to the constraint N + n = const, which expresses the conservation of particles. Substituting Eq. (3.1) in Eq. (3.2) we find

$$\frac{N}{n^2} \frac{m'T}{2\pi\hbar^2} e^{-I/T} = 1, \quad m' = \frac{mM}{m+M}.$$

It then follows that the degree of ionization of the plasma α is given by the formula (usually called the Saha equation):

$$\alpha = \frac{n}{N+n} = \frac{1}{\sqrt{1+K}}, \tag{3.3}$$

where the ionization equilibrium constant K is

$$K = \frac{P}{T} \left(\frac{m'T}{2\pi\hbar^2} \right)^{-3/2} e^{I/T}, \quad P = (N + 2n)\, T. \tag{3.4}$$

The factor that multiplies the exponential in Eq. (3.4) is of order $(\lambda/r)^3$ and is very small for the case of Boltzmann statistics being considered here. These results indicate the degree of ionization can be appreciable at small T/I in a rarefied equilibrium plasma.

The relation in (3.3) can also be used when heating of a neutral gas causes dissociation of the molecules. In this case the dissociation constant is again given by Eq. (3.4) with the sole difference that the quantity I is now the dissociation energy of the molecule while m' is the reduced mass of the atoms formed in dissociation. If the molecule dissociates into a pair of oppositly charged ions the partially dissociated gas obtained by heating constitutes a classical plasma. When the density of such a plasma is increased, the electrostatic forces acting between the particles of the charged component tend to reduce the energy of the system so that dissociation proceeds more easily than in a rarefied plasma. The degree of dissociation (ionization) of this nonideal plasma obtained from the Saha equation is then found to be too low.